Temporary Works

Temporary Works

Principles of Design and Construction

Edited by

Murray Grant and Peter F. Pallett

Published by ICE Publishing, 40 Marsh Wall, London E14 9TP.

Full details of ICE Publishing sales representatives and distributors can be found at: www.icevirtuallibrary.com/info/printbooksales

Also available from ICE Publishing

ICE Manual of Health and Safety in Construction.
C. McAleenan and D. Oloke (eds). ISBN 978-0-7277-4056-4
Deep Excavations, Third edition.
M. Puller and D. Puller. ISBN 978-0-7277-4117-2 (Publication 2012)
Civil Excavations and Tunnelling.
R. Tatiya. ISBN 978-0-7277-3340-5
Buildability: Successful construction from concept to completion.
T. Holroyd. ISBN 978-0-7277-3207-1

www.icevirtuallibrary.com

A catalogue record for this book is available from the British Library

ISBN 978-0-7277-4177-6

© Thomas Telford Limited 2012

ICE Publishing is a division of Thomas Telford Ltd, a wholly-owned subsidiary of the Institution of Civil Engineers (ICE).

Associate Commissioning Editor: Victoria Thompson
Production Editor: Imran Mirza
Market Development Executive: Catherine de Gatacre

Typeset by Academic + Technical, Bristol
Printed and bound by CPI Group (UK) Ltd, Croydon, CR0 4YY

Contents

Foreword

Temporary works are a vital and safety critical part of every construction, building and civil engineering project. Even so, they are only well understood by a handful of engineers. This is surprising. Smart design wins projects; poor design costs time and money and failure, should it occur, often results in fatality.

The consequences of failure were made plain to the UK industry by a number of large-scale falsework collapses in the early 1970s. The lessons were drawn into the seminal Bragg Report and what is perhaps that most excellent of British Standards, BS5975. The term 'temporary works coordinator' sprang from this, and what is set down has given us a pragmatic and safe environment in which to build.

A theme I would like to draw out is the role of the Permanent Works Designer. From an understanding of the process of construction, a clever designer will bring economy and safety. The Construction (Design and Management) Regulations have made this holistic thinking a requirement in law, which is an important step forward. Through history and in the present day all great engineers think this way; it is a cornerstone of our ability to bring value.

While in our industry today the highest risk of catastrophic events might remain on the major construction sites, these are generally well controlled and the most injury is now found in minor works. Small excavations, underpinning, building and alteration works continue to fail and cause fatality. Our industry must focus urgently at this level, and designers of these schemes have a leading role to play.

I commend this book to all involved in the Construction Industry. It is timely, relevant, builds on great wisdom drawn from hard learning and is written by the industry's most knowledgeable. It liberates our engineers to design more fully and to bring better value. My thanks go to those who have provided it for us.

Bill Hewlett MA, FICE, CEng

Vice President of the Institution of Civil Engineers and Chairman of The Temporary Works Forum. Technical Director, Costain

List of contributors

Editors

Eur Ing **Murray Grant** CEng FICE has a total of 38 years in the civil engineering and building industry, and for a large percentage of that time was responsible for the technical function of contractors, both in UK and overseas. He developed many of the design methods that were first published in the falsework code and introduced many innovative methods to the UK market.

He has lectured extensively on construction and temporary works topics and produced several publications himself, as well as being chair of regional committees of ICE and Concrete Society, amongst others.

Eur Ing **Peter F. Pallett** CEng FICE FCS is a civil engineer, educated at Kings College, Taunton and Loughborough University of Technology. Has a total of 43 years experience and over 29 years specialising in temporary works worldwide. Self employed since 1991 on temporary works training worldwide, he formed his own company Pallett Temporary*Works* Limited in 2003.

He is a founder member of the BSI committee for falsework, co-author of the NASC's TG20 on scaffolding, and principally known for Concrete Society publication *Formwork – A guide to good practice*. He is recently certified as an 'Expert Witness – Civil Procedures' with expertise in above ground TW.

Contributors

A. Bell Chief Engineer, Cementation Skanska Limited

Andrew Bell is a geotechnical engineer and Chartered Civil Engineer with over 15 years experience, gained principally in the design and construction of piled foundations and deep basements. Andrew is currently Chief Engineer at Cementation Skanska.

P. Boddy MEng CEng MICE, Head of Temporary Works for Interserve Construction Limited

Currently Head of Temporary Works for Interserve Construction Limited, Paul Boddy has also worked for British Waterways and has a broad experience (both practical and technical) of floating plant from large to small.

G. Bowring BSc CEng FICE

Godfrey Bowring has over 40 years experience, the majority of which has been in heavy civil engineering. He has worked for contractors and consulting engineers; latterly for as Chief Engineer of a large civil engineering contractor. Now partially retired, he maintains an active interest in temporary works and is a member of the BS5975 drafting committee.

M. Brice BSc MSc CGeol FGS, Associate, Applied Geotechnical Engineering

Mike Brice has been a geotechnical engineer for thirty years and has wide experience of the design and construction of earthworks and soil stabilisation.

K. Broughton BSc (Hons) CEng MICE, HOCHTIEF UK Construction

Keith Broughton has worked for of HOCHTIEF UK since 1991, and has been involved in the engineering and tendering of all of their civil engineering projects. He is currently the Director of Technical Services.

R. Filip BEng (Hons) MSc DIC CEng MICE, Temporary works consultant and training provider – RKF Consult Ltd

Ray Filip is a Chartered Civil Engineer with over 20 years experience on site, in principal contractors temporary works design offices and as chief geotechnical engineer with specialist sheet piling subcontractor. Currently self employed temporary works consultant and training provider.

J. Gill MICE BEng Civil Engineering (Cardiff), HOCHTIEF UK Construction

John Gill joined HOCHTIEF UK in 1995 where he is currently the Technical Services Manager, responsible for the support and delivery of technically challenging civil projects.

M. Haynes Sales & Marketing Director, Fagioli Ltd

Martin Haynes has covered most aspects of heavy moves in his career since graduating in 1982, with PSC and since their takeover, with Fagioli.

J. Hislam BSc MPhil CEng FICE MASCE, Director, Applied Geotechnical Engineering

John Hislam has over 40 years experience in foundation engineering with both contracting and consulting companies. He has extensive experience in grouting – having worked in both commercial research and the application of grouting in construction and oil exploration – and in piling, inclusive of basement and retaining construction.

B. Ingham BTech (Hons) CEng MICE MCMI, Engineering Manager, Mabey Hire Services Ltd

After working on permanent bridges for 10 years, with Cleveland Bridge & Engineering and two county councils, Bernard Ingham has spent the majority of his 22 years with the Mabey Group managing all aspects of a broad range of temporary bridge projects.

S. Marchand BA (Cantab) CEng FICE MIStructE. Director, Wentworth House Partnership

Stuart Marchand is the senior director at Wentworth House Partnership and has specialised in temporary works design for 30 years, especially façade retention and deep basements.

A. Massera Engineering Director, Fagioli SpA

Andrea Massera is a Chartered Civil Engineer. He has been responsible for design and fabrication of heavy steel structures and heavy installations internationally since graduating from Pavia (Italy) in 1985. He has been Engineering Director at Fagioli since 2003.

G. Miles MCIOB, Quality Manager, Costain

Geoff Miles previously worked as a Planner, Site Manager and Project Manager and been responsible for planning and implementing Site Set-Up, i.e. mobilisation and de-mobilisation on more than 15 contracts ranging from £2M to £75M value.

J. Murray BEng(Hons) CEng MICE, Engineering Director, PERI Ltd

Jim Murray is a Chartered Civil Engineer and since graduating from the University of Abertay in Dundee has worked in several sectors of the industry holding positions with Consultant Engineers and Contracting companies.

Eur Ing **I. Nicoll** BSc(Hons) CEng MICE, Chief Engineer, Interserve Industrial Ltd

Ian Nicoll is a Chartered Civil Engineer with nearly forty years experience of heavy industrial construction; much of that time working on projects abroad. He is currently totally associated with temporary works and Chairman of the NASC Working Group on TG20 for scaffolding.

A. Rattray BSc CEng MICE, HM Principal Specialist Inspector, Construction Engineering Specialist Team, Health and Safety Executive

Andrew Rattray is a chartered civil engineer with over 30 years experience of the construction industry. He started work as a civil and structural design engineer before joining the HSE as a specialist inspector providing professional and technical advice on the health and safety aspects of civil engineering and building related topics; the role also includes the investigation of a range of construction accidents and incidents, often involving temporary works.

C. Robinson BEng MSc CEng MICE, Technical Manager, Cementation Skanska Limited

Currently Technical Manager with Cementation Skanska Limited, Chris Robinson is a geotechnical engineer and Chartered Civil Engineer with over 15 years experience, gained principally in the design and construction of piled foundations and deep basements.

A. Smith BSc MICE CEng. Contracts Director Joseph Gallagher Ltd

Andrew Smith has been leading tunnelling and shaft projects for 40 years with major and specialist contractors and is now a consultant with Joseph Gallagher Ltd.

Eur Ing **N. Smith** BSc(Eng) MSc CEng FICE FGS, Director, Applied Geotechnical Engineering

Neil Smith has been a specialist geotechnical engineer from the beginning of his career and has lectured on geotechnical aspects of temporary works. Neil has worked for specialist contractors and consultants covering a very wide range of geotechnical work – investigation and specialist processes, interpreting and understanding the ground conditions at sites around the world and applying the knowledge gained to project design.

C. Tate BSc CEng MICE MCIHT, Chief Engineer, VolkerFitzpatrick

Chris Tate is Chief Engineer with VolkerFitzpatrick. For nearly 40 years, he has been involved in the construction of roads and airfield pavements, earthworks and associated temporary works design. He also runs his own ground investigation and materials testing company.

L. York BSc CEng MICE MCIWEM C.WEM MCIHT FFB

After fifteen years involved with the supervision of on-site Temporary Works, Laurie York spent twenty years designing a wide variety of Temporary Works for a major civil engineering contractor, and is now a Temporary Works consultant.

Introduction

Temporary Works: Principles of Design and Construction has been produced for practitioners or would-be practitioners to enable them to apply their skills, usually developed in the larger area of permanent works, in this specialism. It will also be of interest to all technicians, undergraduates and graduates wishing to broaden their professional development to have a basic understanding of temporary works. It therefore does not go into considerable detail of design, or the minutiae of construction, but instead shows the reader the unique philosophy and applications by reference to current methods that will enable this detail specialisation to be applied. You will not find complete worked examples, as an assumption has been made that the reader will either be competent in general engineering principles or will wish to develop those skills not yet possessed.

Where appropriate, each chapter has six main headings of introduction, description of topic (how and why it works), any alternatives worth considering, common methods of construction and principles of design, concluding with references.

Our primary target readership could be considered to be engineers working for the Main Contractor or Design Consultant, or those intending to gain the technical elements of skill needed to perform efficiently in these roles. We would hope that we have also provided something of value to students and their teachers on the more practical engineering courses.

The most economic temporary works is 'no temporary works'. Often designing out the temporary works is impossible on a structure. Where required, it is rarely specified in the pricing for the permanent works – yet the temporary works have a significant impact on the overall cost of a structure. This impacts the industry in two ways. Firstly, it is given minimum coverage in education at colleges. How many readers had lectures on temporary works while at college? Secondly, it has until recently been considered a contractor's issue and left to the construction phase of a project. The result is that the subject of temporary works has expanded into many specialised fields, each having its own experts and, in many cases, being delivered by specialist suppliers.

ICE Publishing realised that to obtain authoritative guidance, a single author would not suffice. Two well-known and respected engineers with detailed knowledge in temporary works were appointed as managing editors to coordinate and proof (and, in some cases, write) the detailed chapters. The very wide-ranging topics inherent in temporary works (27 chapters proved to be necessary), involved 23 of arguably the most knowledgeable engineers and practitioners in their field, writing on their own specialised subjects. The result is an authoritative work, informed by the latest European codes.

Scope of temporary works

A precise use of the Oxford Dictionary would limit our definition of temporary works to any work which is done to enable the creation of a permanent structure or infrastructure element. However, this would preclude the opportunities that often arise to reduce or avoid the work and costs of creating something that will be removed or redundant once the client's needs have been satisfied. To avoid temporary works is often a broader, and more elegant, approach to construction, with less exposure to risk and savings in overall cost. On several occasions in the preparation of this book, the definition of temporary works has been extended to suggest alternative processes, at all times promoting the safety of operations and introducing correct procedures for temporary works.

Before using the detailed information, readers of this book are advised to consider if there may be an alternative process whereby the cost and effort of providing works which serve no permanent purpose could be reduced or even avoided.

Further, readers are advised not to limit their selection of temporary works to those methods chosen for inclusion in this book (simply because they are those most commonly used), but to explore the wide range of engineering for potential solutions to their specific project.

Murray Grant and Peter F. Pallett (joint editors)

Temporary Works: Principles of Design and Construction
ISBN 978-0-7277-4177-6

ICE Publishing: All rights reserved
http://dx.doi.org/10.1680/twpdc.41776.001

Chapter 1
Safety, statutory and contractual obligations

Andrew Rattray HM Principal Specialist Inspector, Construction Engineering Specialist Team, Health and Safety Executive
Peter F. Pallett Pallett Temporary*Works* Ltd

Safety of temporary works is paramount to protect not only site workers, but also the public and others who may be affected by the work. Temporary works should be 'engineered' and given the same degree of care and consideration as the permanent works. It is also important that temporary works are designed to be robust enough to withstand the rigours of site use and detailed to ensure that local or single component failure does not lead to progressive collapse. Knowledge gained from past collapses/incidents and research has informed current temporary works guidance and standards. BS 5975 is an industry consensus view on good practice and provides recommendations for procedures for the design, construction, use and dismantling of all types of temporary works. Statutory legislation has a direct effect on the design and operation of temporary works, imposing duties and obligations on many of the parties involved. In addition, all users of temporary works will have contractual obligations under which they work, often imposing specific requirements for the works.

1.1.   Introduction
'Temporary works' is a widely used expression in the construction industry and is defined in BS 5975: 2008 + A1: 2011 *Code of practice for temporary works procedures and the permissible stress design of falsework* (BSI, 2011) as 'parts of the works that allow or enable construction of, protect, support or provide access to, the permanent works and which might or might not remain in place at the completion of the works'. The construction of most types of permanent works will require the use of some form of temporary works. Temporary works should be an 'engineered solution' that is used to support or protect an existing structure or the permanent works during construction, or to support an item of plant or equipment or the vertical sides or side-slopes of an excavation or to provide access. It is imperative that the same degree of consideration and care is given to the design and construction of temporary works as to the design and construction of the permanent works. The management of temporary works is discussed in Chapter 2 on management.

Examples of temporary works include (but are not limited to) the following.

■ *Earthworks*: trenches, excavations, temporary slopes and stockpiles.

- *Structures*: formwork, falsework, propping, façade retention, needling, shoring, edge protection, scaffolding, temporary bridges, site hoarding and signage, site fencing, cofferdams.
- *Equipment/plant*: tower crane foundations, construction hoists, mast climbing work platforms (MCWPs), any work to support plant and machinery, for example, mobile crane outrigger supports, piling and crane platforms, anchorages/ ties for MCWPs and hoists.

In order to ensure the strength and stability of any temporary works structure, there are three fundamental aspects that need to be considered, which can be simplified as follows.

- *Foundations*: the ability of the ground to carry the loads transmitted from the temporary works structure without failure or excessive deformation or settlement.
- *Structural integrity*: the ability of the temporary works structure itself to carry and transmit loads to the ground via the foundations without failure of the structural elements, including fixings and connections (e.g. by buckling, bending, shear, tension, torsion) and without excessive deflection.
- *Stability*: the ability of the temporary works structure to withstand horizontal or lateral loading without sway, overturning or sliding failure (stability may be inherent in the temporary works structure itself or provided by the permanent works).

Failure to adequately design, construct and maintain temporary works can lead to

- collapse or failure of the temporary works
- structural failures and collapse of the permanent works
- uncontrolled ingress or egress of materials, spoil and water
- collapse of adjacent structures (buildings, transport systems, infrastructure)
- risk of single/multiple fatalities and serious injuries to workers and members of the public
- risk of significant delay and increased costs to construction projects
- significant financial and commercial risks to contractors, subcontractors, designers, suppliers and clients.

The main causes of temporary works failures include

- absence of or an inadequate temporary works procedure
- inadequate site investigation (including geotechnical investigation, identification of underground services, assessment of the structural condition of existing and/or adjacent buildings)
- inadequate or lack of design and/or design brief for the temporary works
- inadequate level of checking of temporary works designs
- lack of awareness on site of temporary works design assumptions
- unavailability of temporary works equipment
- inappropriate use of temporary works equipment
- poorly constructed temporary works and/or absence of checking of adequate erection

- unauthorised changes to an approved temporary works design
- overloading of temporary works, i.e. failure to control loading or lack of awareness of the capacity of the equipment
- inadequate communication of details of the temporary works design to the erectors
- inadequate foundations for the temporary works
- lack of adequate lateral stability for the temporary works.

The code of practice on falsework (BS 5975) was revised in 2008 to provide recommendations and guidance on the procedural controls to be applied to all aspects of temporary works in the construction industry, as well as specific guidance on the design, specification, construction, use and dismantling of falsework. BS 5975 (BSI, 2011) describes procedures as well as technical aspects since the success of falsework and temporary works is closely linked to good management.

1.2. Background

The first report on falsework was by the Joint Committee of the Institution of Structural Engineers and the Concrete Society (1971) and introduced classes of falsework. The British Standard Code of Practice committee was established and, ironically, a fortnight later a major collapse occurred in the UK by the River Loddon near London. This collapse and other significant falsework collapses in the 1970s, together with an apparent lack of authoritative guidance, led to the government setting up the Advisory Committee on Falsework which produced the Bragg Report (Bragg, 1974, 1975) named after the committee chairman. Industry produced the first code of practice (in compliance with one of the recommendations of the Bragg Report) as BS 5975 in 1982 which was informed by the recommendations of the Bragg Report and the earlier Joint Committee report.

The Bragg Report made some very pertinent comments about falsework which apply equally to all temporary works and which still hold true today, including:

> '*Falsework requires the same skill and attention to detail as the design of permanent structures of like complexity, and indeed falsework should always be regarded as a structure in its own right, the stability of which at all stages of construction is paramount for safety.*'

Other key concerns highlighted in the report include

- competency
- design procedures
- design responsibilities
- communication and coordination
- inspection and supervision
- lateral stability.

BS 5975 codified all relevant aspects that should be considered when preparing a permissible stress design for falsework and included recommendations for materials, design and work on site. Because the success of falsework is closely tied up with its management, the code described procedures as well as technical aspects. Recommendations were given on the actions that should be taken and the allocation of duties to individuals. The Bragg Report recommended that the duty of ensuring that all the relevant procedures and checks carried out, be given to one individual known as the Temporary Works Coordinator. Although BS 5975: 1982 adopted the narrower term of Falsework Coordinator, when it was revised in 2008 it incorporated procedural controls for all types of temporary works and reverted back to the term Temporary Works Coordinator.

There have been significant changes to the construction industry since the mid 1970s which have affected how falsework, and more generally temporary works, are dealt with. A Standing Committee on Structural Safety paper (SCOSS, 2002), updated in 2010, identified the principal changes which included the following.

- Few main contractors now have their own temporary works departments, whereas in the 1970s almost all would design temporary works in-house; the responsibility for temporary works now often falls to a specialist contractor/supplier which can result in a lengthy supply chain.
- In the 1970s, most falsework (and temporary works) were constructed from scaffold tube and fitting components whereas proprietary systems now dominate the market; the design skills and knowledge of the performance of the systems therefore now tends to lie within the specialist organisations.
- There has been a gradual but inexorable loss of traditional skills within the construction industry; in practical terms, this means that the site foreman with a lifetime's experience of 'what works' has largely been lost.
- Procurement routes are now largely chosen to maximise commercial benefit and have little regard to considerations of the flow of information; the difficulties caused by long supply chains are further exacerbated when design and erection responsibility are split and when design/supply briefs do not include site visits/inspections.

Health and Safety Executive research (HSE, 2001) into various aspects of falsework produced some worrying findings that were equally applicable to temporary works in general; these included the following.

- A lack of understanding, at all levels, of the fundamentals of stability of falsework and the basic principles involved.
- Wind loading was rarely considered.
- There was a lack of clarity in terms of the design brief and coverage of key aspects such as ground conditions.
- The assumptions for the lateral restraint of the falsework made by designers were often ignored or misunderstood by those on site.
- There was a lack of adequate checking and a worrying lack of design expertise.
- Erection accuracy left a lot to be desired.

Based on the research, a number of key concerns were identified

- competency of the falsework/temporary works designer

- sufficiency of information
- adequacy of supervision
- role of the Temporary Works Coordinator
- competency of those erecting falsework/temporary works.

The actions to deal with these concerns are straightforward and require no more than the application of the good practice given in BS 5975 (BSI, 2011). They also fit well with the aspirations of the Construction (Design and Management) Regulations 2007 (HSE, 2007) in respect of their aim of improving the overall coordination and management of health and safety throughout all stages of a construction project. The European limit state design codes, such as BS EN 12811-1 for scaffolding (BSI, 2003) and BS EN 12812 for falsework (BSI, 2008), have little (if any) reference to procedures or site practice. This means that the procedural items in BS 5975 (BSI, 2011) take on a significant importance.

1.3.   Management of temporary works

The correct design and execution of temporary works is an essential element of risk prevention and mitigation on a construction site. Section 2 of BS 5975: 2008 + A1: 2011 (BSI, 2011) provides recommendations and guidance for a robust set of procedural controls to be applied to the design, specification, construction, use, maintenance and dismantling of all types of temporary works. Compliance with BS 5975 is not a legal requirement, but the code of practice does provide an industry consensus view on what is considered to be good practice. All temporary works should be an 'engineered solution' and it is imperative that the same degree of consideration and care is given to the design and construction of the temporary works as to the design and construction of the permanent works. See Chapter 2 on the management of temporary works.

1.4.   Construction (Design and Management) Regulations 2007

The Construction (Design and Management) Regulations 2007 (CDM, 2007) came into effect on 6 April 2007. They replaced the Construction (Design and Management) Regulations 1994 (as amended in 2000) and were largely limited to a reworking of the existing requirements under the EC Directive, Temporary or Mobile Construction Sites Directive 92/57/EEC. One structural change was the incorporation of most of the requirements of the Construction (Health, Safety and Welfare) Regulations 1996 (CHSWR) into Part 4 of CDM 2007. The CHSWR requirements relating to work at height had already been revoked by and incorporated into the Work at Height Regulations 2005 (WAHR). In Part 4 of CDM 2007, the regulations are grouped into generally related topics, some of which are particularly relevant to temporary works

- safe places of work
- unsafe structures or premature collapse
- excavations
- cofferdams and caissons
- training, inspection and so on.

The duties of all parties under CDM 2007 (Client, CDM Coordinator, Designer, Principal Contractor, Contractor) are set out in the associated Approved Code of

Practice (CDM ACOP) (HSE, 2007) and need to be read and understood by all those involved in the procurement and use of temporary works. CDM 2007 and the CDM ACOP (HSE, 2007) make several specific references to the design and management of temporary works; these are considered below.

1.4.1 Designers

The definition of 'structure' in CDM 2007 (HSE, 2007) includes 'any formwork, falsework, scaffold or other structure designed or used to provide support or means of access during construction work'. In the CDM ACOP (HSE, 2007), designers are deemed to include 'temporary works engineers, including those designing auxiliary structures, such as formwork, falsework, façade retention schemes, scaffolding, and sheet piling'. Specific guidance for all designers is given in CDM07/4 *Industry Guidance for Designers* (CITB, 2007). It is therefore clear that, under CDM 2007, temporary works designers have exactly the same designer duties as Permanent Works Designers, including the following.

- Ensuring that they are competent in their specific field of temporary works design (and able to address the particular relevant health and safety issues).
- Avoiding foreseeable risks, so far as is reasonably practicable, to those involved in the construction, use and dismantling of the temporary works and providing adequate information on the remaining significant risks, for example, by following the principles of the Eliminate, Reduce, Inform, Control (ERIC) model (CITB, 2007) or any other similar risk reduction technique as part of the design process.
- Coordinating and cooperating with others, for example, liaising with the Permanent Works Designers to ensure that designs are compatible and that the permanent works can accommodate any assumed loadings from the temporary works, such as the lateral restraint of falsework.

The equal care and consideration required by the designers of temporary works and the permanent works reflects comments made in the Bragg Report (Bragg, 1975) more than 30 years previously.

1.4.2 Principal contractors and contractors

All contractors should plan, manage, coordinate and monitor their construction work so that it is carried out safely and without risks to health. On a project notifiable under CDM 2007, principal contractors (PCs) should formalise these arrangements in a construction phase plan with a level of detail proportionate to the risks involved. Among the topics that need to be considered when drawing up the construction phase plan, as listed in the CDM ACOP (HSE, 2007), are the arrangements for controlling significant site risks such as the 'stability of structures while carrying out construction work, including temporary structures and existing unstable structures' and 'work on excavations and work where there are poor ground conditions' and 'work in a caisson or compressed air working'. The majority of temporary works are likely to involve significant risks such as working at height, the potential for ground instability and/or collapse and the potential for structural instability and/or collapse. Consequently, the expectation is that the majority of construction phase plans will need to contain the management arrangements for dealing with temporary works, i.e. suitable temporary works procedures.

1.4.3 CDM coordinators

A CDM coordinator (CDMC) should be appointed by the client on all CDM-notifiable projects as soon as is practicable after initial design work or other preparation for construction work has begun. The CDM ACOP (HSE, 2007) notes that 'CDMCs have to take reasonable steps to ensure co-operation between permanent and temporary works designers, in particular to ensure that arrangements are in place to ensure that designs are compatible and that the permanent works can support any loadings from temporary works'. CDMCs also have a duty to advise the Client on the suitability of the PC's initial construction phase plan before work commences on site. As noted above, the expectation is that the majority of such plans should contain details of suitable temporary works procedures and the CDMC should check and advise accordingly. Once work commences on site, the responsibility for the content of the construction phase plan lies entirely with the PC.

1.5. The Work at Height Regulations 2005

The Work at Height Regulations 2005 (WAHR, 2005) impose health and safety requirements applicable to all work activity at height and not just in the construction industry. Work at height can take place at any location either above or below ground level and includes temporary means of access to and egress from such work. The WAHR implemented the requirements of EC Directive 2001/45/EEC and replaced the provisions in the Construction (Health, Safety and Welfare) Regulations 1996 relating to falls, fragile materials and falling objects.

The WAHR (2005) impose duties on employers and the self-employed to assess the risks from work at height and to organise and plan the work so it is carried out safely. The objective is to make sure that work at height is properly planned, including the selection of relevant equipment, appropriately supervised and carried out in a safe manner. The WAHR set out a simple hierarchy for managing and selecting equipment for work at height; duty holders must avoid work at height where they can; use work equipment or other measures to prevent falls where they cannot avoid working at height; and, where they cannot eliminate the risk of a fall, use work equipment or other measures to minimise the distance and consequences of a fall should one occur. Priority should be given to collective protection measures over personal protective measures. When working under the control of another person, all employees and the self-employed have a duty to report any activity or equipment which is defective.

In relation to temporary works, the WAHR place duties on clients and designers to ensure that strength and stability calculations for scaffolding are carried out unless calculations are already available or the scaffold is assembled in conformity with a generally recognised standard configuration (HSE, 2007; schedule 3.2). A recognised standard configuration could be the National Access and Scaffolding Confederation (NASC) Technical Guidance TG20 for tube and fitting scaffolds (NASC, 2008) or the manufacturer's guidance for system scaffolds. In such cases calculations have already been prepared and, provided the scaffolding is erected to the stated rules for the solution adopted, further calculations are not required. The WAHR require that, depending on the complexity of a scaffold, an assembly, use and dismantling plan shall be drawn up by a competent person; such a plan should describe the sequence and methods to be adopted when erecting, dismantling and altering the scaffold, if this is not covered by the published guidance referred to above.

The WAHR state certain requirements for all working platforms. Where there is a risk of falling, there are requirements for guardrails, toe boards, barriers and similar means of protection; the top guardrail should be at least 950 mm high, with intermediate guardrail(s) and toe boards(s) positioned to give a maximum unprotected gap of 470 mm. Where the platform is for a sloping workplace at an angle greater than 10°, the guardrail requirements are more onerous. Although no minimum width of a working platform is stated, the width values given in good practice documents such as BS EN 12811 (BSI, 2004) or TG20 (NASC, 2008) are used.

1.6.   The Health and Safety (Offences) Act 2008

The Health and Safety (Offences) Act 2008 (HSOA, 2008) makes amendments to the Health and Safety at Work etc. Act 1974 (HSWA). HSOA has resulted in the £20 000 maximum fine in the Magistrates' Court applying to most health and safety offences; it does not affect the position in relation to fines for sentences imposed in the Crown Court where fines are unlimited. HSOA also makes imprisonment of individuals an option for many health and safety offences, including employees who do not take reasonable care of the health and safety of others and for Directors and senior managers. The maximum custodial term in the Magistrates' Court is 6 months and in the Crown Court 2 years.

1.7.   Contractual obligations

1.7.1   General

All work is carried out by one party instructing a second party to act; i.e. a contract is offered, consideration is shown and, once accepted, forms a contract between the parties. Although a verbal instruction can be considered a contract, the usual form will be a written and legally binding contract between the relevant parties. Employees have contracts of employment, clients have contracts with professional advisors to design structures, and clients also have contracts with organisations to construct the designed permanent works. It should be noted that unless the work is 'design and build' it is unusual for there to be a contract between the professional designer and the organisation carrying out the construction i.e. the contractor. There may be more extensive contracts for design, build, operate and, in some cases, with finance, often including risk management.

In the UK, there is a separate judicial system for handling the Civil Procedures involved in disputes both under contract law and the law of tort. Under contract law, both parties accept and agree to liabilities and duties whereas tort is a violation of a duty established by law. Liability in tort usually arises from a breach of duty established in law, and includes the tort of negligence. However, although the subject of Contract and Tort Law is outside the scope of this book (see ICE, 2011), its implication for temporary works needs to be considered.

Contracts may be based on existing industry formats such as the ICE Conditions of Contract (ICE, 1999) and the Engineering and Construction Contract (ECC), previously the New Engineering Contract (NEC3) (ICE, 2005). Contracts may also require compliance with detailed specifications. Typical specifications are Highways Agency (HA, 2006), the National Building Specification (NBS) (published annually), Civil Engineering Specification for the Water Industry (CESWI, 2011) and the National Structural Concrete Specification for Building Construction (NSCS) (CSG, 2010). The contract will place an obligation on the contractor to comply. This contractual obligation will frequently be passed on to subcontractors and suppliers, therefore obligating their compliance. The contract may also include lists of standards deemed to be included, thus making a particular British Standard a contractual requirement. Hence, although not legally enforceable as a mandatory statutory requirement, use of a particular British Standard would become obligatory under the contract. Failure to adopt the BS recommendations would therefore risk a court action for damages. This could affect the temporary works design and such obligations should be included in the temporary works design brief (see Chapter 2 on management).

There will also be contractual obligations when utilising proprietary equipment. A supplier/importer of items for use at work essentially has a statutory duty under the Health and Safety at Work Act to give advice about the equipment's use; the user, when placing an order i.e. a contract to purchase or hire such equipment, is obliged contractually to use the equipment as the supplier intended. Often the specific conditions of use assumed by the supplier/importer and incorporated by the Temporary Works Designer are stated on the drawings or in technical datasheets; for example, the use of soffit formwork to provide lateral restraint to falsework when 'top restraint' is assumed (discussed in Chapter 22) places an obligation on the site management and the user to ensure that such considerations exist in practice.

1.7.2 Functions and relationships between parties

The client will have separate contracts with one or more professional advisers and the principal contractor, with implications of privity of contract. The client will appoint a CDM coordinator. The professional adviser may contract with other professional advisers directly. The principal contractor may contract for the supply of labour, materials or both and also for hire of plant and equipment, with or without labour. Many contractors 'manage' only, and let contracts to subcontractors and other 'contractors'. On design, build and operate projects there will be one main contract, but there may be subsidiary contracts with professional advisers and management organisations.

1.7.3 Responsibilities for the temporary works

Particular contractual issues are the effect of temporary works on the permanent design, discussed in more detail in Chapter 2, and who takes responsibility for the temporary works. Responsibility for the temporary works rests with the principal contractor, and the costs are normally included in the build-up of the tender rates in the contract. Rarely is temporary works included as a bill item in the schedule of quantities. The law requires Permanent Works Designers to consider loadings from temporary works. Under certain contracts, clauses can require the contractor to provide calculations of the stresses and strains in the permanent works caused by the temporary works; this can be a significant additional cost. For example, on a major bridge it implies that the contractor has to carry out permanent works design in order to verify the construction sequence and method.

The professional advisor is responsible to the client for ensuring that the contractor's temporary works will produce a finished job which complies with the contract documents, in particular that it is not detrimental to the permanent works. This means that the professional advisor does not have a contractual duty to verify the contractor's temporary works calculations; hence the importance of the independent temporary works design checks recommended by BS 5975 (BSI, 2011) and discussed in Chapter 2. It is always important to establish the responsibilities under the various subcontracts. Phrases in the contract such as 'in accordance with recognised codes of practice' etc. will make the use of certain codes of good practice a contractual requirement.

1.8. Robustness

Temporary works often comprise a structure with many components, junctions and connections and, unlike the permanent works, are often reused a number of times and moved from site to site. Temporary works should therefore be robust enough to withstand the rigours of site use. Careful attention should be paid to the way in which components, connections and junctions are detailed to reduce the dependence on workmanship. For example, the design of a particular joint or component may be justified by calculations using a minimum thickness of section, whereas engineering judgement would dictate that using a thicker/larger section would reduce the risk of damage during transport and when in use, giving a more robust and consequently safer structure. Any critical component or connection should be inherently robust in its own right. Detailing of the temporary works should be such that local or single component failure does not lead to the progressive collapse of the whole structure. This does not imply that the design of temporary works should be over-conservative, but that due consideration should be given to providing alternative load paths so that in the event of the failure of one member or component the load may be redistributed through others. An appreciation of the way the temporary works structure behaves will lead to safe temporary works that do not progressively collapse.

1.9. Public safety

Every year construction work injures and kills people who have no direct connection to it. Some temporary works such as site hoardings, scaffold fans and public protection scaffolds are specifically provided to protect members of the public. However, any construction activity including the erection or dismantling of temporary works has the potential to cause harm not only to the construction workers but also to members of the public. The law states that business must be conducted without putting members of the public at risk. Providing suitable protection for those actually carrying out construction work will often also provide protection for others who may be affected by the works. The precautions which need to be taken to adequately protect members of the public may, however, differ from those taken to protect those working on site. The public are likely to be less aware of the dangers involved with construction activities than those working on site.

In particular, children do not have the ability to perceive danger in the same way as adults do and may see construction sites as potential playgrounds. While the numbers of children being killed or injured on construction sites has reduced, there is no room for complacency. Each year, two or three children die after gaining access to construction sites but many more are injured. Other members of the public have been seriously injured by

- materials or tools falling outside the site boundary
- falling into trenches
- being struck by moving plant and vehicles.

All construction sites require measures in place to manage access to the site through well-defined site boundaries and to exclude unauthorised persons such as members of the public. The site boundary should be physically defined, where necessary, by suitable fencing. In populated areas, this will typically mean a 2 m high small mesh fence or hoarding around the site or work area. Consideration must also be given to the provision of protection from any work activity taking place outside of the site boundary, for example, erection/dismantling of the site fencing/hoarding, utilities excavations, scaffold erection/dismantling and delivery and storage of materials.

Many hazards have the potential to injure members of the public. In particular, the following need to be considered whenever temporary works are being planned or carried out.

- *Falling objects*: ensure that objects cannot fall outside the site boundary.
- *Excavations and openings*: barriers or covers are required.
- *Delivery and site vehicles*: ensure that pedestrians cannot be struck by vehicles entering/leaving site; do not obstruct pavements so forcing pedestrians into the road.
- *Scaffolding and other access equipment*: prevent people outside the site boundary being struck during the erection, dismantling and use of scaffolding and other access equipment.
- *Slips, trips and falls within pedestrian areas*: inadequate protection of holes, uneven surfaces, poor reinstatement, trailing cables and spillage of materials are common causes.
- *Storing and stacking materials*: keep all materials within the site boundary if possible, or provide protection.

More comprehensive guidance on this subject is given in the HSE publication *Protecting the public – Your next move* (HSE, 2009).

1.10. Summary of main points

- The construction of most types of permanent works will require the use of some form of temporary works.
- All temporary works should be an 'engineered solution'.
- It is imperative that the same degree of consideration and care is given to the design and construction of the temporary works as to the design and construction of the permanent works.

- Key issues for the safety and stability of temporary works are adequate foundations, structural integrity and lateral stability.
- Coordination and cooperation is required between the temporary and the Permanent Works Designers to ensure that designs are compatible and that the permanent works can accommodate any assumed loadings from the temporary works, for example, the lateral restraint of falsework.
- The majority of construction phase plans prepared by Principal Contractors should contain the management arrangements for controlling the risks associated with temporary works, for example, suitable temporary works procedures.
- The appointment of a competent Temporary Works Coordinator is an essential step for the safe management of substantive temporary works structures.

REFERENCES

Bragg SL (1974) Interim Report of the Advisory Committee on Falsework. Department of Employment and Department of the Environment. HMSO, London.

Bragg SL (1975) Final Report of the Advisory Committee on Falsework. Department of Employment and Department of the Environment. HMSO, London.

BSI (2004) BS EN 12811-1: Temporary works equipment. Part 1: Scaffolds – Performance requirements and general design. BSI, London.

BSI (2008) BS EN 12812: Falsework – Performance requirements and general design. BSI, London.

BSI (2011) BS 5975: 2008 + A1: 2011 Code of practice for temporary works procedures and the permissible stress design of falsework. BSI, London.

CESWI (Civil Engineering Specification for the Water Industry) (2011) Civil Engineering Specification for the Water Industry, 7th edition. WRc plc, Swindon.

CITB (Construction Industry Training Board) (2007) The Construction (Design and Management) Regulations. Industry Guidance for Designers. Construction Skills, Norfolk.

Concrete Society (1971) Falsework. Report of the Joint Committee of The Concrete Society and the Institution of Structural Engineers. Technical Report TRCS 4. Concrete Society, Crowthorne.

CSG (Concrete Structures Group) (2010) National structural concrete specification for building construction, 4th edition. Publication CCIP-050, The Concrete Centre, Camberley.

HA (Highways Agency) (2006) Specification for Highway Works. Manual of Contract Documents for Highway Works. Highways Agency, London.

HSE (Health and Safety Executive) (2001) Investigation into aspects of falsework. HSE Contract Research Report 394/2001. HSE Books, Sudbury. Available at www.hse.gov.uk/research/crr_htm/2001/crr01394.htm.

HSE (2007) Managing health and safety in construction. Approved code of practice, Publication L 144, HSE Books, Sudbury.

HSE (2009) Protecting the public – Your next move. Publication HSG 151, HSE Books, Sudbury.

HSOA (Health and Safety (Offences) Act) (2008) The Health and Safety (Offences) Act. HMSO, London.

ICE (Institution of Civil Engineers) (1986–1999) *ICE Conditions of Contract*, 5th and 6th editions. ICE Publishing Ltd, London.

ICE (2005) *ECC Engineering and Construction Contract*. ICE Publishing Ltd, London.

ICE (2011) *ICE Manual of Construction Law*. Thomas Telford Publishing Ltd, London.

NASC (National Access & Scaffolding Confederation) (2008) TG20: Guide to good practice for scaffolding with tube and fittings. NASC, London (including TG20 Supplement, February 2011).

NBS (National Building Specification) (annually) Formed finishes, Section E20. National Building Specification Ltd, Newcastle-upon-Tyne.

SCOSS (Standing Committee on Structural Safety) (2002) Falsework: full circle? SCOSS Topic Paper SC/T/02/01. SCOSS, London.

WAHR (Work at Height Regulations) (2005) SI 2005/735: The Work at Height Regulations. HMSO, London (and Work at Height (Amendment) Regulations 2007).

FURTHER READING

Burrows M, Clark L, Pallett P, Ward R and Thomas D (2005) Falsework verticality: leaning towards danger? *Proceedings of ICE, Civil Engineering*, February 2005: 41–48.

ICE (Institution of Civil Engineers) (2010) *ICE Manual of Health and Safety in Construction*. Thomas Telford Publishing Ltd, London.

NASC (National Access & Scaffolding Confederation) (2010) SG25: Access and Egress from Scaffolds. NASC, London.

Smith NJ (2006) *Managing Risk in Construction Projects*, 2nd edition. Blackwell Publishing, Oxford.

Useful web addresses

http://www.hse.gov.uk/construction/index.htm

http://www.twforum.org.uk

http://books.hse.gov.uk

Temporary Works: Principles of Design and Construction
ISBN 978-0-7277-4177-6

ICE Publishing: All rights reserved
http://dx.doi.org/10.1680/twpdc.41776.015

Chapter 2
Management of temporary works

Godfrey Bowring Consultant

This chapter examines why and how temporary works and the interface between the permanent works and temporary works designers are managed and controlled. The importance and independence of the Temporary Works Coordinator (TWC) and support upon which the TWC depends from the construction team are discussed. The categories of design check to protect the team (including the operatives) from errors, omissions, misunderstandings and perhaps even the pressures of contract, programme and cost are reviewed.

2.1. Introduction

Temporary works are traditionally defined in the Institution of Civil Engineers (ICE) *Conditions of Contract* in very general terms, no doubt to preclude contractors from trying to argue that an aspect of temporary works, not specifically listed, would in some way give rise to a variation.

The *Conditions of Contract* (ICE, 1986), known as the ICE 5th Edition, defines temporary works, permanent works and the works as follows:

> ' "Permanent Works" means the permanent works to be constructed, completed and maintained in accordance with the contract. 'Temporary Works' means all temporary works of every kind required in or about the construction completion and maintenance of the Works. "Works" means the Permanent Works together with the Temporary Works.'

Temporary works could therefore be described as those elements of civil engineering works which are required to either support or enable the permanent works. Temporary works are, however, not confined to civil engineering. They are required in building, in refurbishment and in maintenance (in fact, in all areas of construction). Temporary works principles and materials are often applied to similar types of construction, for example, set design for the media, open-air concerts and temporary grandstands, all of which require temporary structures.

Traditionally, temporary works were the responsibility of the contractor with the Engineer or the Permanent Works Designer (PWD) only required to provide specific details of the permanent works design to allow the contractor to design the temporary works. With this one exception, there was negligible liaison between the permanent

15

and temporary works designers; a situation which is inconsistent with the Construction Design and Management (CDM) Regulations (HSE, 2007). See Chapter 1 on the contractual and legal aspects. Strangely, the mindset of this traditional division of responsibilities can still be found on notes on permanent works drawings to the effect that the temporary works or temporary stability of the permanent works are the responsibility of the contractor. The guidance to the CDM Regulations, *Industry Guidance for Designers* (CITB, 2007), is clear, stating that 'all designers should take full account of the temporary works, no matter who is to develop those works'. This therefore requires that both permanent works and temporary works designers consider the temporary works.

While it is often tempting to provide a list of typical temporary works such as formwork, falsework, excavation support, temporary access, scaffolding, façade retention, temporary slopes, hoardings, cofferdams, trenching, temporary jetties and crane foundations, a list can never be either exhaustive or exclusive and is something that the ICE contractual definition attempts to avoid.

Temporary works and permanent works, and the operatives and public who are entitled to depend upon their safe execution and use, are identical insofar as their being dependent upon the application of the same engineering principles. It therefore follows that the temporary works and permanent works deserve the same rigour and respect.

In the late 1960s and early 1970s, there was unfortunately a series of significant collapses of falsework and of permanent works in a temporary condition together with associated fatalities. The number and scale of these collapses was sufficient to prompt the government to commission a report into the failures. The Government Advisory Report known as the Bragg Report (Bragg, 1975) was an industry milestone, which is still held in respect. It identified a series of causes and made numerous recommendations, the most significant of which were the adoption of procedural controls, coordination between designers of permanent and temporary works, proper management of the process from inception through to loading and unloading and the appointment of a falsework coordinator to manage and be responsible for the process. Industry wisely realised that the Bragg recommendations for falsework applied equally to all temporary works and adopted the more general term Temporary Works Coordinator (TWC).

The core Bragg recommendations, which were subsequently incorporated into BS 5975 which was first published in 1986, remain as valid today as when first written. The adoption of the recommended procedural controls for temporary works in general has served industry well and has been instrumental in preventing further major collapses and failures and in promoting safe practice.

Nevertheless, research commissioned by the Health & Safety Executive (HSE, 2001; Burrows et al., 2005) showed that the basic concepts were being forgotten. This was further supported by the Standing Committee for Structural Safety (ICE/SCOSS, 2002) stating that there was 'a lack of understanding of the fundamentals of stability, at all levels of industry' and 'a lack of adequate checking and a worrying lack of design expertise'. All this serves to reinforce the Bragg recommendations and to caution against complacency.

The Bragg recommendations (Bragg, 1975) relating to coordination between designers of permanent works and temporary works (and communication between all parties in general) anticipated the fundamental principles of the CDM regulations by some 20 years. To ignore Bragg therefore risks designers being at odds with CDM regulations.

In 2008, the procedures recommended for falsework were formally introduced for *all* temporary works by publication of an updated edition of BS 5975: 2008 + A1: 2011 (BSI, 2011). This British Standard also includes the permissible stress design of false-work; see Chapter 22 on falsework for more information.

Although the use of the procedures in British Standards is not mandatory, every organisation has a legal duty to ensure that it is operating a safe method of work. This is usually embodied in its company procedures, written and specifically adapted for the operations carried out by the particular company/organisation. In many cases, the procedures recommended by BS 5975 (BSI, 2011) are incorporated into Quality Manuals, Best Practice Guidance etc., and should be followed. Company procedures are often made binding on subcontractors to ensure they follow the relevant company procedures/forms.

2.1.1 Principle objective in the management of temporary works

The principle objective is to provide temporary works that are safe in use, are sustainable, do not compromise the integrity of the associated permanent works and, finally, are cost effective to programme. This requires that all the interested parties take a disciplined and responsible approach and are informed by the lessons of the past and by current regulations and standards.

This chapter reflects UK practice, though much of what is written will apply elsewhere. It follows the procedural controls embedded in BS 5975 (BSI, 2011), but makes no attempt to either list or replicate every aspect.

2.2. The parties
2.2.1 Clients

Clients need to understand the risks associated with temporary works and ensure that the contractual and commercial framework, within which the main or principal contractor has to work, does not compromise their integrity. Moreover, clients have general responsibilities under the CDM regulations and are required 'to take reasonable steps to ensure that suitable management arrangements are in place (so that work can be carried out safely and without risk to health)' (HSE, 2007).

2.2.2 CDM Coordinator

Similarly, the CDM Coordinator (CDMC) and designers have duties under CDM (HSE, 2007). Permanent works designers must not produce designs that cannot be constructed safely (HSE, 2007; para 125) and must provide information about the risks associated with the design that will need to be managed by others (HSE, 2007; para 131–134). In simple terms, the Permanent Works Designer should consider the buildability of any temporary works required and communicate clearly the residual risks including design assumptions to the designer of the temporary works. It is no longer acceptable for a designer to attempt to abdicate responsibility by the provision of a note on the drawing stating that the contractor is responsible for all checks of temporary conditions and/or loading of the permanent works. The CDM Coordinator has a duty to ensure cooperation between the permanent and temporary works designers and ensure that the permanent works can support any loadings from temporary works (HSE, 2007; para 104). There is an argument that the coordination roles of the CDMC and the TWC overlap; both parties should therefore ensure that their coordination does not lead to omissions or ambiguity.

2.2.3 Temporary Works Designer

The Temporary Works Designer (TWD) will most likely be from a contractor, subcontractor or specialist design organisation. The TWD may utilise the services of the proprietary equipment supplier's staff, while retaining overall responsibility for design of the whole temporary works. Although the PWD has an important influence on the temporary works through drawings and specifications, the PWD will generally have little direct involvement in the design process for the temporary works; this will normally involve the contractor, subcontractor, TWD and equipment supplier. Whether the CDM Regulations encourage PWDs and TWDs to become more closely involved remains to be seen.

If all the good advice is followed, the implementation of temporary works should be relatively risk free. Regrettably, that is not always the case. The principle factors which continue to put temporary works at risk are listed in Table 2.1.

2.3. The controls

The procedural controls recommended in BS 5975 (BSI, 2011) can be summarised as follows.

2.3.1 Designated Individual

Organisations which are responsible for temporary works need to appoint a Designated Individual (DI) to be responsible for the establishment and maintenance of a procedure for the temporary works that that organisation undertakes. The DI is envisaged as being the company Chief Engineer/Operations Director or someone of similar experience and authority. BS 5975 (BSI, 2011) does not restrict the definition of an organisation to contractors. It is therefore arguable that authorities, government agencies, consulting engineers, clients and suppliers should have their own procedures, reflecting the requirements of BS 5975 and regulations in respect of their activities.

2.3.2 Temporary Works Coordinator

The next control is the appointment, for each site, of a Temporary Works Coordinator (TWC). The TWC, who is to be appointed in writing by the DI, is the named person responsible for the safe and timely management of the temporary works on site. It may also be appropriate for the DI to appoint a Deputy TWC to control the works

Table 2.1 Risk considerations in temporary works

Factor	Effect
Package management and subcontracting	Loss of ownership and therefore of responsibility for the temporary works by the principle contractor. Design interfaces and responsibilities established by commercial framework, with insufficient attention being paid to the engineering risks
Supplier design	The advice received will be partial in that the design will inevitably incorporate only the supplier's own equipment and there will be aspects which will either make fundamental assumptions or require separate design. Falsework foundations and top restraint are typical examples
Lack of understanding of temporary works and buildability by permanent works designers of permanent works	Temporary works design will be made more difficult and therefore with a higher risk. Interface between and interaction of temporary and permanent works not fully addressed
Lack of understanding of the importance of procedural control of temporary works by those entering the industry/profession	Temporary works, despite the recommendations of Bragg to the contrary in 1975, is not embedded in civil engineering education
The procedural controls within BS 5975 are not adhered to	The controls, if complied with, reduce the risk of failure to an acceptably low level. Non-compliance, either in part or in the whole, significantly increases the risk of failure

when the TWC is absent for any reason. The key point is that this deputy has both the authority and responsibility to act as the TWC when and if the TWC is absent from site for any reason.

BS 5975 makes it clear that, for a given site, the principal contractor should appoint a TWC.

It is important to realise that the TWC manages the process. It is only on the TWC's authority that the temporary works are either loaded or unloaded. The Project Manager (PM) therefore has to be aware that the TWC's role is critical to the progress of the works and is there to protect, in terms of safe working practice, the operations and operatives on site. The PM must therefore support, and moreover be seen to support, the TWC.

Interestingly, it is the PM's responsibility to manage the erection of the temporary works in the same way that it is the PM's responsibility to manage the permanent works. The

TWC's role of technical independence and responsibility for permits to load is therefore deliberately separated from the role and pressures of production, therefore minimising the risk of being compromised. In the event that the TWC believes that the support is lacking, that the role is being compromised in some way or that other duties are preventing the proper execution of the role, it is essential that the DI is informed. This confirms the earlier point that the DI has to be someone in the organisation with sufficient authority and experience to ensure that the temporary works are not compromised.

2.3.3   Temporary Works Supervisor

BS 5975 (BSI, 2011) introduced the concept of a Temporary Works Supervisor (TWS). This was intended to recognise that

- on small contracts, the appointed TWC may not have the resources to be everywhere since he is responsible for several sites or for a large complex site
- subcontractors may have responsibility for elements of temporary works within their work package.

In both cases, the Principal Contractor may find it advantageous for one or more TWSs to be nominated to act as a point of reference and to handle the day-to-day temporary works. It is therefore feasible for a subcontractor to nominate a TWS to be technically responsible for that subcontractor's temporary works within a given site, while remembering that the TWC (as a single point of reference and authority for all temporary works on that site) has the overall responsibility. Any TWS is therefore technically responsible to the TWC on all relevant matters; although the TWS may on certain sites be permitted to sign permits, this should only occur when specifically authorised.

2.4.   Principal activities of the TWC

The principal activities of the TWC, which are fully defined in BS 5975 (BSI, 2011), are to ensure that

- a register is established and maintained
- a design brief is prepared, in full consultation with all the interested parties
- residual design risks identified by the designer of the permanent works are included in the brief and considered by the designer of the temporary works
- the temporary works are properly designed
- an independent design check is undertaken, working from first principles
- the temporary works are in accordance with the checked drawings and, if so, ensure that a permit to load (bring into use) is issued
- a permit to strike/unload (take out of use) is issued when it can be demonstrated that the permanent structure has gained adequate strength and/or stability.

Each of these key activities is discussed in the following sections.

2.4.1   The temporary works register

The register is the important control document for temporary works on a site. The register should have been started during the tender period, even if the temporary works were included in subcontract packages, and should be updated and maintained throughout a contract. This ensures that the temporary works are properly identified and managed, whatever the method of procurement. The register may include items that, through methods of working, prove not to be required; it is infinitely preferable to have a register that has a number of items which are not required rather than one from which items are missing.

It should be a live register which is regularly distributed by the TWC. Moreover, it can be used to demonstrate to interested parties (including HSE inspectors and QA auditors) that the site and the temporary works are being managed safely and properly.

2.4.2 The design brief

This is probably the most important stage in the whole process; ironically, this is the stage that is probably the most frequently missed, generally by the inclusion of the temporary works packages in subcontracts. Why bother with this stage? The first key point is that the designer (and the design checker) are generally remote from site and are therefore at a disadvantage, not being privy to the TWC's detailed knowledge of the requirements and site conditions. The second key point is that having a design brief ensures that the TWC and the site team think the problem through and discuss it with all the interested parties, in particular verifying that the actual site conditions are as assumed. Check lists are an invaluable starter.

The brief should include the programme, any materials that are available, preferred methods of working and the key information from the designer of the permanent works (e.g. relevant borehole information and design risks and assumptions). It should also define the limits of responsibilities. This is best exemplified by proprietary supplier's designs for falsework which will, almost without exception, exclude the necessary foundation design and make fundamental assumptions about the ability of the permanent works to provide top restraint (see Table 2.1). In both cases, it is essential that the TWC understands the engineering principles involved and ensures that the brief identifies and resolves these and similar points fully. Note that although the TWC role is to manage the temporary works, the appointed person has to have the technical competence to understand the issues involved relevant to the nature of the work.

It should be noted that TWCs and site personnel who make decisions about methods of working or materials to be used are taking on the role and responsibilities of the designer under the CDM regulations. They may have a greater potential to affect the safety in use of a particular temporary works scheme than the designer who proves, in analytical terms, a concept that has already been decided and included in the brief. This principle is reinforced by a legal maxim in respect of design and build, which predates and even predicted the CDM Regulations to the effect that 'he who decides, designs'. This maxim is salutary.

Finally, the brief should set down the required level of information (or output) to be provided by the designer, which should comprise appropriate layouts (such as sketches and/or clear working drawings) with the particular design risks and design assumptions clearly communicated to those who need to know. This principle applies equally to a standard solution, for which the information source should be available and the limits of use and the design risks of such a solution should be clearly communicated to the TWC. Interestingly, the design risks for a standard solution will in all probability be more extensive and restrictive than for a specific bespoke design of similar character.

While all this may appear obvious, there are still proprietary suppliers whose design output is limited to a computer printout. It is therefore worth reflecting on the following points.

- Designs of temporary works and permanent works, and the operatives and public who depend upon their safe execution, depend upon the same engineering principles.
- The Project Manager and the site team expect to be provided with working drawings and specification for the permanent works. Is it not reasonable for the same team to be provided with equivalent drawings/sketches and specifications for the temporary works?
- The person undertaking the design check is required to check from first principles, given that the check is not a simple arithmetical check or a check of calculations (ICE/SCOSS, 2002). This therefore presumes that the checker should be working from drawings/sketches.
- The TWC is expected to ensure that the temporary works is inspected before loading. In so doing, it is not unreasonable to assume that the TWC requires the relevant layout and information; this may be from sketches, brochures or a number of drawings (which have been subject to a design check) against which the check prior to loading is carried out.

2.4.3   Design check

The design can be carried out in a number of ways: by individuals on site, by use of a standard solution, by company temporary works offices, by suppliers of proprietary equipment, by specialist consulting engineers and by subcontractors. Each of these will attract different risks, which should be identified in the design brief.

All temporary works designs require to be independently checked. The degree of checking should be related to the scale of the temporary works; a simple scheme may be checked by someone in the same office, whereas a more complex scheme might have to be checked by an outside organisation. The level of check may also depend on the location and the adequacy of the team members. For example, a major contractor, with many years' experience and competent operatives, would consider a 4 m trench as routine work and relatively low risk in terms of the team's competence and compliance with good practice and procedures. A small house builder, rarely digging deeper than 1 m and whose team has limited experience of significant temporary works, would, however, consider 4 m as high risk.

The four recommended categories of design checks for temporary works in BS 5975 (BSI, 2011) are listed in simplified form in Table 2.2.

It is important that the principle of a 'higher' level category of check being required when the temporary works are more complex is not misunderstood. Any design check should

Table 2.2 Categories of temporary work design check
Data taken from BS 5975 (BSI, 2011)

Category	Scope	Independence
0	Restricted to standard solutions	Site issue – by another member of site team or design team
1	Simple design: includes falsework, which does not assume top restraint (see note)	By another member of design team
2	More complex design: excavations, structural steelwork, foundations and falsework that assumes top-restraint, etc.	By individual not involved in design and not consulted by the temporary works designer
3	Complex or innovative design	By another organisation

Note: top-restrained falsework is the method by which the temporary structure is stabilised for lateral movement by connection to external restraints at its head (e.g. to the permanent works of columns or adjacent walls) provided that these elements have been designed to provide the required restraint

be carried out, by the checker, to a degree of rigour which the checker considers appropriate to enable the design check certificate to be signed. The degree of check should not vary depending on whether it is designated Category 0, 1, 2 or 3. The checking process may be more straightforward for items which have a lower category, but the checker is only ever carrying out a check that is sufficient to enable him to sign, whatever the category. The significance of the various check categories is only that they determine the degree of independence that the checker has in relation to the designer. Some items of temporary works design therefore require greater independence than others for the design check, whether because of the need to involve the thinking or experience of a second organisation or because of contractual requirements or constraints. The risk is that some checkers may consider that a lesser check is acceptable for lower category items.

Other forms of contract may have other requirements for certification of the temporary works, particularly those from the Highways Agency (HA). Temporary works on HA contracts which have a public interface will be subject to an Approval in Principle (AIP or equivalent) followed by the associated design and check certificates.

On rail contracts, a 'Form C' is required for all temporary works that affect the safety of the railways. There is also a Network Rail (NR) form covering the design, design check, NR approval and, if applicable, issue by subcontractor and approval by the zone civil engineer.

It should always be remembered that checks that are required by, or undertaken by, other organisations should in no way be considered as an alternative to or as a reason to reduce or omit any of the checking stages that the organisation responsible for the temporary works is required to undertake.

The TWC should provide the checker with the design brief, the relevant layouts and information (drawings/sketches) and the residual design risks identified by the designer of the permanent works; calculations are not normally provided. The checker's role is to carry out an independent check of the concept, working from first principles (which is why calculations are not provided). With the increasing use of computers and other design aids, the importance of simple rule-of-thumb checks should not be overlooked. The check is therefore *not* an arithmetic check of the original designer's calculations, due to the risk that a fundamental error may be repeated by the checker. The checker must issue a check certificate, which lists all the documents and drawings as necessary with their revision status. Indeed, without such a list, the design check certificate is of questionable value.

Although BS 5975 (BSI, 2011) recommends the four categories shown in Table 2.2, individual companies may have different views on the scale of works and 'simple' versus 'complex' or 'minor' versus 'major' can have different meanings. Often the categories of temporary works are defined in other terms, but the essential philosophy remains that all temporary works designs are checked from first principles. Note that use of 'unclassified' can never be used as a scale because, fundamentally, all items of temporary works have to be given a category (even if it is only 'Category 0').

2.4.4   On-site supervision and control

As referred to, the PM is the person who is responsible for the proper execution of the permanent works on site by the site team. The TWC has to ensure that the PM and the team are provided with clear drawings and other information about the temporary works design. This distinction is deliberate. In addition, any TWS (if appointed) would need to be kept informed.

2.4.5   On-site checking

In procedural terms, the TWC is responsible for ensuring that an inspection of the completed temporary works is carried out when, in the opinion of the Project Manager, it is complete. On large projects the TWC is on site and is part of the site team. It therefore follows that with any substantial temporary works erected over a period of time, the TWC and TWS should be making regular or informal inspections as the work progresses and should be notifying the site team of any issues observed. As an example, it would be sensible to carry out an inspection of the foundations before falsework was erected. None of this will compromise the TWC's independence or the final inspection. As already discussed, a TWS may be delegated by the TWC to carry out the day-to-day operations on site, which may include the checking of completed temporary works. If the TWS observes differences between the erected temporary works and the checked drawings/sketches, then the TWC should be informed. It may be necessary for the TWC to refer back to the TWD.

Finally, and only when the TWC is in all respects satisfied, the TWC (or TWS where authorised) signs and issues a permit to load to the Project Manager, which will generally be limited in time. If the TWS is authorised to sign the permit, the TWC must also be included in the process as the single point of authority and responsibility. It would be incorrect to issue a permit to load falsework some weeks in advance of a pour date, given the inclination of site teams to use misplaced initiative and 'borrow' key components for another element of temporary works. Falsework permits are therefore normally issued the day before and are valid for the following day only. The actions of anyone on the site team who wilfully loaded temporary works in full knowledge that the permit had been withheld or had not been issued would normally be treated as a disciplinary matter.

The TWC can inevitably come under immense commercial pressure from the site team to sign and avoid delay and cost. It is in these situations that the TWC has to have sufficient strength of character and the confidence and full support of the PM. Given the consequence of failure, the presumption is that the TWC has to withhold permission if there is sufficient doubt.

Checklists for some temporary works have been issued; refer to available guidance on falsework (Concrete Society, 1999), formwork (Concrete Society, 2001) and trenching (CIRIA, 2001).

2.4.6   Permit to unload

This is the final stage. While the loading of the temporary works is formally controlled, the unloading or transfer of load to the permanent works must also be assessed and controlled. This stage can generate loadings of the temporary works (and permanent works) that are significantly different to those imposed when they are loaded. A particular case would be the transfer of load through multi-storey structures when back-propping. It is therefore clear that the unloading requires communication and cooperation between the TWC and the designers of the permanent and temporary works, as required by the CDM regulations.

For concrete structures, the value and method of assessing the concrete strength at the time of striking should be agreed beforehand with the PWD and carefully controlled on site. Modern methods of strength assessment are now available; see Chapter 24 on soffit formwork.

Structures that combine temporary works with prestressing of the permanent works or multi-storey floor slab construction with a requirement for back-propping need careful planning and control. The exact order of removal of supports can affect the load transfer, so the permit to unload should state any required sequence or procedures for striking or unloading the structure.

2.5.   Summary

This chapter describes the background to and the reasons why and how temporary works are managed and controlled. It has not sought to repeat fully the detailed procedural points in BS 5975 (BSI, 2011). The TWC's role is to protect the team, including the operatives, from errors, omissions, misunderstandings and perhaps even the pressures of programme and cost. The TWC can be assisted by a TWS, but remains the responsible person.

Failures of temporary works can all too easily cause serious injury or fatalities with the associated distress to families and, in all probability, legal action. Contracts will incur delay and cost that is difficult to recover. The industry relies upon and therefore owes it to those who work with, within, on, or under temporary works to follow the established procedures. In the event of failure and enquiry or legal action, individuals must be able to demonstrate that established practice rules have been followed.

Finally, while it can never be an absolute rule, failures are generally caused by a series or combination of factors. It follows that such failures can best be prevented by the consistent application of a similar series of checks and balances; this is why temporary works are controlled.

REFERENCES

Bragg SL (1975) Final Report of the Advisory Committee on Falsework. Department of Employment and Department of the Environment. HMSO, London.

BSI (2011) BS 5975: 2008 + A1: 2011 Code of practice for temporary works procedures and the permissible stress design of falsework. BSI, London.

Burrows M, Clark L, Pallett P, Ward R and Thomas D (2005) Falsework verticality: leaning towards danger? Proceedings of ICE, *Civil Engineering*, February 2005: 41–48.

CIRIA (Construction Industry Research and Information Association) (2001) *Trenching Practice*, 2nd edition. CIRIA Report 97, London.

CITB (Construction Industry Training Board) (2007) The Construction (Design and Management) Regulations. Industry Guidance for Designers. Construction Skills, Norfolk.

Concrete Society (1999) Checklist for Erecting and Dismantling Falsework. Ref CS123. Concrete Society, Crowthorne.

Concrete Society (2003) Checklist for the Assembly, Use and Striking of Formwork. Ref CS144. Concrete Society, Crowthorne.

HSE (Health and Safety Executive) (2001) Investigation into aspects of falsework. HSE Contract Research Report 394/2001, HSE Books, Sudbury. Available at www.hse.gov.uk/research/crr_htm/2001/crr01394.htm.

HSE (2007) Managing Health and Safety in Construction, Approved code of practice. Publication L 144, HSE Books, Sudbury (including Construction (Design and Management) Regulations 2007).

ICE (Institution of Civil Engineers) (1986) *ICE Conditions of Contract*, 5th edition. Thomas Telford Publishing Ltd, London.

ICE/SCOSS (Institution of Civil Engineers/Standing Committee on Structural Safety) (2002) Falsework: Full Circle? Report on Temporary Works, Topic Paper SC/T/02/01, London.

Useful web addresses

http://books.hse.gov.uk
http://www.construct.org.uk
http://www.temporaryworks.info
http://www.twforum.org.uk

Temporary Works: Principles of Design and Construction
ISBN 978-0-7277-4177-6

ICE Publishing: All rights reserved
http://dx.doi.org/10.1680/twpdc.41776.027

Chapter 3
Site compounds and set-up

Geoff Miles Quality Manager, Costain

Typically, a construction project manager may be responsible for completing the design and build of a new £40M facility over a timescale of 2.5 years. In terms of his role and responsibilities, that makes him the equivalent of the CEO of a small-to-medium 'start-up' enterprise, with revenue of £16M in the first year. In most other industries, manufacturers already have their permanent, sophisticated, production facilities fully operational before they take on new orders for clients. Upon award of a new contract, and within just a few weeks, Builders and Civil Engineers have to first create their 'temporary factory and welfare facilities' on a distant site before they can start their client's work. They establish (or set-up) this often concurrently with commencement of delivery of the permanent works. Set-up requires management of a very large number of trades. This chapter provides advice on the range of items that may need to be designed, costed and included in the project preliminaries cost plan.

3.1. Introduction

Apart from the obvious operational needs to provide production facilities, the following legislation imposes obligations on all parties involved when working in the UK: The Health and Safety at Work Act (1974); The Management of Health and Safety at Work Regulations (1999); The Construction (Design and Management) Regulations (2007); The Workplace (Health, Safety and Welfare) Regulations (1992).

Under the CDM regulations (2007), Clients, Designers, Principal Contractors and Contractors all have specific duties.

The Client must make sure that the construction phase does not start unless there are suitable welfare facilities and a construction phase plan in place. The Principal Contractor must plan, manage and monitor the construction phase in liaison with contractors; prepare, develop and implement a written plan and site rules (the initial plan must be completed before the construction phase begins); ensure that suitable welfare facilities are provided from the start and maintained throughout the construction phase; and secure the site.

The Contractor must plan, manage and monitor their work and that of their workers and ensure there are adequate welfare facilities for their workers. Where contractors are involved in design work, including for temporary works, they also have duties as designers. When working overseas or in other jurisdictions, advice should be sought

27

regarding any local requirements and obligations. Otherwise, the UK standard is a good model to use to provide a safe and healthy working environment for employees in any location, at home or overseas.

The best time to plan and quantify the detailed compound, offices and welfare requirements is during the Early Contractor Involvement or Tender Planning stage. It is important to have a detailed solution in place in order to estimate the preliminary cost budget accurately.

Table 3.1 provides a generic list of what may need to be planned, designed and costed. This should be carefully considered and edited to exclude any unnecessary items. Equally, any missing site-specific items missing should be added.

A detailed description of issues including land and access; communications, energy, clean water supply and waste water disposal; office and welfare accommodation space planning; and materials (unloading, distribution, fabrication, handling, storage and testing) is provided in the following sections.

Table 3.1 Generic list of items possibly requiring attention

Subject	Description	Design output required
Land	Environmental survey: flood risk, tidal impact, earthquakes, subsidence landslides, etc.	Report
	Land survey of site	Survey drawing 1 : 100
	Soils geotechnical survey	Soils report
	Phasing and location to suit permanent works	Drawings and programme
	Existing utility services survey	CAT survey, CCTV survey, drawings and utility correspondence
Access	Highways entrance/exit and diversions	Design, layout drawing 1 : 100, details 1 : 20, 1 : 10 and specification
	Wharf/harbour/jetty	Design, layout drawing 1 : 100, details 1 : 20, 1 : 10 and specification
	On site haul roads and pathways	Design, layout drawing 1 : 100, details 1 : 20, 1 : 10 and specification
	Bridges (vehicle and pedestrian)	Design, specification, layout drawing 1 : 100, base (civils) details and steel fabrication drawings
	Vehicle weighbridge	Design, specification, 1 : 100 layout drawing, base (civils) details and weighbridge drawings
	Wheelwash	Design, specification, 1 : 100 plant layout drawing, and base (civils) details
	Airstrip and/or helipad	Design, layout drawing 1 : 100, details 1 : 20, 1 : 10 and specification

Table 3.1 Continued

Subject	Description	Design output required
Access	Public access, diversions	Design, layout drawing 1:100, details 1:20, 1:10 and specification
	Traffic light controls	Design, layout drawing 1:100, details 1:20, 1:10 and specification
	Rail branch/siding/platform	Design, layout drawing 1:100, details 1:20, 1:10 and specification
	Highways licences	Application form and letter of submission
Water	Desalination plant	Design, specification, 1:100 plant layout drawing and base (civils) details
	Borehole and treatment plant	Design, specification, 1:100 plant layout drawing and base (civils) details
	Metered water supply from existing infrastructure	Design, layout drawing 1:100, details 1:20, 1:10 and specification
	Tanker/Bowser hard-standing and connection point	Design, layout drawing 1:100, details 1:20, 1:10 and specification
	Water storage tank, pumps and distribution pipework	Design, specification, 1:100 plant layout drawing and base (civils) details
	Dust suppression and wheelwash	Design, layout drawing 1:100, details 1:20, 1:10 and specification
	Trenches, ductwork for buried services	Design, layout drawing 1:100, details 1:20, 1:10 and specification
	Fire-fighting provisions for compound and building work in progress	Design, layout drawing 1:100, details 1:20, 1:10 and specification
	Insulation and trace heating to protect pipework	Design, layout drawing 1:100, details 1:20, 1:10 and specification
Electricity	Metered electricity supply from existing network	Design, layout drawing 1:100, details 1:20, 1:10 and specification
	Generator and diesel tanks, refuelling logistics (emergency or permanent)	Design, specification, 1:100 plant layout drawing and base (civils) details
	Electrical distribution power and lighting including 110 V, major plant, etc.	Design, layout drawing 1:100, details 1:20, 1:10 and specification
	Substation/switchgear building	Design, specification, 1:100 layout drawing, building details and plant drawings
	Trenches and ductwork for buried services	Design, layout drawing 1:100, details 1:20, 1:10 and specification
	Construction site electrical regulation testing regime	Specification and method statement

Table 3.1 Continued

Subject	Description	Design output required
Electricity	Environmental impact assessment (for diesel spillage, etc.)	Report
	Security fencing to protect electrical equipment	Design, layout drawing 1:100, details 1:20, 1:10 and specification
	PAT testing regime	Specification and method statement
Gas	Metered gas supply from existing network	Design, layout drawing 1:100, details 1:20, 1:10 and specification
	Bulk LPG tank	Design, specification, 1:100 plant layout drawing and base (civils) details
	Gas distribution pipework	Design, layout drawing 1:100, details 1:20, 1:10 and specification
	Gas valve and meter building	Design, specification, 1:100 plant layout drawing and building details
	Trench and ductwork for buried services	Design, layout drawing 1:100, details 1:20, 1:10 and specification
	Construction site gas regulation testing regime	Specification and method statement
	Environmental impact assessment (for gas leakage, etc.)	Report
	Security fencing re gas equipment	Design, layout drawing 1:100, details 1:20, 1:10 and specification
	Automatic safety and shutoff systems	Design, layout drawing 1:100, details 1:20, 1:10 and specification
Voice and data	Aerial/dish mast base	Design, layout drawing 1:100, details 1:20, 1:10 and specification
	Satellite receiver switched link	Design, layout drawing 1:100, details 1:20, 1:10 and specification
	Cooper wire, switched link	Design, layout drawing 1:100, details 1:20, 1:10 and specification
	Fibre-optic, switched link	Design, layout drawing 1:100, details 1:20, 1:10 and specification
	Data and voice wiring network	Design, layout drawing 1:100, details 1:20, 1:10 and specification
	Cable ducts and draw-pit layout	Design, layout drawing 1:100, details 1:20, 1:10 and specification
	Voice and data equipment schedule	Schedule
	Internal communication system – radios	Schedule
Security	Fire alarm system	Fire alarm system schematic drawing 1:100 and specification

Table 3.1 Continued

Subject	Description	Design output required
Security	Intruder alarm system	Intruder alarm system schematic drawing 1 : 100 and specification
	CCTV system/webcam systems	CCTV system/webcam system schematic drawing 1 : 100 and specification
Wastewater	Outfall connection to existing sewers	Design, drawing 1 : 100, details 1 : 20, 1 : 10 and specification
	Temporary foul and surface water drainage above and below ground	Design, drawing 1 : 100, details 1 : 20, 1 : 10 and specification
	Sewage storage/treatment plant	Design, drawing 1 : 100, details 1 : 20, 1 : 10 and specification
	Land drainage	Design, drawing 1 : 100, details 1 : 20, 1 : 10 and specification
	Sewage collection and removal from site	Assessment of tanker size and number of visits
	Environmental impact assessment of wastewater	Report
Welfare	Facilities for all site personnel	General arrangement layout drawing 1 : 100
	Predicted manpower plan	Labour histogram produced from bar-chart programme
	Canteen	Detailed room drawings 1 : 50
	Drying room	Detailed room drawings 1 : 50
	Changing room	Detailed room drawings 1 : 50
	M and F toilets	Detailed room drawings 1 : 50
	Showers and emergency showers	Detailed room drawings 1 : 50
	Living accommodation on site	Detailed room drawings 1 : 50
	Health and first-aid	Detailed room drawings 1 : 50
	Remote welfare facilities about site	Detailed room drawings 1 : 50
Offices	Facilities for all management staff	General arrangement layout drawing 1 : 100
	Management organogram	Organisation chart
	Subcontractors offices	Detailed room drawings 1 : 50
	Main contractors offices	Detailed room drawings 1 : 50
	Office furniture layout	Detailed workstation and furniture layout drawing 1 : 50
	IT office equipment	Detailed IT, printing and office equipment layout drawing 1 : 50
	Filing system/room	Detailed room drawings 1 : 50
	Stationery store	Detailed room drawings 1 : 50
	Cleaners store	Detailed room drawings 1 : 50
	M and F toilets	Detailed room drawings 1 : 50
	Print room	Detailed room drawings 1 : 50
	Drawings room	Detailed room drawings 1 : 50

Table 3.1 Continued

Subject	Description	Design output required
Offices	Meeting rooms	Detailed room drawings 1:50
Gantry	For congested sites (usually inner city)	Structural steelwork design layout and fabrication drawings
	Highways licence	Application form and letter of submission
Materials	Storage buildings	Design, drawing 1:100, details 1:20, 1:10 and specification
	Lay down areas	Design, drawing 1:100, details 1:20, 1:10 and specification
	Unloading plant	Plant and equipment specifications
	Unloading labour	Labour histogram
	Racking	Design, drawing 1:100, details 1:20, 1:10 and specification
	Pallets and packing timber	Assessment of quantities required
	Tarpaulins	Assessment of quantities required
Materials handling	Crane	Schedule of lifts (hook time analysis)
	Forklift	Assessment of loads/quantities
	Lorry	Assessment of loads/quantities
	Tractor and trailer	Assessment of loads/quantities
Materials testing	Laboratory	Design, drawing 1:100, details 1:20, 1:10 and specification
	Sample room small items	Design, drawing 1:100, details 1:20, 1:10 and specification
	Sample testing external storage area	Design, drawing 1:100, details 1:20, 1:10 and specification
	Samples area external	Design, drawing 1:100, details 1:20, 1:10 and specification
Compound	Temporary soil heaps	Location and design drawing 1:100, and specification
	Hard-standings	Design, drawing 1:100, details 1:20, 1:10 and specification
	Fencing	Design, drawing 1:100, details 1:20, 1:10 and specification
	Hoarding	Design, drawing 1:100, details 1:20, 1:10 and specification
	Noise Screens	Design, drawing 1:100, details 1:20, 1:10 and specification
	Gates	Design, drawing 1:100, details 1:20, 1:10 and specification
	Vehicle entry barrier	Design, drawing 1:100, details 1:20, 1:10 and specification

Table 3.1 Continued

Subject	Description	Design output required
Compound	Security hut	Design, drawing 1 : 100, details 1 : 20, 1 : 10 and specification
	Electronic turnstile	Design, drawing 1 : 100, details 1 : 20, 1 : 10 and specification
	Lighting	Design, drawing 1 : 100, details 1 : 20, 1 : 10 and specification
	Car-park and cycling racks	Design, drawing 1 : 100, details 1 : 20, 1 : 10 and specification
	Footpaths	Design, drawing 1 : 100, details 1 : 20, 1 : 10 and specification
	Signage	Design, drawing 1 : 100, details 1 : 20, 1 : 10 and specification
	PA system	Design, drawing 1 : 100, details 1 : 20, 1 : 10 and specification
	Fire stations and assembly	Layout drawing 1 : 100
	Designated smoking areas	Layout drawing 1 : 100
Waste management	Skip standing and segregation area	Design, drawing 1 : 100, details 1 : 20, 1 : 10 and specification
	Concrete plant 'wash out' area	Design, drawing 1 : 100, details 1 : 20, 1 : 10 and specification
	Food refuse bins and storage	Design, drawing 1 : 100, details 1 : 20, 1 : 10 and specification
	Incinerator	Design, drawing 1 : 100, details 1 : 20, 1 : 10 and specification
Plant maintenance	Refuelling station and fuel storage	Design, drawing 1 : 100, details 1 : 20, 1 : 10 and specification
	Recharging station; battery-powered vehicles	Design, drawing 1 : 100, details 1 : 20, 1 : 10 and specification
	Vehicle repairs and maintenance bay	Design, drawing 1 : 100, details 1 : 20, 1 : 10 and specification
Workshop buildings	Onsite fabrication shop	Design, drawing 1 : 100, details 1 : 20, 1 : 10 and specification
	Welding shop	Design, drawing 1 : 100, details 1 : 20, 1 : 10 and specification
	Painting shop	Design, drawing 1 : 100, details 1 : 20, 1 : 10 and specification
	Pre-cast concrete factory	Design, drawing 1 : 100, details 1 : 20, 1 : 10 and specification

3.2.   Land and access
3.2.1   Site visit and inspection
A visual feel for the site, its surroundings and accessibility is critical. Sufficient time should be taken to walk the site perimeter and across the central areas, and photographs taken or a film made.

Access routes should also be walked, especially in remote areas away from major roads or in congested town centres where many restrictions can apply (e.g. limited access in length, width, height and axle-weight). Look for overhead cables, noise and time limitations.

To prepare for a site visit, contact all relevant authorities and request copies of their drawings showing all existing infrastructure, i.e. roads, sewers, water mains, electricity cables, gas mains and communications cables. During the site visit make a point of finding physical proof of items such as manholes, draw-pits, valve access covers, fire hydrants, substations and cable pylons or poles shown on the drawings provided. Also identify all potential locations for the site compound(s).

3.2.2   Site surveys for topography, ground conditions (geotechnical) and environmental impact
If not already done, arrange for these surveys to be carried out as early as possible; it can take between four weeks and three months to procure, carry out and publish the survey reports. The analysis, testing, reports and recommendations on their findings are just some of the fundamental prerequisites before being able to begin designing and drawing details of the temporary compound and accommodation. The remaining pre-requisites are the work breakdown schedules, programme, resource histograms, methods statements, general attendance and special attendance requirements of the package contractors. This information should be requested and submitted with their quotations as supporting documentation. All tender enquiries for the permanent work packages must therefore be sent out and quotations returned during the same period that survey reports are being prepared. This approach ensures that all the information needed is available to start detailed compound and temporary facilities designs.

3.2.3   Locating the compound
The ideal location for the compound is one that can remain in place for the full duration of the contract, and not interfere with the permanent works or compromise the working space to carry them out.

Finding that location requires detailed analysis and sketch modelling of the drawings and specifications provided for the permanent works. The timing of the availability of such information depends very much on the two principal methods of procurement, either

■ traditional: the Client provides a complete, fully detailed design, specification and bill of quantities for the main contractor/specialist subcontractors to price or
■ design and build: the Client provides a schematic design and performance specification requiring the main contractor/specialist subcontractors to complete the detailed design, specification, materials take-off and cost plan.

Figure 3.1 Site compound for a road project
Courtesy of Costain

In cases where the detailed design will not be completed pre-tender or pre-guaranteed maximum price, then the following options must be considered

- the use of a piece of land or an existing building close to the site (this removes the risk of the temporary set-up being in the way of the permanent works), or
- include for relocating the set-up in the tender cost budget.

On high-security sites such as nuclear facilities, prisons and airports, it is beneficial to have two contractor's compounds. One should be located outside the secure perimeter to make people access, deliveries and storage easier to manage and control. Office space for Project Management, Commercial and Administration support staff is best placed in this compound. A second compound should be located inside the secure perimeter to provide welfare facilities for operatives and office space for the Production Management staff.

Lease negotiations for land and premises can take a considerable time. This will involve securing the option to lease contracts and obtaining outline planning approval during the tender or 'early contractor involvement' period. Without these, it would be irresponsible to include assumptions about their availability for use in any tender submissions.

See Figures 3.1 and 3.2 for typical compound layouts for a road project and a small site.

Figure 3.2 Compound GA for a small site
Courtesy of Costain

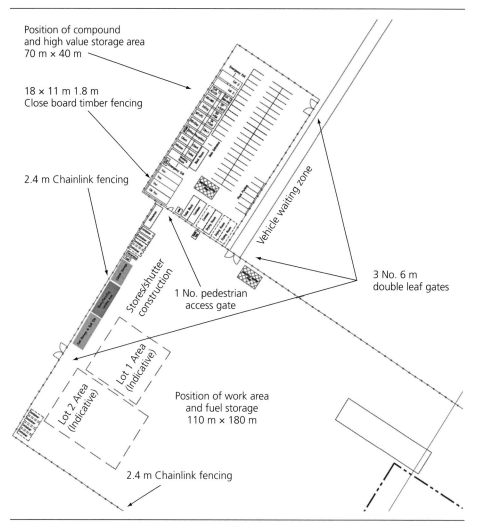

Position of compound
and high value storage area
70 m × 40 m

18 × 11 m 1.8 m
Close board timber fencing

2.4 m Chainlink fencing

Stores/shutter
construction

Lot 1 Area
(Indicative)

Lot 2 Area
(Indicative)

1 No. pedestrian
access gate

Vehicle waiting zone

3 No. 6 m
double leaf gates

Position of work area
and fuel storage
110 m × 180 m

2.4 m Chainlink fencing

3.2.4   Infrastructure link-up

In well-developed areas there are two other important matters to consider

- the proximity of utilities to connect up to, i.e. sewers, water mains, electricity mains, gas mains, telecommunications cable network, and
- access between the road network and site for cars and heavy goods vehicles.

Established roads and utilities infrastructure may not exist in remote or under-developed areas and so energy and water sources, water treatment, communications and transport links have to be considered from first principles. Provision for designing and constructing the following should be included.

- Energy source: power station, substation, overhead transmission cables.
- Water source: pipeline, borehole, river or sea water intake, dam with a reservoir.
- Water treatment: purification plant for clean water, sewage treatment plant for waste water.
- Communications: overhead cables, satellite receiver dish, aerial mast.
- Transport links: roadway, airstrip, harbour with quayside, helipad, railway siding, canal.

3.3. Communications, energy, clean water supply and wastewater disposal

3.3.1 Communications

It is now the expected business standard to provide internet access on site for all management personnel. Advances in technology for mobile devices means we now only need a single lightweight handheld device for laptop and mobile phone. These are very handy but have a short battery time and limited upload/download capacity. For the longer term, a larger keyboard, display screen and computing power in the site office, hard-wired up to the internet via fibre-optic links, is still a necessity.

IT systems, software and support are high cost overheads. Profit margins in construction are notoriously low, generally between 1 and 2%. Budgets for IT investment are therefore very low compared to other, more profitable industries. As a result, only basic services and systems are affordable.

In the UK, the mobilisation lead time for a new cable internet link, measured from placing an order to commissioning, is on average 20 weeks. However, there is rarely more than 4–6 weeks between signing contracts and being expected to make a start and have a management team based on site.

Two types of IT solution are therefore required as follows.

1 During the first 20 weeks, use mobile 3G or satellite receiver systems. These provide an instant email and database service. Performance is variable and often frustratingly slow, but is better than no service at all.
2 In the period leading up to week 20, the local area cable network (LAN), switchgear and fibre-optic/copper-wired link will be installed and 'go live'. The LAN will be used from week 20 for the remaining duration of the project, linking users to shared equipment such as printers, plotters, scanners, internet and telephones. Access to the project database and documents will be available at acceptable upload/download speeds.

Before deciding on a system and placing supplier orders, two steps are required. For the first step, a briefing document must be drawn up to pass to the IT system designer. This is comprised of three parts: as follows.

1 A questionnaire asking for site address and project duration with the start and completion dates; number of users; software required and the type of web-based

document sharing system; and types and number of shared equipment such as printers, plotters, scanners, internet, telephones, projectors, etc.

2   A compound layout drawing and a detailed office plan layout drawing showing the positions of communications hub room, work stations, printers, plotters, scanners, telephones and projectors. Positions of data socket outlets should be drawn on the plan, including some in the meeting room(s). It is prudent to have a few extra socket outlets included for visiting 'hot desk' users.

3   A site location map.

The brief is passed to the IT systems designer in the second step so that a fully costed IT system specification and design can be produced. This should always be checked and explained to ensure that the proposals are a correct interpretation of the brief.

3.3.2   Energy

Electricity is the most popular and flexible energy to use. Reliable sources include either: national grid or local distribution cable networks; or hired electricity generators (commonly diesel engine powered). Generators can also be driven by gas engine or turbine or even jet engine. The choice of fuel will depend on safety risk assessment, availability and cost. Isolated wind power and hydro-electric alternatives are not reliable.

Estimating demand for electricity

In estimating demand for electricity, the first step is to produce a schematic electrical system layout which resembles a hierarchical pyramid. Start at the base by naming each temporary building or purpose zone within the compound and list every electrical energy-consuming item within each along with its energy consumption rating in kilowatts, including the following.

■   In offices: power socket outlets, light fittings, space heaters, water heaters, domestic appliances, office equipment, IT and communications switchgear, fire alarm, intruder alarm, access control, trace heating.

■   In welfare facilities: power socket outlets, light fittings, space heaters, water heaters, domestic appliances, kitchen equipment, fire alarm, intruder alarm, access control, trace heating.

■   Compound: external lighting, CCTV system, access control, vehicle entry barrier, weighbridge, wheel-wash, battery charging plug-in sockets for large battery-powered moving plant.

■   Materials storage shed: power socket outlets, light fittings, space heating, fire alarm, intruder alarm, access control, dehumidifier.

■   Materials testing laboratory: power socket outlets, light fittings, space heating, fire alarm, intruder alarm, access control, trace heating, cube curing tank, special test equipment.

■   Maintenance workshop: power socket outlets, light fittings, space heating, fire alarm, intruder alarm, access control, welding equipment, hoist and vehicle inspection ramp.

■   Fabrication workshop: power socket outlets, light fittings, space heating, fire alarm, intruder alarm, access control, overhead gantry crane, manufacturing plant, welding equipment.

- Items of major plant located in the compound or elsewhere on site, for example, tower cranes, concrete batching/mixing plant, mortar silo mixers, materials or passenger hoists, etc.
- Site distribution to transformers on all floor levels to provide power outlets for 110 V power tools, welding points in plant rooms, etc.
- Site distribution to all floor levels for temporary lighting, fire alarm system, etc.

Using the schematic described above as well as utilisation factors, the total electricity demand can be calculated and used to pick the most economical source of supply.

The second step is to prepare a detailed distribution layout plan showing cable sizes, routing and switchgear locations. In order to do this, the electrical engineer will need the completed detailed compound layout plan and temporary buildings layout plans. Distribution of electricity on site is covered by BS 7375 (BSI, 2010).

3.3.3 Clean water supply

All the water needed on a project for both welfare and construction purposes must be clean and free from impurities (potable is preferable). The daily consumption should be estimated over the duration of the project to establish the required quantity and flow rate of water required. To carry out this estimate, a schematic diagram will be drawn up to show all hot and cold water appliances in welfare facilities and draw-off points for standpipes, mortar silo mixers, concrete mixers, wheel-wash plant, etc. The water treatment, storage and distribution pipework/pumping scheme can then be designed. For high-rise or multi-storey buildings, vertical risers are required with a tap-off point on each floor level. Include an allowance for frost protection by having trace heating and insulation to all pipework.

Once the total quantity and flow rate required has been calculated, the next step is to decide upon a water source. Depending upon the location, the choices of source will be one of the following.

- Connect to the existing water mains supply. Obtain an application form from the relevant water supply company and apply for a new (temporary) metered water supply pipe. They provide a proposal and quotation for the supply. Once they have received payment for the quoted sum, they then install their pipework from their mains (including a water meter) up to a stop valve located at the site boundary. Water usage is paid for on a rate per cubic metre.
- Import water by bulk tanker. Again, obtain an application form from the relevant water supply company and apply for them to supply water in bulk tankers. They provide a proposal and quotation for the supply. Once they have received payment for the quoted sum, they will commence deliveries. Water usage is paid for on a rate per cubic metre. A tanker hard-standing area is required with suitable valve chambers to allow the tanker discharge pipes to be connected to the site network.
- Extract water from a river, a borehole or the sea. Water extraction licences and borehole drilling licences have to be applied for and granted before proceeding

with this option. Water pumps, purification plant and clean water 'buffer' storage tanks are required. When using seawater, desalination plant is also needed.

- Build a dam and form a reservoir. This option would only be the choice of last resort. Obtaining local planning permission will be necessary before proceeding. Water pumps, purification plant and clean water 'buffer' storage tanks are required.

3.3.4 Wastewater disposal

Foul water from all toilets, sinks, wash basins and canteen equipment has to be collected and treated before it can be discharged back to nature. A system of pipework and manholes needs to be designed and drawn, to connect up all the waste outlets and drain into one of the following

- an existing main foul water sewer system adjacent to the site
- a waste collection tank located above or below ground (this will require frequent emptying by a suction tanker and the waste transported to the nearest sewage works for disposal and treatment)
- temporary sewage treatment works built on site (last-resort option which requires local planning permission to be obtained before proceeding).

Similarly, surface water from roofs, guttering, hard-standings, car parks and roads has to be collected by a system of pipework, manholes, petrol interceptors and disposed of by one of the following methods

- connecting to a main storm-water sewer system adjacent to the site
- connection to underground soakaway constructed on site as part of the system
- connection to a Catchment and Settlement pond constructed on site (if there is a watercourse adjacent, the pond can have an overflow; otherwise they are designed large enough to rely upon evaporation).

Groundwater arising from the works has to be properly disposed of by a controlled method. This water can be from one of several sources, as listed below.

- From ground surface run-off during rainstorms. A system of ditches, land drains and silt traps linked to a soak-away should be designed.
- From groundwater seeping into excavations. This is normally dealt with by excavating sump holes to collect the water and then pump it into a settlement tank, before pumping it to a soakaway or settlement pond.
- From the de-watering of deep substrata to allow excavation below the water table. A typical dewatering scheme will comprise a series of well points connected via a common header collection pipe to the suction side of a large pump. The pump runs constantly and the discharge water is passed into a segmented settlement tank. The water is then discharged into a soakaway or settlement pond. Water quality should be monitored by daily sampling. Consideration should be given to include piezotubes in the de-watering design to allow water sampling at depth.

3.4.   Office and welfare accommodation space planning

Detailed work on drawing up plans for site offices, meeting rooms, changing rooms, toilets, drying rooms, canteens, etc., can only start once the number of people that have to be catered for and the time they will spend on the site has been estimated. A detailed bar chart programme of work and a resource histogram for both management and operatives is therefore needed.

Once these quantities are known, the following must then be considered.

- Segregation or integration: the need to separate people relative to their job roles, work groups, different employers and for reasons of privacy. Bringing multi-disciplinary teams together in an open-plan environment has become common practice. There will be a requirement to provide different-sized meeting rooms for privacy and confidentiality.
- Productivity and quality: open-plan offices should not be assumed. Construction site offices are notoriously noisy. Many technical and managerial job roles require privacy, relative quietness, wall space to display bar chart programmes, table-top space to layout two AO or A1 size drawings side by side, filing cabinet, cupboard and a desk. Providing individual offices where needed will improve productivity, quality and staff motivation. Regular team meetings should be used to open up lines of communication.
- Communication and motivation: operatives need a good-quality canteen and welfare facilities. Break times are short and time spent away from the workface must be minimised. Design seating and table layouts that allow sufficient places for all to be served in 'one sitting'. Employees should not have to sit in a van to eat due to lack of space. Equally important are changing, clothes drying and shower rooms. Workers should not be expected to travel to work in their overalls or dirty clothes. The induction/training room needs to be a dedicated space and large enough to accommodate daily new arrivals for Safety, Health and Environment (SHE) inductions and to accommodate all operatives for shift briefings.
- Storage and records: separate and secure rooms with ventilation and temperature control for IT switchgear 'hub' cabinet and document filing.
- Modular or volumetric accommodation system: there are numerous suppliers and systems to choose from. Cost comparisons will need to take into account any foundations required, setting up and dismantling, craneage and transport and connectivity (i.e. prewired and only needing to be 'plugged in').

Deciding upon and drawing up room layout and furniture plan is a fairly straight-forward exercise. Most suppliers of modular accommodation have standard generic drawings available to use or modify into site-specific layouts. In cases where existing buildings are used as temporary facilities, obtain floor plans from the landlord or carry out a dimension survey of all rooms and draw the floor plan. The completed furniture layouts are also used to show small power, data and voice socket outlet positions. Figure 3.3 shows a typical layout of office and welfare facilities.

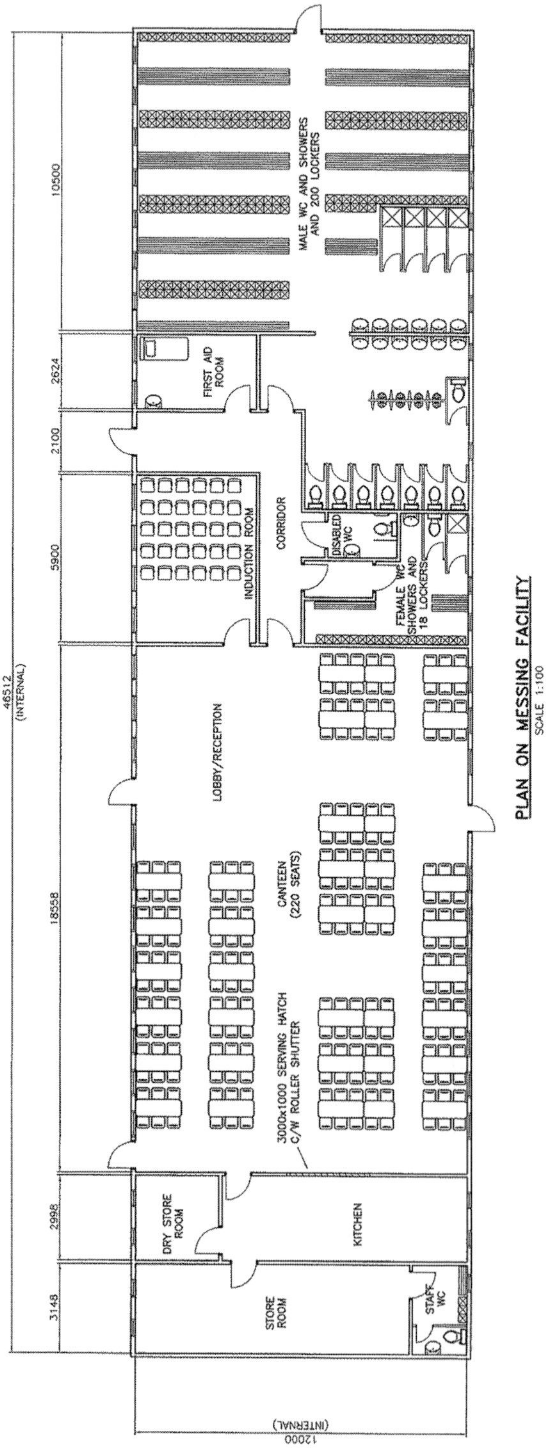

Figure 3.3 Site office and welfare example
Courtesy of Costain

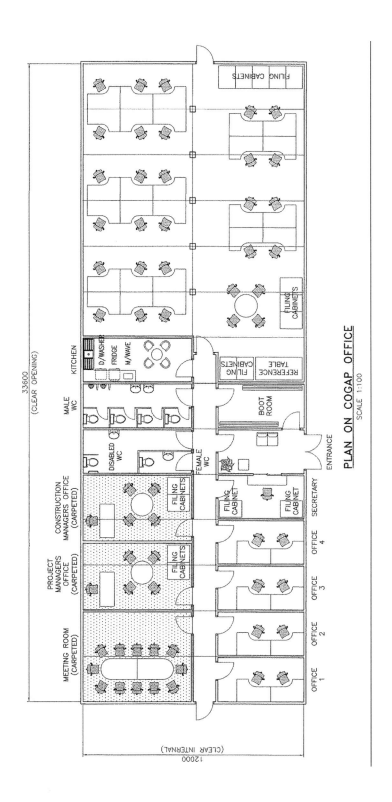

PLAN ON COGAP OFFICE
SCALE 1:100

43

3.5. Materials (distribution, fabrication, handling, storage, testing and unloading)

There is a huge variety of length, width, height, weight, shape and physical nature of construction materials and components ranging from lightweight, small items such as screws or nails up to heavyweight, large prefabricated modules.

When considering the choices for deciding on the load size, the method of delivery onto site, storage and movement to the workface, principal considerations including the following.

- Roads, hard-standings and bridges: weight and size restrictions/requirements.
- Mechanical handling plant: self-weight, lifting capacity, availability and utilisation efficiency.
- Manual handling: maximum weight restrictions.
- Temporary storage areas or buildings: capacity, weight and size limitations/ requirements, dry environment.
- Off-site or on-site fabrication.
- Traffic restrictions on the access to site.

Alternative methods and designs for providing a solution for each of these have to be drawn up and fully costed so that they can be compared and allow the most practical, efficient and cost-effective combination to be determined. Main Contractors usually rely upon specialist suppliers and subcontractors to provide details of their requirements.

REFERENCES

BSI (2010) BS 7375: Distribution of electricity on construction and demolition sites. Code of practice. BSI, London.
Construction (Design and Management) Regulations (2007) HMSO, London.
Health and Safety at Work Act (1974) HMSO, London.
Management of Health and Safety at Work Regulations (1999) HMSO, London.
Workplace (Health, Safety and Welfare) Regulations (1992) HMSO, London.

FURTHER READING

Hall F and Greeno R (2001) *Building Services Handbook*, 5th edition. Butterworth Heinemann, Oxford.

Useful web addresses
http://www.legislation.gov.uk

Temporary Works: Principles of Design and Construction
ISBN 978-0-7277-4177-6

ICE Publishing: All rights reserved
http://dx.doi.org/10.1680/twpdc.41776.045

Chapter 4
Tower crane bases

Laurie York Consultant

Tower cranes are widely used in the construction industry, especially for building construction. They are normally supplied on hire and the customer, usually the Principal Contractor, is responsible for the design and construction of the base upon which the crane will be erected. Details of loadings imposed on the base by the chosen crane are provided by the crane supplier and the customer designs the base as temporary works. Loadings are normally provided for 'in-service' conditions (when the crane is working but wind speeds are restricted to 'working wind' speed) and 'out-of-service' conditions (when the crane is not working but is free to weather-vane, and maximum wind speeds may occur). A further set of loadings is sometimes also provided, related to the erection of the crane. The temporary works base design process will include checking that the loading details are appropriate for the location in which the crane is to be erected (particularly with regard to the wind speed used by the crane supplier in deriving the loadings) and will also entail liaison with piling contractors (if the base is to be piled) and the Permanent Works Designer (if the crane base is to impose temporary loading on any part of the permanent works during the construction operations). Similarly, if the tower crane mast is to be supported off an adjacent structure, the temporary works designer must liaise with those responsible for that structure.

4.1.   Introduction
The process of foundation design for tower cranes which are to be used on construction projects starts during the tender preparation. A particular crane type and configuration will be identified, for example, saddle-back or luffing, with decisions made concerning whether the crane is to be static or mobile and assessments made concerning the requirements for the maximum loads to be lifted, the height required under the hook and the maximum radius required about the mast for handling the loads. Other factors which influence the choice of crane type and configuration include the number of cranes needed, the proximity of hazards and any restrictions on oversailing which may have been imposed under the contract conditions.

Figure 4.1 shows typical tower crane coverage of a site using a mobile tower crane. The track upon which the crane travels may be curved in plan (subject to minimum radius of curvature conditions, as advised by the crane manufacturer) if this is more suitable for the area to be serviced by the crane.

Similar considerations are involved when static tower cranes are to be utilised. Figure 4.2 shows typical tower crane coverage of a site, using two static tower cranes. Care is

Figure 4.1 Typical mobile tower crane coverage of site

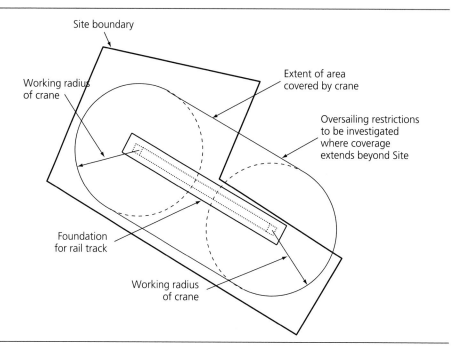

Figure 4.2 Typical coverage of site using two static tower cranes

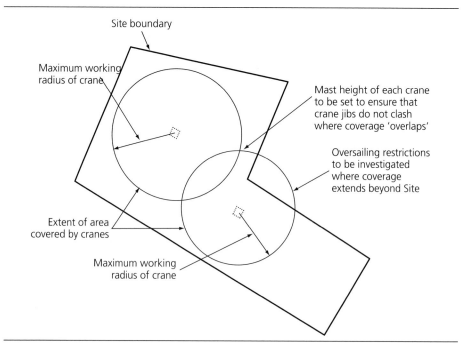

required if more than one crane is to be used to ensure that, where the coverage areas of two (or more) cranes overlap, the jib lengths and mast heights are set for each crane so that they cannot clash with each other.

The location for each tower crane base will be determined by taking account of the proposed permanent works to be constructed. Sufficient temporary works design for the foundation will be undertaken at tender stage to enable financial provision for the construction (and sometimes subsequent removal) of the base to be included in the tender, and for the crane erection to be planned within the construction programme.

Following award of the contract, full design and detailing is undertaken by the temporary works designer. CIRIA Report C654 *Tower crane stability* (Skinner *et al.*, 2006) provides guidance to designers on all aspects of tower crane foundation design. Details of overturning moments, vertical and horizontal loads and slewing torques which will be imposed on the foundation are provided by the crane supplier. This information is normally supplied in the units of kilonewtons (kN) and metres (m), and the foundation designer must take care to ensure that corresponding units are used throughout the design process.

Foundation construction utilises basic groundworks processes, provided that these design methods have been adopted. However, it is prudent to use trades and methods (e.g. piles) already chosen for the permanent works and particular care is necessary if the crane is to load the permanent works.

4.2.   Design of foundation for mobile tower crane
4.2.1   Mobile tower crane foundation
Mobile tower cranes typically travel on a pair of parallel rails set 4.5–10 m apart (depending on the crane type). At the base of the mast is a square chassis with a bogie at each corner consisting (usually) of a pair of wheels. Because the crane cannot be tied down to resist overturning, sufficient kentledge is provided with the crane and installed around the base of the crane mast to ensure that vertical loading on the rails from the crane is always downwards.

All overturning moments on the crane (from the load on the crane hook, crane counter-weights and wind loading) are converted into vertical loads acting, through the bogies, on to the foundation. Details will be provided by the crane supplier. The temporary works designer must then design a suitable foundation for each of the rails, incorporating either structural fill (ballast as for railway tracks) or reinforced concrete beams. Loads provided by the crane supplier will normally be unfactored working loads, but this must be checked by the foundation designer before any design is commenced. The crane supplier should also give full details of suitable rail sections, the fixings used to connect the rails to any foundation and the spacing of ties required between the two beam foundations.

4.2.2   Ground support
If the ground is good and the loadings imposed by the chosen crane are low, it may be possible to spread the load from each bogie sufficiently by means of properly laid and

compacted structural fill. The foundation will then be similar in principle to a railway track foundation, with the loads from the bogies spread through the layers of track support and at 45° through the structural fill and the various soil strata below. The bearing pressures on each stratum are then compared with allowable bearing pressures. The temporary works designer should obtain advice from a suitably qualified geotechnical engineer with regard to the load-spreading ability of the fill material. Additional supervision may also be necessary during the time that the crane is in operation on the site, to monitor any settlement of the foundation and to apply any remedial measures as necessary.

4.2.3   Preliminary design of the concrete foundation

If the ground is not suitable for the provision of support without a concrete foundation, a short length of reinforced concrete beam is designed to be capable of supporting the most heavily loaded bogie under all conditions (in-service, out-of-service or during erection), taking account of the minimum width and depth of section necessary to accommodate the rail fixings. This beam acts in the manner of a concrete pad foundation and, for the purposes of design, is considered to be concentric with the crane bogie. The length of the beam considered for the design obviously cannot be greater than the distance between bogies or overlapping of loading from each of the two bogies on one rail will occur on the ground under the beam. The area of the underside of the beam should be such that the unfactored loading from the bogie, together with the unfactored load from the beam itself, creates a bearing pressure on the ground under the beam which is less than the allowable bearing pressure of that ground. Typical beam widths are 1–2 m. Consideration can be given, at this stage, to the beam section dimensions which will best allow simple and economic reinforcement arrangements. A shallow beam may save on concrete quantities but require significantly more reinforcement, both in the main bars along the beam and in the shear links.

Extreme conditions involving large loads from the bogies and poor ground may result in the need for piled foundations. In such cases (which are rare), the foundation is designed as a continuous beam supported by piles and loaded by the two bogies on the rail. Care is needed to ensure that all necessary design cases are considered to provide the worst-case sagging and hogging moments, shear and pile loadings.

4.2.4   Design for adequacy of ground support to the concrete foundation

The assumed beam length L, width B and depth d are used to determine its self-weight. The maximum loading applied to the foundation by a crane bogie, whether in-service or out-of-service, is then added to the beam self-weight and the total (unfactored) is then used to determine the bearing pressure (considered as a uniformly distributed load) on the ground under the beam (Figures 4.3 and 4.4).

The bearing pressure is therefore

$$\frac{P + W_{base}}{L \times B}$$

Figure 4.3 Section through base along line of rail

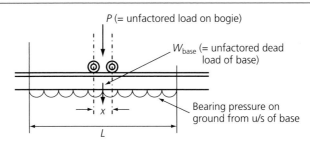

This bearing pressure is then compared with the allowable bearing pressure. This process can be applied iteratively to achieve the best solution for the beam section.

4.2.5 Design of the reinforced concrete beam

Having checked the suitability of the beam section size to transmit the loading from the crane (and from the beam itself) into the ground, it is necessary to design the reinforced concrete beam section to transmit that loading. Because the beam itself is cast on the ground, it is supported evenly over its full area and the beam's self-weight is balanced by the ground-bearing pressure. The beam must therefore be designed to suit the loading from the crane bogie alone. Although BS 8110 *Structural use of concrete* (BSI, 1997) is used for this design, guidance concerning partial safety factors for the loads is given in CIRIA Report C654 (Skinner *et al.*, 2006). This is because the details provided by the crane suppliers do not generally split dead, imposed and wind loads. The CIRIA report recommends that the values listed in Table 4.1 are used as partial load factors γ_f to determine design loadings for ultimate limit state design, as used in BS 8110.

Having obtained the design loadings for in-service and out-of-service, they are then compared and the more onerous case used for the beam design. This design loading, from the bogie, is considered to be spread evenly over the full width and length of the beam adopted for the design (Figure 4.5). The reinforced concrete section is then designed, both longitudinally and transversely.

Figure 4.4 Section through base across line of rail

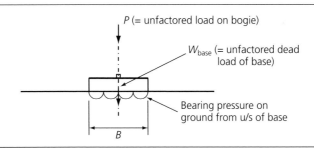

Table 4.1 Partial (load) safety factors for design of foundation beam
Data taken from CIRIA C654

	In-service condition	Out-of-service condition
Unfactored loading from bogie (from crane supplier)	$\gamma_f = 1.6$	$\gamma_f = 1.4$

In the longitudinal direction, the beam is considered to be loaded in an upwards direction by the uniformly distributed load generated by the ground support and 'supported' at its mid-length point by the wheel (or pair of wheels) forming the bogie.

The maximum bending moment in the beam occurs below the centres of the bogie wheels; its value is

$$\frac{P}{L} \times 0.5 \times \left(\frac{L-x}{2}\right)^2$$

The maximum shear in the beam occurs at the same location but, in accordance with BS 8110, recognition of the enhanced shear strength of beams near their supports allows the beam to be designed to suit the shear at a distance, equal to the effective depth of the beam d, away from the centres of the bogie wheels. The value of the shear at these points is:

$$\frac{P}{L} \times \left(\frac{(L-x)}{2} - d\right)$$

In the transverse direction, a 1 m length of the beam is considered 'supported' by the rail, with upwards loading as for the longitudinal direction. For simplicity, the width of the rail is neglected (Figure 4.6).

The maximum transverse bending moment in a 1 m length of the beam is therefore:

$$\frac{P}{L \times B} \times 1.0 \times 0.5 \times \left(\frac{B}{2}\right)^2$$

Figure 4.5 Section through base along line of rail

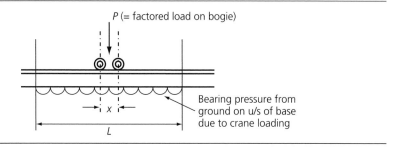

Figure 4.6 Section through base across line of rail

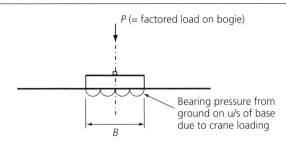

and the shear (calculated in the same way as for the longitudinal direction) is

$$\frac{P}{L \times B} \times 1.0 \times \left(\frac{B}{2} - d\right)$$

This design process, using BS 8110 (section 3.4) and incorporating the appropriate partial material factors γ_{m}, will produce reinforcement requirements for the bottom of the beam and for shear links. It is unlikely that shear links will be required in the transverse direction but, if the calculations indicate that shear reinforcement is required in that direction, consideration should be given to modifying the chosen section dimensions in order to remove this requirement, as fixing shear links in both directions within a beam can be difficult. It is also prudent to detail minimum reinforcement content, in accordance with the recommendations of BS 8110, for the top of the beam. This will resist any tension in the top of the beam caused by moments resulting from the beam 'spanning' between the bogies, and will assist in the fixing of the shear links.

On completion of the design of the reinforced concrete section, the reinforcement should be detailed similarly throughout the full length of each of the rail foundations.

When it is necessary to adopt a piled foundation, the beam supporting the crane rail is designed to suit the various combinations of loads from the crane bogies at all positions along the rail. The loads are factored, using the appropriate values of γ_{f} noted above, and the beam designed with reference to BS 8110 as before.

4.3.   Design of foundation for static tower crane
4.3.1   Static tower crane foundation
There are two basic types of static tower crane. One is similar to a mobile tower crane, with a base which accommodates the necessary kentledge to maintain stability of the crane with no residual uplift on the foundation. Such cranes may be supported by foundations incorporating structural fill, similar to mobile tower crane tracks. Indeed, mobile tower cranes can be used as static tower cranes by erecting them on a track which is only long enough for the crane to operate in one location. Alternatively, static tower cranes can be erected on purchased, disposable, mast base units which are

specially fabricated by the crane manufacturer and which are cast into a reinforced concrete base. The reinforced concrete base is designed by the temporary works designer, either as a ground-bearing pad or as a piled foundation, to withstand the loads and over-turning moments as advised by the crane supplier. The minimum depth requirement for the ground-bearing pad or for the pilecap will be advised by the crane supplier, ensuring that the embedment depth of the crane mast into the concrete is sufficient to be capable of transmitting the loads from the crane into the foundation.

The choice of whether to adopt either a crane which utilises kentledge at the base of the mast to provide stability or a crane which has its mast cast into the foundation is probably dictated by space available on the site. A tower crane with kentledge around the mast can take up a significant area whereas a crane with a cast-in mast base section only occupies a limited space, particularly if the foundation is constructed with its top at (or below) existing ground level.

4.3.2   Preliminary design

For foundations incorporating crane mast base units which are cast into a concrete pad or pilecap, the first step in the foundation design process is to choose a concrete block with dimensions that allow for the required embedment depth for the crane mast (as advised by the crane supplier) and which produce a foundation having an adequate factor of safety against the crane overturning, whether in-service, out-of-service or during erection. If it is clear with regard to the condition which creates the worst case loading from the data provided by the crane supplier, those loadings are used for the design. If it is not clear, then preliminary design must be undertaken for each loading case and the foundation detailed to suit the worst. Because the crane rotates through 360°, it is rare for the foundation to be anything other than square in plan (Figure 4.7).

Figure 4.7 Plan of base

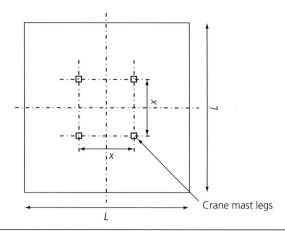

Figure 4.8 Section through base

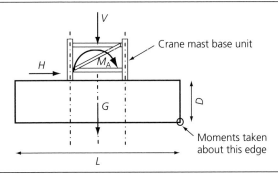

The chosen size for the concrete block is taken and its self-weight calculated. Depending on the crane type and configuration, base sizes are often in the range 1–1.5 m deep and 4.5 m square–6 m square. The (unfactored) vertical load from the crane (as provided by the crane supplier) is then added to the unfactored self-weight of the foundation. Moments are then taken about one of the bottom edges of the concrete block, using unfactored values (Figure 4.8).

Self-weight of concrete block (G) is

$$L \times L \times D \times 24$$

where $24 \, (\text{kN/m}^3)$ is taken as the density of concrete.

The overturning moments imposed by the crane on to the foundation (M_O) are

$$M_A + (H \times D)$$

the stabilising moment (M_S) is

$$(V + G) \times \frac{L}{2}$$

and the self-weight of the concrete block must be such that

$$M_S \geqslant 1.67 \times M_O$$

This process may be applied iteratively to achieve the best base size for stability.

4.3.3   Design for adequacy of ground support
Having determined a suitable base size to provide stability to the crane, the bearing pressure imposed by the base on the ground below is compared to the allowable bearing pressure. Maximum bearing pressure occurs under the base when the over-turning moments are applied about a diagonal axis.

Figure 4.9 Plan of base

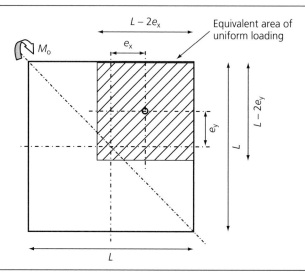

Meyerhof's (1953) construction for the transformation of a non-uniform loading distribution to an equivalent uniform pressure over a reduced rectangular area is used. This is done by 'splitting' the overturning moments (about the diagonal axis) into the components acting in the two directions parallel to the sides of the base. The base being square, the two components will be equal (due to the diagonal being at 45°) so that the design process only needs to be carried out for one direction, with the results applying to both directions (Figure 4.9).

The unfactored overturning moment component is

$$M_O \times \cos 45°$$

the eccentricity of the transformed uniform pressure (e_x) is

$$\frac{M_O \times \cos 45°}{V + G}$$

and the length of side of the area over which the transformed uniform pressure is imposed on the ground is $L - 2e_x$. The transformed uniform pressure imposed on the ground by the crane foundation is therefore

$$\frac{V + G}{(L - 2e_x)^2}$$

This unfactored bearing pressure is then compared to the allowable bearing pressure on the soil under the base.

At this stage, it may be appropriate (if possible) to review the overall dimensions of the concrete block to reduce the imposed bearing pressure on the soil without reducing the overall stability factor of safety below 1.67.

Table 4.2 Partial (load) safety factors for design of block foundation
Data taken from CIRIA C654

		In-service condition	Out-of-service condition
Self-weight of foundation (G)	Adverse	$\gamma_f = 1.4$	$\gamma_f = 1.4$
	Beneficial	$\gamma_f = 1.0$	$\gamma_f = 1.0$
Vertical load imposed by crane (V)	Adverse	$\gamma_f = 1.6$	$\gamma_f = 1.4$
	Beneficial	$\gamma_f = 1.0$	$\gamma_f = 1.0$
Overturning moment (M_A) imposed by crane		$\gamma_f = 1.6$	$\gamma_f = 1.4$
Horizontal load (H) imposed by crane		$\gamma_f = 1.6$	$\gamma_f = 1.4$

If a concrete block which will provide adequate stability without overstressing the soil below cannot be designed using the approach described above, it will be necessary to design a piled foundation.

4.3.4 Design of the reinforced concrete base (without piles)

If the required stability of the crane can be achieved using a concrete block which does not overstress the soil below, it is then necessary to design the reinforced concrete section of that block. The block is designed to suit the upwards loading from the ground support. This loading is derived in a similar way to that noted above for the determination of the bearing pressure on the ground, except that partial safety factors are used with the various loads. Because the foundation block is cast on the ground, the self-weight of the block may be subtracted from the upwards loading. BS 8110 is used for the design but, because the details provided by the crane suppliers do not split dead, imposed and wind loads, guidance is given in CIRIA Report C654 concerning the appropriate values for the partial load factors γ_f for use in the design (refer to Table 4.2).

A similar design process to that used to determine the bearing pressure on the ground is then followed for both in-service conditions and for out-of-service conditions, using the appropriate partial load factors and the partial material factors γ_m in accordance with the guidance in BS 8110.

The transformed uniform pressure derived less the factored bearing pressure due to the self-weight of the block ($\gamma_f = 1.0$) (as noted in Table 4.2) is then used to design the foundation block reinforced concrete section (Figures 4.10 and 4.11). An example of this calculation can be found in CIRIA Report C654 (Skinner et al., 2006).

4.3.5 Piled foundation design

There are a number of factors which the temporary works designer must take into account when making a preliminary choice for the arrangement of the piles. For a pile to provide the full design support it must be spaced at least three times its diameter away from other piles. Piles should be positioned to be clear of the tower crane mast

55

Figure 4.10 Plan of base

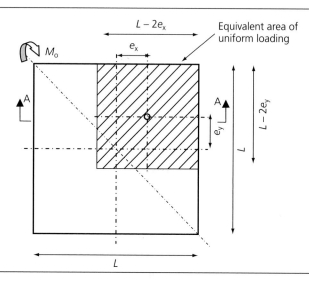

legs, in plan, so that congestion of reinforcement at the pile top does not create problems for positioning the mast base section. The pilecap should extend a reasonable distance in plan beyond the piles in order to avoid problems associated with punching shear around the pile perimeter. If piles are being installed elsewhere on the site, it is recommended that the tower crane foundation is designed using similar piles. It is often possible to design foundations incorporating four piles. This is recommended and any foundation should, if possible, be square with a symmetrical arrangement of piles.

The depth of the pilecap is chosen to suit the embedment requirements of the tower crane mast cast-in section and plan dimensions chosen, assuming four piles. In a similar manner to that adopted when carrying out the design of a foundation without piles, initial analysis uses unfactored loads and moments and is carried out for both in-service and out-of-service conditions,with the overturning moment imposed by the

Figure 4.11 Section through base

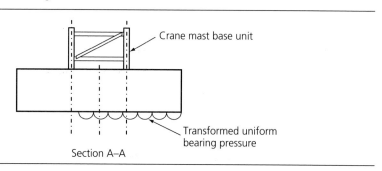

Section A–A

Figure 4.12 Plan of pilecap

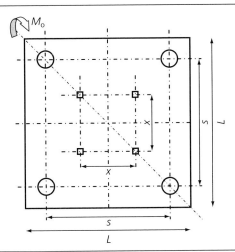

crane applied about a diagonal axis (Figure 4.12). An example of this calculation can be found in CIRIA Report C654 (Skinner *et al.*, 2006).

The final working load combinations of vertical and horizontal loads, as calculated, must be checked with the pile designer to ensure that the piles will be suitable for the loading predicted.

4.3.6   Ultimate pile loading for foundation stability

Having derived working pile loads, it is necessary to check the ultimate pile loading providing stability for the base. This is done using factored loads and moments and applying the overturning moment, which is imposed by the crane, about an axis which passes through the centre of the pilecap and is parallel to one of the sides. Guidance is given in CIRIA Report C654 (Skinner *et al.*, 2006) concerning the partial load factors γ_f to be used (see Table 4.3).

A similar design process to that used to determine the pile working loads is then followed for both in-service conditions and for out-of-service conditions, using the appropriate partial load factors (Figure 4.13). Having derived maximum and minimum ultimate pile loads, a comparison with the equivalent working pile loads will normally show

Table 4.3 Partial (load) safety factors for checking capacity of piles to provide stability to base
Data taken from CIRIA C654

	Vertical load	Horizontal load	Moment
For maximum pile load	$\gamma_f = 1.1$	$\gamma_f = 1.5$	$\gamma_f = 1.5$
For minimum pile load	$\gamma_f = 0.9$	$\gamma_f = 1.5$	$\gamma_f = 1.5$

Figure 4.13 Plan of pilecap

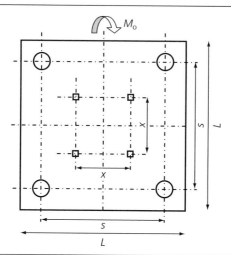

that piles designed to suit working loads will meet the requirements for stability; normal pile design is based on the working pile loads and incorporates a factor of safety of at least 2 in compression and 3 in tension. If, however, the ultimate pile loads for stability are greater than the pile design loads, the pile design must be reviewed by the pile designer.

4.3.7   Design of the reinforced concrete pilecap

There are various ways in which the pilecap can be designed. BS 8110 (BSI, 1997) provides guidance on two approaches and CIRIA Report C654 (Skinner *et al.*, 2006) includes a worked example.

Alternatively, the pilecap may be designed incorporating reinforced concrete beams within the pilecap section which support the tower crane mast legs and which are supported by reinforced concrete beams (again within the pilecap section) which span between pairs of piles (Figure 4.14). The width of the beams can normally be taken as 1 m, but guidance is provided in BS 8110.

Loading on the beams within the pilecap is assumed to be imposed through the tower crane mast legs. These loads are derived from the in-service and out-of-service load combinations advised by the crane supplier, converted into loads in the individual mast legs.

For the beams shown, four load cases are considered: with the overturning moment from the crane applied about the axis parallel to each of the sides of the pilecap, and about each diagonal axis. The guidance given in CIRIA Report C654 can be adapted to give the appropriate values for the partial load factors γ_f for use in the design, as listed in Table 4.4.

Figure 4.14 Plan of pilecap

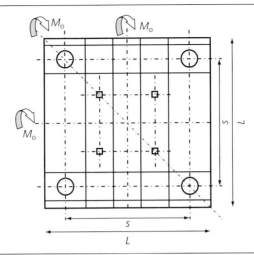

Maximum sagging and hogging bending moments and maximum shear can be determined for each beam and the reinforced concrete section designed in accordance with BS 8110 using the appropriate values for γ_m. It is often the case that, due to the depth of the pilecap necessary to provide the embedment for the tower crane mast legs, the reinforcement content in both the top and the bottom of the beams will be determined by the minimum content required in accordance with BS 8110. On completion of the design of the four beams, if the pilecap is square and there is a symmetrical arrangement of the tower crane mast and piles, the arrangement of reinforced concrete beams may be repeated for the other direction across the pilecap with no further design. Finally, top and bottom reinforcement, similar to that detailed for the beams, is incorporated in the remaining areas of the pilecap. As with foundations not incorporating piles, it is not normally necessary to check the section for punching and pull-out shear around the tower crane mast legs, as the legs will have been designed by the crane manufacturer to suit the embedment requirements which they stipulate. Checks on punching shear at the pile tops should, however, be undertaken.

Table 4.4 Partial (load) safety factors for design of pilecap
Data taken from CIRIA C654

		In-service condition	Out-of-service condition
Self-weight of pilecap	Adverse	$\gamma_f = 1.4$	$\gamma_f = 1.4$
	Beneficial	$\gamma_f = 1.0$	$\gamma_f = 1.0$
Vertical load imposed by crane mast legs	Adverse	$\gamma_f = 1.6$	$\gamma_f = 1.4$
	Beneficial	$\gamma_f = 1.0$	$\gamma_f = 1.0$

REFERENCES

BSI (1997) BS 8110 Part 1: Structural use of concrete. BSI, London.

Meyerhof GG (1953) The bearing capacity of foundations under eccentric and inclined loads. *Proceedings of 3rd International Conference on Soil Mechanics and Foundation Engineering*, Zurich, 1: 440–445.

Skinner H, Watson T, Dunkley B and Blackmore P (2006) Tower Crane Stability. C654, CIRIA, London. ISBN 978-0-86017-654-1.

Useful web addresses

http://www.ciria.org

Temporary Works: Principles of Design and Construction
ISBN 978-0-7277-4177-6

ICE Publishing: All rights reserved
http://dx.doi.org/10.1680/twpdc.41776.061

Chapter 5
Site roads and working platforms

Christopher Tate Chief Engineer, VolkerFitzpatrick

Except on very compact construction sites, vehicles are likely to be used to transport materials from place to place. Site traffic may comprise road-going vans and delivery lorries, or construction plant ranging from dumpers weighing a few tonnes to tipper trucks of thirty-five tonnes or more. In order for these vehicles to move safely and efficiently across terrain that might be rough and undulating with poor load-carrying capacity, temporary site roads are needed; these should be distinguished from 'haul routes' used by heavy earthmoving equipment. Site roads generally fulfil only the most basic function of a permanent carriageway and will often be designed for a relatively short working life; they are generally constructed cheaply using unbound granular material or stabilised soil and must be capable of being simply and rapidly repaired should localised failure or excessive rutting occur during service. Purpose-built working platforms are needed to support heavy construction plant operating in defined locations; for example, tracked piling rigs and cranes and mobile cranes with outriggers. Platforms must be strong enough to ensure that the ground underneath is not overstressed during peak loading and they should be relatively flat and level so there is no risk of plant toppling during manoeuvring.

5.1. Introduction

Provision for the efficient movement of delivery vehicles, muck-away lorries and construction plant across a site is vital, yet may be given little forethought and a low or non-existent budget. Ground that appears hard and able to support traffic in a hot summer season can quickly be transformed into a quagmire as the autumn and winter rain arrives; production is curtailed and minds become focused on the problem of transporting materials from A to B. Temporary site roads capable of functioning all year round should be central to project planning. If designed appropriately and built before ground conditions are allowed to deteriorate, site roads are cost effective; they will of course have a tangible cost but should more than prove their worth by keeping supply lines open (Figure 5.1).

Working platforms are considered by some to be a luxury. Cases of mobile cranes tilting or toppling during a heavy lift or piling rigs unable to extract casing as a result of poor ground support suggest otherwise. Correctly designed platforms enable lifting or piling operations to be undertaken with confidence at any time of year and whatever the foreseen ground conditions, and have a place on most projects.

Figure 5.1 The need for a properly designed and constructed site road
Courtesy of Tensar International Ltd

This chapter deals primarily with the design and construction of temporary roads and working platforms for use by site vehicles and plant. The temporary diversion of public roads within the site is a special case, which is covered briefly.

5.2.   Site roads: principles and design
5.2.1   Alignment

In most cases there is little need to be concerned with the finer points of vertical and horizontal alignment. The vertical alignment should as far as is practicable follow the terrain in order to minimise regrading costs. Unbound granular material with a longitudinal gradient of 10% or less can be traversed without difficulty by road-going vehicles; if unavoidable, the gradient could be increased to 15% on straight sections where no stopping/starting is anticipated. In the horizontal plane, sight-lines are important on congested sites where it may be necessary for traffic to weave between obstacles; across open fields on a new highway construction project, the shortest convenient route between any two points is the most favoured.

A minimum road width of 3.5 m will accommodate normal site traffic in single file, with local widening (typically 32/R) on short radius (R) bends to allow for the passage of long or articulated lorries. Passing places 15 m long with 1:5 tapers should be provided at suitable intervals and at blind bends; the length may be reduced to 12 m if site traffic is not expected to include articulated lorries. For two-way working, a 6.5 m wide road will avoid passing vehicles running too close to an edge and causing excessive haunch damage.

5.2.2　Traffic loading

To prevent costly over-design or premature failure it is essential to make the best estimate of traffic likely to use the road (both during and after its construction). This will involve itemising the weights/volumes of the various building materials involved in the project and assessing the transport needed to supply the imported materials and dispose of any surplus site arisings. The transport (probably mostly comprising vans and lorries) should be categorised by fully laden weight; unladen vehicle movements are usually neglected, as are car movements. On top of this, the day-to-day activities of dedicated construction plant (excavators, dumpers, forklift trucks, etc.) should be considered since this type of traffic will, on occasions, also make use of the site roads. The resulting number of movements of vehicles of each type, and the likely distribution of traffic across the site, will enable the magnitude of traffic loading to be calculated for each branch of a site road network.

The damage inflicted on a road by the passage of a vehicle is related to the axle loading. Current knowledge is that there is a fourth power relationship; i.e. doubling the vehicle axle loading results in 16 times the damage. This effect is taken into account by assigning each type of vehicle likely to be using the site roads a number of 'standard' axles (a standard axle is 8160 kg or 80 kN). Table 5.1 lists the numbers of standard axles associated with various types of road vehicle and construction plant operating at full payload (BritPave, 2007). It is clear that a single fully laden lorry will have as much influence on the structural design of the road as a fleet of vans.

In the absence of data for a particular item of wheeled construction plant, its number of standard axles (sa) can be estimated from the manufacturer's technical specification

Table 5.1 Equivalent standard axles for typical vehicle types (fully laden)
Data taken from BritPave (2007) courtesy of Alex Lake

Vehicle No.	Vehicle description	Gross vehicle weight: tonnes	Equivalent number of standard axles: sa
V_1	6-axle articulated lorry	44	5.15
V_2	5-axle articulated lorry	38	4.70
V_3	4-axle articulated lorry	35	7.35
V_4	3-axle articulated lorry	26	5.65
V_5	4-axle draw bar lorry/trailer	35	5.40
V_6	4-axle rigid lorry	32	5.35
V_7	3-axle rigid lorry	26	4.80
V_8	2-axle rigid lorry	17	3.15
V_9	Van	5	0.02
V_{10}	Car	2	0.0005
V_{11}	5-tonne forklift	11	0.40
V_{12}	3-tonne forklift	7	0.07
V_{13}	3-axle dump truck	34	11.26
V_{14}	6-tonne dumper	10	0.39

using the fourth power relationship:

$$sa = \sum (\text{gross weight on each axle in kg}/8160)^4$$

Tracked plant is designed to exert a relatively low ground pressure while travelling and its effect on the road design compared to say, a fully laden four-axle tipper lorry, will be insignificant.

On large civil engineering projects where heavy dump trucks or motorised scrapers are employed for earthmoving, it is not normal practice for haul routes to be hardened since the pattern of plant movements may be subject to continual change. Earthworks operations by their nature generally take place in the late spring to early autumn period; at this time of year the ground itself is able to provide the necessary support for the vehicles involved (albeit with continual re-profiling of an often well-rutted surface). Heavy earthmoving plant would therefore not be routinely included in the traffic-loading assessment for site roads, although in special circumstances some account may need to be taken (e.g. should haul routes cross site roads).

The product of the anticipated number of movements (n_1, n_2, n_3...) of each fully laden type of vehicle (V_1, V_2, V_3...) and the number of standard axles associated with that vehicle (sa_1, sa_2, sa_3...) should be summed for all the expected vehicle types:

$$sa_{(total)} = n_1 sa_1 + n_2 sa_2 + n_3 sa_3 \ldots$$

This will give the total number of standard axles to be carried by each branch of the site road network over its lifetime. Because site roads are likely to have a relatively uneven surface, there will be an element of dynamic loading not usually considered in the design of public roads; to take account of this it is suggested that the calculated total number of standard axles be doubled. The resulting number of standard axles is the design traffic loading:

$$sa_{(design)} = 2 sa_{(total)}$$

In cases where the site road is merely the foundation layer for a permanent road to be built at a later date, a more simplistic approach to assessing design traffic loading can be adopted. There are published data relating the number of standard axles expected during construction to both

- the length of permanent road under construction (Powell *et al.*, 1984) and
- the size of the development served by the permanent road (BSI, 2001).

5.2.3   Ground conditions
Having established the design traffic loading, the subgrade must be evaluated in order to formulate a design for the site road.

If a comprehensive ground investigation report is available for the site it may well contain some or all of the information needed. Such information includes

- current subgrade California bearing ratio (CBR) or undrained shear strength (fundamental properties for the thickness design of the road)
- plasticity index as a guide to equilibrium CBR and performance of the subgrade when saturated (Powell *et al.*, 1984)
- soil grading (to determine whether the soil can be incorporated into the road structure directly as a granular layer, or after stabilisation with lime or cement)
- moisture condition value (MCV) and compaction-related data, including remoulded CBR (only important if significant site regrading is needed to achieve a satisfactory road alignment)
- soil chemical suite comprising organic matter, sulphate/oxidisable sulphide and pH value (only necessary if soil stabilisation is being considered)
- an indication of ground permeability; for example, soil infiltration rate (to assess whether provision for temporary drainage needs to be made).

Should information be lacking it will be necessary to excavate trial pits at intervals along the proposed route to sample and test the ground to obtain the required data. If time is short, in situ testing may substitute for some of the laboratory tests. For example, a Mexe-probe or Transport Research Laboratory (TRL) dynamic cone penetrometer (DCP) could be used to estimate current CBR (HA, 2009) and a hand vane to measure undrained shear strength. For a clay soil, shear strength can be converted to CBR using the approximate relationship:

$$CBR(\%) = \text{shear strength (kPa)}/y$$

where $y = 23$ for fill (Black and Lister, 1978) and $y = 30$ for undisturbed ground.

Basic soakage tests (BRE, 1991) performed in the trial pits would help decide if the site roads need to be drained or whether natural percolation into the subgrade will suffice.

If the trial pits expose weak ground that would benefit from stabilisation, or soil stabilisation is being considered in lieu of granular material for the road construction, it is essential that bulk samples be taken to a specialist laboratory to determine the feasibility and most economic method of stabilising (i.e. which type of binder is most suitable and the necessary percentage addition). Chemical tests and swelling tests must also be undertaken to ensure there are not elevated levels of undesirable or potentially disruptive substances in the soil (HA, 2007).

5.2.4 Formulating the design

Most site roads are unpaved, at least for the temporary construction condition. They normally comprise unbound granular material, with or without geosynthetic reinforcement, or stabilised soil (usually with an unbound granular protection course).

5.2.4.1 Unreinforced unbound granular roads

Elastic analysis can be used for the design of unbound granular site roads but for temporary works it is simpler to use an empirical method aimed at limiting rut depth. Powell *et al.* (1984) quote an equation (rearranged below) to determine the thickness *h* (in mm) of unbound granular material that will limit rut depth to 75 mm for a given traffic loading (sa_{design}) and subgrade CBR (%):

$$h = 190 \log_{10}(sa_{design})CBR^{-0.63} \tag{5.1}$$

The equation was first presented by Giroud and Noiray (1981) and relates to low permeability subgrade soils (clay/silt); the granular material itself should have a CBR > 80%.

For example, for traffic loading of 1000 standard axles (approximately 100, 4-axle tippers with 20 tonne payloads and dynamic loading allowance) and a subgrade CBR of 2.5% (firm clay), the thickness of unbound granular material (well-graded crushed rock) needed for the temporary road would be:

$$h = 190 \log_{10}(1000)2.5^{-0.63} = 320 \text{ mm (to the nearest 10 mm)}$$

While a rut depth of 75 mm is acceptable for a temporary site road, it is too much if the granular layer is to become the foundation for a permanent road. For the latter case, Powell *et al.* (1984) present a second equation (rearranged below) where the unbound granular material is Type 1 subbase and the rut depth is limited to 40 mm:

$$h = 190[\log_{10}(sa_{design}) + 0.24]CBR^{-0.63} \tag{5.2}$$

Using the above example, the thickness of unbound granular material increases to:

$$h = 190[\log_{10}(1000) + 0.24]2.5^{-0.63} = 350 \text{ mm (to the nearest 10 mm)}$$

The use of both design equations is generally restricted to $sa_{design} \leqslant 10\,000$. The subgrade CBR used for design purposes should be the lesser of

- the value measured in the trial pits at the time of the ground investigation
- the equilibrium value based on soil type and plasticity index (Powell *et al.*, 1984)
- the value estimated from Mexe-probe/DCP/hand vane testing at the time of construction.

Having calculated a suitable thickness for the granular road, the following rationalisation should be adopted.

- If the subgrade is weak and the design CBR falls below 2.5%, formulate an alternative design incorporating geogrid reinforcement; as well as saving on the thickness of granular material, the geogrid should give better support for construction plant during placing and compaction.
- For subgrades with a design CBR of 2.5% or more, the calculated thickness of unbound granular material may be adopted, subject to the following provisos.
  (i) Where the design CBR does not exceed 15%, a *minimum* road thickness of 225 mm would be prudent.

Figure 5.2 Summer construction on chalk subgrade; temporary site road not required

(ii) On non-clay subgrades with a design CBR in the range >15–30%, the road thickness should not be less than 150 mm.

(iii) On subgrades of gravel where the CBR is >30%, it may not be necessary to provide a road structure at all if the ground is relatively free-draining (soil infiltration rate $>10^{-4}$ m/s).

(iv) Subgrades of chalk can be troublesome. Even though low-density chalk can generally be trafficked directly during the drier seasons (Figure 5.2), it may be impassable during winter (particularly if damaged by frost) when the CBR can drop below 2.5%. The site road design should be assessed accordingly.

It should be noted that if the site road is also the foundation layer for a permanent public road there may be special requirements in respect of layer thickness and the quality of materials used; the views of the supervising highway authority should be sought.

5.2.4.2 Geosynthetic-reinforced unbound granular roads

Geosynthetic reinforcement includes geotextiles (fabrics), geogrids (semi-rigid ribbed meshes) and geocells (honeycombed mattress-like structures). All three types of reinforcement are manufactured from polymer-based material (e.g. polypropylene, polyester) and, in the right circumstances, have the potential to reduce the thickness of granular material needed to accommodate any given traffic loading. The overall benefits can be considerable where the subgrade is (very) weak (CBR < 2.5%), and may also be worthwhile on stronger ground.

A geotextile covered with compacted unbound granular material to form a road needs the subgrade to deform significantly under wheel loading in order to function as a

Figure 5.3 Interlock of aggregate and geogrid increases lateral restraint (confinement)
Courtesy of Tensar International Ltd

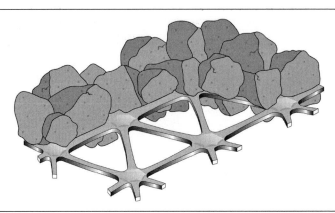

'tension membrane' (i.e. a state in which it both confines the granular material and reduces the pressure applied to the subgrade soil). Therefore, a rut must develop before the full contribution of the geotextile occurs; typically the rut depth would be ≫75 mm, which limits the effectiveness of geotextiles as reinforcement in permanent works. However, a geotextile could act as reinforcement in the special case of a narrow temporary site road where traffic is channelised and a regime for maintenance of rutting is implemented. While a geotextile may not in most circumstances permit a reduction in the thickness of the unbound granular layer, it may confer other benefits. For example, it could prevent the intermixing of the aggregate with a soft cohesive subgrade soil (separation) and filter any soil water rising up into the granular layer on wet sites (filtration). Guidance on designing with geotextiles is available from manufacturers (e.g. Terram, 2010).

By comparison, a geogrid functions in unpaved road applications by restraining lateral displacement of aggregate subjected to a vertical stress without the inherent need for subgrade deformation; the load-spreading capability of the granular layer is thereby improved and pressure on the subgrade soil reduced. The bearing capacity of the subgrade is also increased as it is relieved of horizontal shear stress at the interface. The net effect may be regarded as a form of mechanical stabilisation (Figures 5.3 and 5.4), which enables the granular layer to be thinned by 30% or more.

Design software for geogrid-reinforced site roads (and working platforms) is available from a leading manufacturer (Tensar, 2010). Based on the output from this software, Figure 5.5 compares the thicknesses of granular material needed to accommodate a range of traffic loading with and without geogrid reinforcement. A geogrid can be supplied with a factory-attached geotextile (i.e. as a geocomposite) to provide the combined benefits of confinement, separation and filtration.

Geocells are an extension of the geogrid principle, effectively increasing the depth of the 'ribs' to the full thickness of the granular layer. The quality of aggregate used to fill the

Figure 5.4 Increased restraint (confinement) at base of unbound layer leads to better load spreading and improved subgrade bearing capacity
Courtesy of Tensar International Ltd

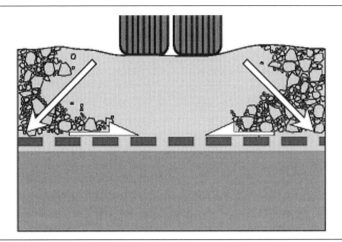

cells may be inferior to that needed with geotextiles or geogrids, thereby recouping some of the extra cost of the geocell structure. Reinforcement of unpaved granular roads is a relatively new application for geocells and empirical design guidance needs to be sought from manufacturers.

5.2.4.3   Stabilised soil roads

If the physical and chemical properties of the ground are suitable, soil stabilisation (in situ or ex situ) could be considered as an economic alternative to unbound granular material. Details of this technique are discussed fully in Chapter 7 (Lime and Cement Stabilisation). Either of the following two design approaches may be adopted.

(i)   Calculate a suitable thickness of granular material (Type 1 subbase) using Equation 5.2 and substitute stabilised soil with a similar stiffness (taken to be 7-day soaked CBR > 50%). For temporary roads, a protective granular topping is needed to provide a durable skid-resistant surface course, which will also afford a small measure of frost protection for the stabilised layer over the winter period. The topping should not be thinner than 110 mm and may be included as part of the design thickness. Stabilised soil should be constructed in layers not thicker than about 250 mm to ensure that adequate full-depth compaction is achieved by surface rolling; the minimum desirable thickness is 150 mm.

(ii) Use a stabilised soil mixture with a higher stiffness and thereby reduce the road thickness needed when compared to unbound granular material. Reference should be made to Chaddock and Atkinson (1997) for the equivalency between Type 1 subbase and a range of stabilised materials. A granular topping is still considered desirable, except perhaps where the stabilised material is compressive strength class C3/4 or higher.

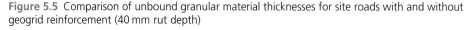

Figure 5.5 Comparison of unbound granular material thicknesses for site roads with and without geogrid reinforcement (40 mm rut depth)

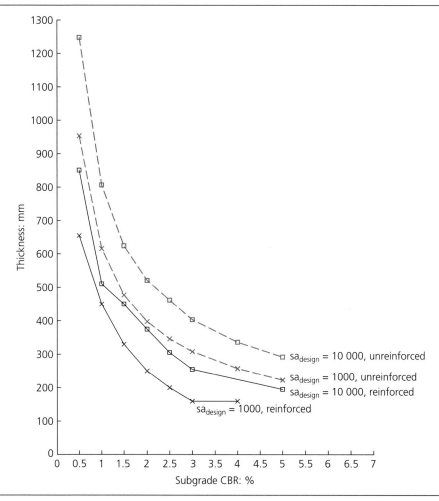

5.3.   Working platforms: principles and design

Dedicated platforms are often required at specific locations to support working heavy plant; for example, a tracked piling rig or crane, or mobile crane outriggers (Figure 5.6). Platforms may also be needed for falsework to bridge decks and for general scaffolding. In each case, the function of the platform is to provide reliable support by dissipating the imposed loads sufficiently to keep settlement within tolerable limits and avoid yielding of the underlying ground. A secondary function is to create a working environment that can be kept relatively clean and dry.

For lightly loaded platforms used for storage or supporting falsework on firm ground, a thin concrete blinding layer could suffice (in conjunction with timber sleepers below

Figure 5.6 Geogrid-reinforced platforms for tracked sheet piling rig and mobile crane outriggers

concentrated loads such as scaffolding standards); a spread of load at 45° through the support is normally assumed for design purposes. At the other extreme, piled foundations might be needed for heavy gantries where the ground is marshy with negligible bearing capacity. Traditional soil mechanics methods can be used for the design of these types of platforms.

5.3.1 Working platforms for tracked plant

Platforms for use by tracked piling rigs and cranes are mostly constructed from unbound granular material (often incorporating geogrid reinforcement), although soil stabilisation (in situ or ex situ) is an increasingly popular alternative. Platform thicknesses can vary from a nominal minimum of 300 mm, up to 1600 mm or more for the most onerous combinations of loading and subgrade strength.

The frequently used Building Research Establishment design method (BRE, 2004) determines the thickness of platform needed to resist punching shear under the tracks or bearing plates of the operating plant. The method is only applicable where the working platform is significantly stronger than the subgrade and is not appropriate for very soft cohesive subgrades (undrained cohesion <20 kPa). While the BRE method can be used for the thickness design of a platform to support the outriggers of mobile cranes, trafficking by the wheeled vehicles themselves should be assessed in accordance with Section 5.2.

For a platform on a very soft cohesive subgrade (undrained cohesion <20 kPa) geogrid reinforcement is considered essential, not least to facilitate construction. Geogrids can

Figure 5.7 Comparison of unbound granular material thicknesses for typical piling platform with and without geogrid reinforcement

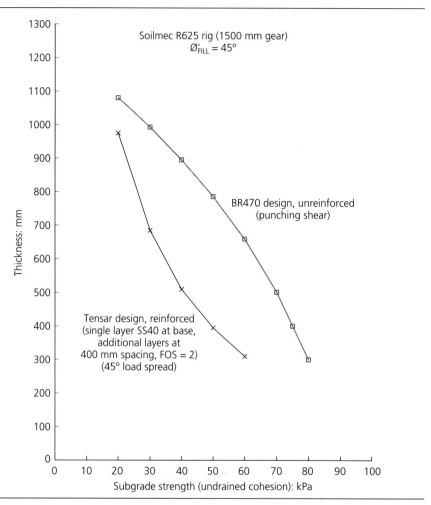

Soilmec R625 rig (1500 mm gear)
$\emptyset'_{FILL} = 45°$

BR470 design, unreinforced
(punching shear)

Tensar design, reinforced
(single layer SS40 at base,
additional layers at
400 mm spacing, FOS = 2)
(45° load spread)

Thickness: mm (y-axis)

Subgrade strength (undrained cohesion): kPa (x-axis)

also reduce the overall thickness of granular material needed on stronger subgrades (Figure 5.7). The relevant design method (Tensar, 2010) assumes a spread of load through the reinforced granular layer of 45°, the platform being made sufficiently thick to limit the pressure on the subgrade to less than its safe bearing capacity. As with site roads, the geogrid placed at the base of the granular layer serves to restrain outward displacement of aggregate subjected to a vertical stress, thereby improving load-spreading ability and increasing subgrade bearing capacity. For platforms more than about 400 mm thick, a second geogrid may be needed within the body of the granular layer to extend the zone of confinement.

A sound understanding of ground conditions in the environs of the working platform is an integral part of the design process. A programme of ground investigation as outlined for site roads should be undertaken, with emphasis on undrained shear strength rather than CBR as the fundamental design property for cohesive subgrades. The investigation would need to be expanded to include standard penetration testing (to estimate the angle of shearing resistance) should the subgrade prove to be of a granular nature.

It is generally recommended that the gradient of platforms used by tracked cranes and piling rigs with raised masts be restricted to 10% (which includes access ramps), although a level surface is preferable. At the base of a ramp it is good practice to increase the platform thickness by 50%.

5.4.   Temporary roads for public use

On some construction projects, particularly highway works, it may be found necessary to close a section of public road for a period. When no suitable diversion route exists, there may be no option but to build a temporary road within the site for use by public traffic. Since the road must be paved to normal highway standards, the route will always be made as short as possible in order to minimise costs.

Road alignment, marking and signing will need to be approved by the local highway authority; temporary lighting may be stipulated at potentially hazardous locations (e.g. short radius bends and junctions).

The thickness design of the temporary road pavement and its foundation can be based on well-established principles relating to traffic loading (number of standard axles) and subgrade strength. However, the intended short life means that the current design charts for highway pavements (HA, 2006) will not necessarily give an economic design, since the minimum thickness limit for the bound layer(s) has been set relatively high.

Reference could be made to earlier design guides for bituminous roads (Powell *et al.*, 1984) and concrete roads (Mayhew and Harding, 1987) where data are provided for traffic loading as low as 100 000 sa.

For even lower traffic loadings, Figure 5.3 in Powell *et al.* (1984) could be extrapolated back to 1000 sa using the following equation to estimate the required thickness of bitumen-bound material, h_{DBM100} (in mm):

$$h_{DBM100} = 190(sa_{temp} \times 10^{-6})^{0.2} \qquad (5.3)$$

where sa_{temp} is the traffic loading (standard axles) expected over the lifetime of the completed road. The bitumen-bound material should comprise a binder course and a surface course; the surface course should have adequate skidding resistance.

The thickness h (in mm) of Type 1 subbase needed as the road foundation may be derived from Equation 5.2 where sa_{design} is a measure of the traffic (standard axles) employed in the building of the road.

For example, consider a temporary public road diversion 200 m long built on a subgrade with CBR 6% to carry 5000 standard axles after construction:

$sa_{design} = 1000$ (minimum recommended input); $sa_{temp} = 5000$

$h = 190[\log_{10}(1000) + 0.24]6^{-0.63} = 200$ mm Type 1 subbase (to next 10 mm)

$h_{DBM100} = 190(5000 \times 10^{-6})^{0.2} = 70$ mm DBM100 (to next 10 mm)

In practice, it would be unwise to use a subbase thinner than 225 mm as a platform on which to place and compact bitumen-bound material (relaxed to 150 mm should the subgrade CBR exceed 15%). Also, where the thickness of the bound layer is less than 110 mm, there is a risk of premature failure occurring as a consequence of occasional very heavy wheel loading on hot days.

Because temporary roads can be relatively thin they may suffer winter damage when a prolonged period of freezing is experienced and the subgrade is highly frost-susceptible (e.g. chalk). There is no way to mitigate this risk cheaply and the consequences of premature failure during a harsh winter need to be assessed.

5.5.   Construction
5.5.1   Materials and maintenance
Granular material for building temporary roads/platforms may be derived from site if suitable deposits of gravel or moderately strong rock occur naturally in the ground; on brownfield sites it should be possible to process demolition arisings to create acceptable granular material. If site-won granular material is unavailable, a design that includes geogrid reinforcement would reduce the volume of import needed and should prove more economic; in these circumstances, stabilisation of the subgrade also becomes an attractive option.

For convenience, granular materials are classified in accordance with the *Specification for highway works* (HA, 1998) and should be compacted accordingly. The standard designs for roads (Equations 5.1 and 5.2) require the use of well-graded crushed rock gravel or Type 1 subbase. For lower-quality material, for example, Type 2 subbase or Class 6F2 capping, an increase in the design thickness is needed. This could be as much as 100% based on material equivalency (BSI, 2001), although realistically a 50% increase is considered more appropriate providing the lower-quality materials have negligible plasticity and are relatively free-draining. No such increase in the design thickness is considered necessary for geogrid-reinforced granular roads, although it is important that the maximum particle size of the aggregate remains compatible with the selected geogrid mesh size. The use of granular material with a rounded particle shape should be avoided (at least near the surface of the road) since it may lack stability under wheel contact pressure.

Where secondary (recycled) aggregates are imported (these will normally be cheaper than primary aggregates), they must have been recovered under an acceptable quality protocol (e.g. WRAP, 2010).

For working platforms where the design criteria are different, the angle of shearing resistance ($\emptyset'$) of the granular material must be known. This can be determined by a large shear box test in the laboratory but, since the maximum particle size that can be included in the test specimen is 20 mm, the result may underestimate the potential of the material. It is the author's experience that for 75 mm maximum size, well-graded, moderately strong crushed rock or crushed concrete, $\emptyset' = 45°$ may be safely presumed, provided that the material is non-plastic and relatively free-draining. At the other extreme, naturally occurring sand/gravel deposits with slight plasticity complying with the requirements for Type 2 subbase (commonly referred to as 'hoggin') will have $\emptyset' \sim 35°$.

Site roads and working platforms constructed from unbound granular material must be kept clear of mud and slurry otherwise the desirable free-draining properties will be adversely affected. Any localised deep rutting or haunch damage should be reinstated with fresh material at the earliest opportunity, or progressive failure will result.

Soil stabilisation is a specialist operation and should not be attempted by the inexperienced (refer to Chapter 7). A strong material (equivalent to or stiffer than unbound granular material) can be formed from most soil types by using an appropriate binder. The binder may be Portland cement, quicklime, fly ash, ground granulated blast furnace slag or combinations of these. It is important for a stabilised road/platform to be protected against surface abrasion by site traffic, standing water and frost. To this end, a topping of granular material should be provided except perhaps in cases where the stabilised soil is compressive strength class C3/4 or higher. One disadvantage of stabilised soil construction is that, should premature failure occur, it is not usually practicable to replace the damaged layer with like material. The only option is to dig out the affected area and substitute compacted granular material, which might result in a recurrent 'soft-spot'.

On small sites, or for short-term and one-off applications, the placing of proprietary mats could be considered for traffic or plant access over soft ground. Access mats are made variously from heavy-duty flexible plastic composites, aluminium extrusions/plates or timber and can be bought, or more usually hired, from specialist outlets. Some types are lightweight and capable of being man-handled into position; they can be used to good effect where damage to existing surfacing (e.g. turf) must be avoided. Access mats function by increasing the load contact area; the restraint offered by adjoining linked mats serves to restrict deformation. However, they can prove to be prohibitively expensive for long-term or widespread use.

Inevitably, traffic leaving a construction site will have picked up mud from the site roads or piling platforms. The provision of a wheel-wash facility (or at least a rumble strip) close to the exit will help minimise the spread of mud to the adjoining public roads. On larger sites where bulk excavation is taking place, a purpose-made wheel/vehicle wash unit is essential (models are available that recycle the wash water and extract/dewater the suspended solids).

It is important that plant operators and drivers using the site roads and working platforms are aware of the layout and boundaries. Edges should be defined by fencing or timber sleepers; in circumstances where there is an abrupt drop over the edge, a physical restraint should be provided, which might comprise an earth bank or pre-fabricated barrier units.

5.5.2   Drainage

During inclement weather rainwater could accumulate in unbound granular construction layers, resulting in softening of the underlying stabilised soil (where used) or cohesive subgrade (particularly where the soil infiltration rate is $<10^{-6}$ m/s). Potentially, this could lead to early failure of the site road or working platform.

For site roads, both the surface of the granular layer and the underlying stabilised soil or subgrade should be shaped to a crossfall (5% if feasible, but 2.5% minimum) to shed water, the run-off being channelled away from the edges of the road in drains or temporary shallow open ditches ('grips').

Working platforms may be much wider than site roads and providing a crossfall is not necessarily practicable. It is also desirable that the surface of the platform be relatively level to avoid construction plant tilting. Shaping the underlying stabilised soil or subgrade to fall in two, or even four, directions towards the edges of the platform may be a solution, in conjunction with perimeter drains or grips. Alternatively, for very wide platforms constructed entirely of unbound granular material, shallow land drains could be installed in a herringbone pattern below the platform to channel any water reaching the subgrade to a common outfall; these drains need not be piped, but may simply be slots in the subgrade filled with a free-draining granular drainage medium.

When disposing of water drained from site roads and working platforms it is essential to avoid pollution of aquifers and watercourses. Recourse to silt traps and oil interceptors may be needed and Environment Agency guidance should be sought.

Drainage of surface water from a paved temporary public road would normally be to a filter drain on the low side of the carriageway with an outfall into the existing highway drainage system. In built-up areas, kerbs could be used to direct surface water back to the main highway.

REFERENCES

Black W and Lister NW (1978) The strength of clay fill subgrades; its prediction and relation to road performance. In: *Clay Fills*, Proceedings of the Conference held at the Institution of Civil Engineers 14–15 November 1978. ICE, London.

BRE (Building Research Establishment) (1991) BRE Digest 363: Soakaway design. IHS BRE Press, Watford. (Revised 2007.)

BRE (2004) BR 470: Working platforms for tracked plant. BRE Bookshop, Watford.

BritPave (2007) Concrete hardstanding design handbook: Guidelines for the design of concrete hardstandings. 2nd edition. British In-situ Concrete Paving Association, Camberley.

BSI (2001) BS 7533-1: Pavements constructed with clay, natural stone or concrete pavers (Part 1: Guide for the structural design of heavy duty pavements constructed of clay pavers or concrete paving blocks). BSI, London.

Chaddock BCJ and Atkinson VM (1997) Stabilised sub-bases in road foundations: structural assessment and benefits. TRL Report 248. Transport Research Laboratory, Crowthorne.

Giroud JP and Noiray L (1981) Geotextile-reinforced unpaved road design. *Proceedings of the American Society of Civil Engineers, Journal of the Geotechnical Engineering Division*, **107**, No. GT9.

HA (Highways Agency) (1998) Specification for highway works. Manual of contract documents for highway works Vol. 1. HMSO, London. (Amended 2009.)

HA (2006) Pavement design. Design manual for roads and bridges Vol. 7, Section 2, Part 3. HD 26/06. HMSO, London.

HA (2007) Treatment of fill and capping materials using either lime or cement or both. Design manual for roads and bridges Vol. 4, Section 1, Part 6. HA 74/07. HMSO, London.

HA (2009) Design guidance for road pavement foundations (Draft HD25). Interim Advice Note 73/06 Revision 1 (2009). HMSO, London.

Mayhew HC and Harding HM (1987) Thickness design of concrete roads. Department of Transport, TRRL Research Report 87. Transport and Road Research Laboratory, Crowthorne.

Powell WD, Potter JF, Mayhew HC and Nunn ME (1984) The structural design of bituminous roads. Department of Transport, TRRL Report LR1132. Transport and Road Research Laboratory, Crowthorne.

Tensar (2010) TensarPave. Available from Tensar International Limited, Blackburn.

Terram (2010) Geotextiles. Terram Limited, Pontypool. Available at http://www.terram.com (accessed September 2010).

WRAP (Waste and Resources Action Programme) (2010) Guidance notes for the producers' compliance checklist. Banbury. Available at http://www.wrap.org.uk (accessed September 2010).

FURTHER READING

BritPave (2007) *HBM and Stabilisation 2: The design and specification of residential and commercial road pavements.* British In-situ Concrete Paving Association, Camberley.

Jewell RA (1996) *Soil reinforcement with geotextiles.* CIRIA SP123. London (Construction Industry Research and Information Association).

WRAP (Waste and Resources Action Programme) (2006) *Guidance on the use of HBM in working platforms.* Banbury.

ICE Publishing: All rights reserved
http://dx.doi.org/10.1680/twpdc.41776.079

Chapter 6
Control of groundwater

Neil Smith Director, Applied Geotechnical Engineering

The main purposes of controlling groundwater are to enable the construction of below-ground works in the dry and to improve the stability of the ground below the sides and base of an excavation. In order to plan and design a control scheme, it is necessary to obtain good-quality information on the stratigraphy, the groundwater regime and the mass permeability of the ground. A number of techniques are available, each being applicable to particular circumstances. The principal parameters governing design are permeability and drawdown. Even with good site investigation, the mass permeability of the ground surrounding a proposed excavation is only approximately known. Sensitivity analysis is therefore an important part of the design process, to give the designer an appreciation of the possible range of flows needed to produce the required outcome. Monitoring of groundwater control schemes is essential to ensure that sufficient drawdown or pressure reduction is achieved and maintained. Environmental aspects must also be considered, to check the quality of the water being extracted from the ground and of the water being discharged from the process. Consents are required, both to abstract the water from the ground and to dispose of it.

6.1. Introduction

Where excavations are required to extend below the groundwater level, it is essential to plan beforehand the means of dealing with the water. There are generally four possible methods as follows.

1 Exclude the water by surrounding the area to be excavated with a cut-off wall (there are various ways of doing this; see Chapters 8, 9, 11, 13 and 14).
2 Extract sufficient groundwater to depress the level below the excavation surface. (Methods (1) and (2) may be used in combination, where a partial cut-off reduces the volume of water to be extracted.)
3 Reduce the pore water pressure in the soil sufficiently to stabilise the ground around and below the excavation.
4 Excavate below water (refer to Chapter 15 on Caissons and Shafts).

Groundwater control can be achieved either by Method (2) or (3). It is important to realise that low flow does not necessarily mean low pressure and high flow does not necessarily require a high pressure. The techniques for controlling groundwater are

- sump pumping
- wellpointing

- deep wells
- ejectors.

The rarely-used technique of electro-osmosis is based on different principles and will not be considered here.

6.2. Techniques
6.2.1 Selection of appropriate technique

Figure 6.1 illustrates the ranges of application of the various different pumped systems for groundwater control. The blurred boundaries are deliberately chosen to emphasise their approximate nature. The particle sizes shown below the permeability k axis are a guide only. Note that where there are strata of widely differing permeabilities, it may be necessary to use more than one technique.

6.2.2 Sump pumping: extraction from the surface of the excavation

This is probably the most commonly used system of groundwater control. At its simplest, it consists of a shallow well (such as a perforated 45 gallon drum) placed into a hole excavated below the general base level of an excavation, with a suction pump inlet within the drum. One of the drawbacks of this method is that the water flows towards the excavation and may issue from the lower sides as well as the base, which can

Figure 6.1 Relations between pumped well systems, permeability and drawdown
Adapted from Roberts and Preene (1994a)

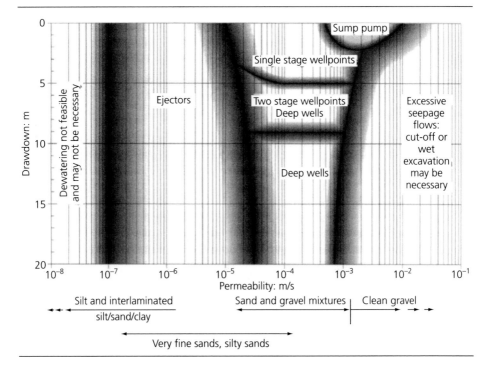

Figure 6.2 The main features of a wellpoint

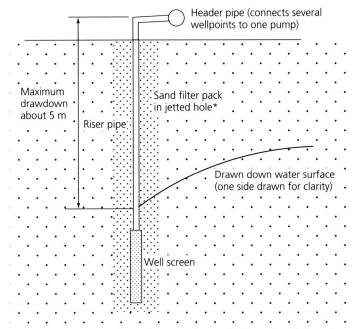

Header pipe (connects several wellpoints to one pump)

Maximum drawdown about 5 m

Sand filter pack in jetted hole*

Riser pipe

Drawn down water surface (one side drawn for clarity)

Well screen

*A filter is essential in stratified soil. May not be needed in well-graded sandy gravel

reduce the stability of the soil close to the excavation surface. The sump can be fed by a pattern of trenches or French drains leading from the perimeter of the excavation. Sump intakes can be filtered by granular, geotextile wrapping or combined filters.

6.2.3 Deep wells, wellpoints and ejectors: extraction from below the excavation

Wellpoints work by suction pumping and so the head which they can lift is limited by atmospheric pressure and suction efficiency. Figure 6.2 illustrates the main parts of a wellpoint.

Note that the header pipes, which connect a number of wellpoints to a pump, can obstruct surface activities as can be seen from Figure 6.3 (in which the tops of wellpoints and pumps can also be seen).

In practice, the achievable drawdown is limited to about 5 m but the use of a second stage of wellpoints can increase the drawdown to around 9 m. In rare instances, multiple levels of wellpoint can be used (Figure 6.4). Wellpoints can be used to enclose an excavation or simply to dewater a length of trench, for example, to install services. To dewater long trenches, sections of wellpoints which extend beyond both ends of the open trench are activated progressively as the work proceeds.

Figure 6.3 Wellpoint header pipe around excavation
Courtesy of WJ Groundwater Ltd

Deep wells are not limited in the drawdown they can achieve because the water is sucked into the bottom of the well and then pushed up the discharge pipe. Pumps operate from within prepared wells which have had lining tubes and surrounding filters previously installed.

Figure 6.4 Three stage well-point system. Note rise of water level below excavation; a similar rise is present with deep wells

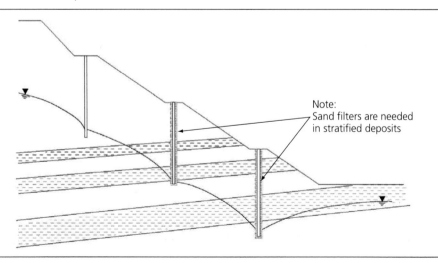

Note:
Sand filters are needed in stratified deposits

Ejectors work on the principle of a nozzle and venturi pump. Water fed to the base of a hole is forced to flow back up the hole through a nozzle and venturi to pull groundwater in from below. The practical depth limit on their use is about 50 m. They tend to be used for the control of pore pressure in fine-grained soil. (There is some similarity with the airlift system in that fluid is introduced at the bottom of a discharge pipe (riser) to cause an upward flow.)

6.2.3.1 Development
It is important to 'develop' deep wells. This is, effectively, a cleaning process to remove drilling debris from the hole and also, in suitable ground, wash out fine particles from joints or fissures, thus increasing the effective size of the well. Removal of debris before installing the pump also reduces pump wear. In carbonate rocks such as limestone or chalk, concentrated hydrochloric acid can be added to dissolve slurry and clean fissures. This process releases carbon dioxide in large quantities and should only be carried out by appropriately experienced personnel.

6.2.4   Filters
Whenever groundwater is pumped from a soil, seepage pressures are set up at the point of entry of the water into the well. The seepage pressures can dislodge particles from the soil near the borehole wall so that the flow carries them into the system. This can have deleterious effects both on the system and the ground. Excessive sediment transport will cause wear or clogging to the pump and pipework. Removal of fines from the ground is a common source of settlement of ground in the vicinity of dewatering schemes.

In order to prevent the removal of soil particles, filters are installed. Traditionally, these were made from soil with a grading specified to meet criteria relating the particle size distribution of the filter to that of the aquifer. In some cases, two layers of filter were needed. Filter rules are described in detail in Preene *et al.* (2000).

Woven geotextiles have been developed to provide sophisticated filtering systems. Manufacturers should be consulted for information on the attributes of their particular products.

6.2.5   Hazards
Hazards resulting from the application of the techniques described above include the following.

- Settlement: when the groundwater level is reduced, the effective stress between soil particles increases. At shallow depth and in compressible soil, this increase can be significant, causing settlement of the ground in the drawdown zone surrounding the system and consequential damage to structures.
- Removal of fines: if the filtration system does not function properly, the flow of water can lead to the extraction of fines from the surrounding ground and the creation of voids. In some circumstances, this can lead to catastrophic collapse of the surface.

■ Fouling and clogging: the effectiveness of wells, wellpoints and ejectors can deteriorate over time because of fouling of the screen by bacterial growth and/or encrustation by chemicals precipitated from the water.

■ Corrosion: some groundwater (for example, saline water at sites near the sea) has a chemical composition which may cause corrosion of pipework and pumps.

6.2.6   Recharge

Where settlement is considered to present a hazard, the effects of dewatering can be ameliorated by pumping water back into the ground within the area of drawdown outside the excavation. This will change the groundwater profile during system operation and reduce the drawdown below the surrounding ground.

6.2.7   Monitoring and maintenance

It is essential to confirm that the dewatering system is effective and that it continues to be effective. Plant which is on standby should be regularly checked and run. Groundwater levels must be measured sufficiently frequently over a wide enough area. The flow rate from the system should be checked and collated with groundwater levels. In normal circumstances, the initial pumping capacity used to drawdown the water level will be significantly greater than (perhaps twice) that needed to maintain the reduced level. Monitoring the initial stage will show when some of the system can be shut down and put onto standby in case of mechanical or other problems. The occurrence of fouling or clogging is a gradual process and should be monitored by continuing measurement of water levels and flow rates at suitable intervals. In some circumstances it may be necessary to replace wells which have become ineffective.

It may also be necessary to monitor water quality (both the chemistry and the concentration of suspended solids), particularly for discharge or recharge purposes. Where the ground conditions dictate, accurate settlement monitoring should be undertaken; this should begin well before the dewatering is turned on. Note that in some areas close to tidal water, the ground surface can move with the tide. Any natural variation in level could make it very difficult to interpret ground level data during operation of the groundwater lowering system.

6.2.8   Consents

It is normally necessary to obtain a license from the Environment Agency (EA) to extract more than $20 \, m^3/day$ of water from the ground. The abstracted water is classified in a legal sense as trade effluent. As such, a discharge permit is required before the water can be fed to surface water, the sea, water courses or recharged back into the ground. Note that, even if nothing else is done to the abstracted water, exposure to the atmosphere may cause chemical changes to occur. Advice about obtaining permits from the EA can be found on their website.

6.3.   Investigation for dewatering

The stratigraphy of the area which will be affected by the dewatering can be found from an array of suitably deep boreholes. Samples should be taken to allow the various strata to be classified by testing and their structure be determined by splitting open and describing samples of intact soil.

Direct measurements of permeability can be made in a number of ways, but there are significant drawbacks to most methods. Testing can be carried out in situ during drilling of site investigation boreholes. However, the ground just below the bottom of the borehole may have been disturbed and there may be problems in allowing enough time to establish an accurate rest level. Additionally, sediment can be deposited at the bottom of the borehole as a thin low-permeability layer, especially during inflow tests. If the head is reduced too far for a rising head test, the ground around the base of the hole may be disturbed by 'blowing'. Where piezometers are installed, tests can be carried out which are similar to the in-borehole tests. The rest level should have been determined by repeated measurements and the risk of silting or blowing should be minimal. However, tests in boreholes and piezometers suffer from the small volume of ground tested. In most circumstances, it is necessary to carry out a number of tests in different places at different depths.

Permeability tests can be carried out on samples in the laboratory, but sample disturbance may be a problem. Tests which pass a vertical flow through a tube sample may measure a misleadingly low permeability if the sample is anisotropic, as many soils are. To obtain sufficient flow in low permeability soils, it is generally necessary to apply a much higher hydraulic gradient to the specimen than would occur in practice; this can lead to misleading results. The sample size may not be large enough to include representative fabric (soil structure). Particle size distributions can be used to provide an estimate of permeability in certain soils – uniform sands are most suited to this (see Equation 6.2). In a layered soil, the different soil layers should be separated before taking specimens for particle size distribution testing.

The best way to measure permeability at the scale required for a dewatering scheme design is by a pumping test. This is effectively a small-scale trial of the dewatering system. The test pumping well should be surrounded by a number of monitoring wells so that the drawdown curve can be determined, ideally in two orthogonal directions. These tests are relatively expensive and take between 1 and 2 weeks to conduct. Their major advantage is that the mass permeability of the soil is measured under conditions which are similar to those which will confront the actual dewatering system.

6.4. Analysis and design
6.4.1 Steps in analysis and design

- Draw ground cross-sections to establish the stratigraphy.
- Measure k and determine a most probable value and a range for all strata.
- Find the equilibrium groundwater level and consider whether this may vary (long-term monitoring data may be available for the locality from the Environment Agency).
- Determine the required drawdown (depth and area).
- Consider the type of system needed (see Figure 6.1).
- Idealise the system: well, slot or combination.
- Estimate potential flow rate (most probable and range).

- Detail the system (e.g. determine depths and spacings for wellpoints or deep wells).

6.4.2 Permeability

One-dimensional flow in saturated soil is governed by Darcy's Law which states that the velocity of laminar fluid flow through a soil is proportional to the gradient of fluid pressure (head) between the two ends of the element. Turbulent flow in soil is only likely in coarse gravels with high flow. Darcy's Law is defined:

$$q = -k\frac{(h_o - h_i)}{l} \tag{6.1}$$

where q is the velocity of flow (m/s), h_o is the head (m) at the point where the fluid emerges from the element, h_i is the head (m) at the point where the fluid enters the element, l is the length (m) of the element and k is the coefficient of proportionality (m/s), referred to as the permeability.

The flow is positive in the direction of negative gradient. Between clay and coarse gravel there is a huge range of permeability, c. 10^{-10} to 10^{-1} m/s. (An equivalent range of distance is from 1 m to 2.5 times the distance from the Earth to the Moon.) In highly favourable conditions, the most accurate determination of permeability is within a factor of c. 3.

The permeability is related to pore size which, in uniform soil, is related to the particle size. Hazen's formula can be reliable for some sands and gives a general indication of the order of magnitude of k:

$$k = 0.01D_{10}^2 \tag{6.2}$$

where D_{10} is the sieve size (mm) which allows 10% of the soil by weight to pass through and k is measured in m/s.

Permeability is not a constant, because the pore size decreases if the soil is compressed. This can be important in soft soil (e.g. organic clay) where significant changes in permeability can occur as a result of consolidation, which may be a result of the groundwater lowering.

Soil is not homogeneous. Even in what might appear to be a uniform soil, the permeability is almost always greater in the horizontal direction than the vertical. Many soils are layered. Thin clay layers in a sand stratum can reduce the vertical mass permeability dramatically. Glacial soils are very heterogeneous. Predominantly clayey glacial soil can contain pockets, lenses or ribbons of coarse granular material which may provide a conduit to a source of water.

Equation (6.1) shows that the rate of flow is also proportional to the difference in head along the element. In a dewatering scheme this is equivalent to the drawdown, that is, the difference between the equilibrium water level and the lower level required for construction.

Ground cross-sections are seldom uniform and simplifications in geometry may be needed to make analysis possible. The mass permeabilities of the different strata are key parameters in design.

6.4.3 Analysis of pumped well dewatering systems

The flow of water to a dewatering system is three-dimensional. In many circumstances, however, the groundwater regime is simplified to a two-dimensional system using either planar or radial coordinates. Plane flow can be used for lines of wells, for example, dewatering a trench for the installation of services. The idealised equivalent to a row of wells is termed a 'slot'. Radial flow applies in the case of flow to single wells; where a group of wells surrounds an excavation, it can be treated as an equivalent single well or as a combination of slots for the sides and wells for the corners.

Figure 6.5 shows the two principal 'ideal' aquifer conditions (confined and unconfined) with partially penetrating wells or slots. Fully penetrating wells, as the name suggests, reach down to the top of the impermeable base layer.

Equations have been derived for volumetric flow rates to wells and slots for confined and unconfined aquifers. As might be expected, the principal variables are the permeability and the required drawdown. In determining the required drawdown, allowance must be made for the increase in head with distance from the well. In the case of a group of wells around an excavation, the head at the centre of the group is higher than the head at the wells themselves (see Figure 6.3).

The expression for radial flow to a fully penetrating well in a confined aquifer is given by the Theim equation:

$$Q = \frac{2\pi k D (H - h_w)}{\ln(R_o / r_e)} \tag{6.3}$$

where Q is in m^3/s if k is in m/s and D, H and h_w are in m.

There are similar relationships for a well in an unconfined aquifer and for planar flow to slots in confined and unconfined aquifers. The equations, together with factors for flows from partially penetrating wells and slots, are given in Preene et al. (2000).

The parameters are defined in Figure 6.4. Note that r_e is the equivalent well radius. Where a group of wells is distributed around a rectangle $a \times b$, r_e may be taken as $(a + b)/\pi$. If only a single well is being considered, $r_e = r_w$ (i.e. the well radius).

When three-dimensional analysis is required, or for complex two-dimensional geometries, computer programs providing numerical solutions are available. It is, however, advisable to engage the services of a groundwater specialist to make such analyses. Bond (1994) provides advice on the use of geotechnical software.

Figure 6.5 Definitions of parameters for flows to wells and slots

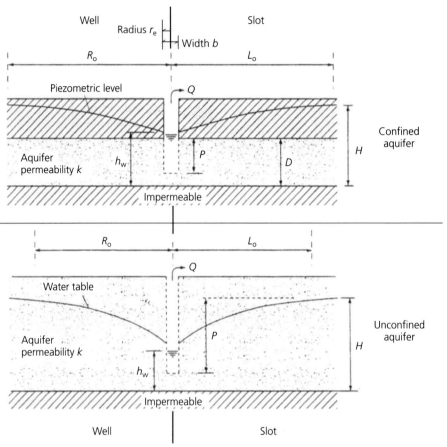

However sophisticated the analysis, the design of the dewatering system must take account of the uncertainties in both the actual values of permeability and in the structure of the ground affected by the process. It is essential to monitor the effectiveness of the system, ideally starting the process with enough time allowed in the programme to adjust the design if the drawdown is insufficient. When starting a dewatering scheme, it is wise to be aware of where and how quickly additional resources can be obtained (if they are not actually held in reserve). As far as pump capacity is concerned, an immediate need to increase capacity can often be met by use of a standby pump(s) which should be on hand in case of breakdowns.

REFERENCES

Bond A (ed.) (1994) *Validation and use of geotechnical software*. Association of Geotechnical and Geoenvironmental Specialists, Kent.

Preene M, Roberts TOL, Powrie W and Dyer MR (2000) Groundwater control – design and practice. CIRIA Report C515. CIRIA, London.

Roberts TOL and Preene M (1994) Range of application of groundwater control systems. In *Groundwater Problems in Urban Areas*, Wilkinson WB (ed.) Thomas Telford, London, 415–423.

FURTHER READING

Roberts TOL and Preene M (1994) The design of groundwater control systems using the observational method. *Géotechnique*, **44(4)**: 727–734.

Useful web addresses

A comprehensive listing of available geotechnical programs can be found at http://www. ggsd.com, including various groundwater categories (found within the Geoenvironmental program index).

Information on the regulations surrounding abstraction and disposal of groundwater can be found at http://www.environment-agency.gov.uk.

Temporary Works: Principles of Design and Construction
ISBN 978-0-7277-4177-6

ICE Publishing: All rights reserved
http://dx.doi.org/10.1680/twpdc.41776.091

Chapter 7
Lime and cement stabilisation

Mike Brice Associate, Applied Geotechnical Engineering
Neil Smith Director, Applied Geotechnical Engineering

Weak soils can be improved in strength and workability by the addition of lime and/or cement. The use of the process as a temporary measure is generally to provide a sound working surface for construction (though the treated soil has been altered permanently). Lime is usually applied to the soil in the form of quicklime. This has an immediate effect in taking moisture from wet soils and is especially effective in soft, wet, plastic clay. The lime also reduces the plasticity of the clay and so makes it both stronger and more workable. If added in sufficient quantity, it produces a cementing effect with considerable additional increase in strength over time. Cement also reduces the moisture content and plasticity, although less effectively than lime. It does, however, have a greater cementitious effect. It is more suitable for treating lower plasticity or non-plastic soils. The results of adding lime or cement are very soil-specific, so preliminary testing is essential to ensure that the desired effect(s) can be achieved and to find the optimum concentration and type of additive. The effects vary with plasticity and other properties, so that a substantial test programme is needed in variable soils such as glacial till. Blends of lime and cement can be used and other cementitious agents, such as pulverised fuel ash (PFA), may be incorporated.

7.1.   Introduction

This chapter deals with the use of lime and cement additives to improve the strength of near-surface soils for temporary works construction. In a temporary works context, the addition of lime or cement is most likely to be required in the context of haul road or working platform improvement (see Chapter 5), and in the rendering of wet material suitable for use as a general fill. In some circumstances, such as the enhancement of thick soft deposits, deep methods such as lime mixing or lime columns may be beneficial. These require highly specialised plant and are of a different character to superficial lime and cement mixing. They are not considered further here.

The two additives differ in their actions: lime is of more benefit in the rapid drying of soils and as an additive to improve 'heavy' plastic clay soils. In low plasticity clay soils (PI < 10%) and in predominantly granular soils lime may be used as a drying agent, but otherwise its effectiveness is limited and cement is of greater benefit.

7.2.   Materials and their effects on the soil
7.2.1   Lime
Lime is available in two forms: quicklime and slaked lime. In Europe quicklime is most

commonly used for soil treatment, being significantly more effective in drying out a soil by the heat of hydration than slaked lime, and is less dusty to handle. Only quicklime is discussed below.

In the first instance, the addition of lime dries the soil both by absorbing water directly (up to 32% of the dry lime weight) and by driving off water by the exothermic nature of the hydration reaction. As a rule of thumb, the reduction in soil moisture content amounts to approximately 1% per percentage point of added quicklime. This effect is seen in all soils. In cohesive soils there is also a chemical reaction with clay minerals in the soil; the lime will alter the nature of the clay minerals, greatly increasing the plastic limit and thereby reducing the plasticity. Both of these reactions are immediate and are not affected by ambient temperature. They can combine to transform a soft plastic soil into a dry friable material, making it significantly stronger and easier to work. Together they are termed soil modification. The effectiveness of the second reaction is dependent upon the nature of the clay minerals within the soil (montmorillonite being more affected than illite and chlorite for example), and the clay content and mineralogy will also affect the quantity of lime required.

The proportion of lime required is small; between 1 and 3% (by dry weight) of lime to soil is needed in order to effect soil modification. It has been noted that 0.5% lime addition should be adequate for the majority of British plastic clays that have been classified as unacceptable on the basis of excess moisture content (Perry *et al.*, 1996a).

If a higher proportion of lime is added then the pH of the soil is elevated to pH > 12 and a cementitious action of the lime on the clay minerals in the soil occurs, leading to an increase in strength with time (typically weeks, although measurable strength increases will still occur after several years). Above 5–8% lime (depending on the original clay content of the soil), the effect is lost and long-term strength begins to decrease. Such high proportions of lime may not be economical in any event. This cementitious reaction is affected by soil temperature, and the reaction will be suspended for as long as the temperature falls below 4–5°C. It also requires the presence of water, therefore wetting of treated fills may be required if the cementitious effect is to be relied upon. The cementitious action is termed 'soil stabilisation'.

A resting ('mellowing' or 'maturing') period between mixing and compacting the fill is recommended where the stabilisation component of the lime treatment is important. The resting period, which is typically 24–72 hours for lime-treated soils, allows the lime to hydrate and migrate through the soil thereby fully effecting the changes in plasticity index and general handling improvements. Following this resting period, the soil is remixed and compacted. If the resting period is too protracted then carbonation of the quicklime becomes appreciable, and less quicklime is then available for the stabilisation reaction.

For high-strength end products (such as road-capping layers), compaction to less than 5% air voids is usually required and control of the moisture content is needed to ensure this is achievable.

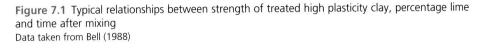

Figure 7.1 Typical relationships between strength of treated high plasticity clay, percentage lime and time after mixing
Data taken from Bell (1988)

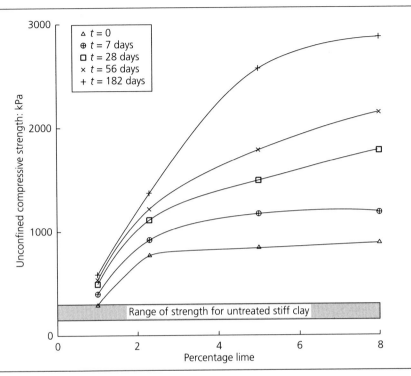

Figure 7.1 depics data for the strength of a lime-treated high plasticity clay from Bell (1988). The flattening of the $t = 0$ line at lime concentrations above 2% clearly shows the limitation of the modifying effect. The subsequent strength gains largely reflect the stabilisation process.

7.2.2 Cement

Cement is used predominantly for soil stabilisation, similar to the cementitious action of excess lime. There is a modest immediate drying effect (soil modification) on first mixing the cement with the soil. This amounts to a 0.3–0.5% reduction in overall moisture content per percentage point of cement added, but this is usually viewed as a secondary benefit. The cementitious action is far faster than the equivalent action in the lime stabilised soil and is not dependent on the presence of clay minerals. The reaction is again suspended below a soil temperature of 5°C, but the period over which the treated soil is susceptible to low temperature is so much shorter than with lime treatment that cement additives might confidently be used closer to the winter season. The faster 'set' of a cement additive means that there is far less leeway in the duration of the resting period. Testing is required to establish the optimum duration of the resting period.

Figure 7.2 Relations between lime/cement content, compressive strength and original clay plasticity
Data taken from Christensen (1969)

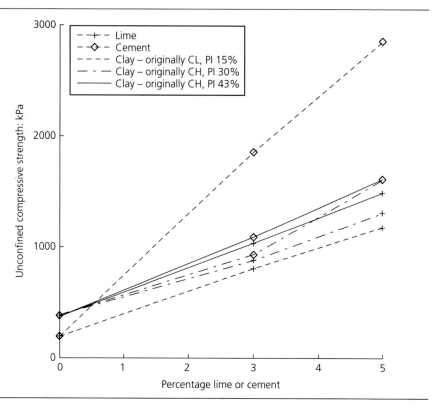

Figure 7.2 presents data from Christensen (1969) for lime- and cement-modified soils of different plasticity, tested for strength at 7 days. It can be seen that there is little difference between the effects of the lime and cement for the high plasticity soil, but a very marked difference in the results for low plasticity clay.

7.2.3   Blends

In some cases a combined treatment with a lime/cement blend may be appropriate. In any case it is imperative, in view of the significant costs of lime/cement treatment, that pre-contract laboratory testing is carried out. The best additive to use for a given soil and the proportions in which it is to be added in order to achieve the required performance must be established.

Where it is only required to produce a modest increase in strength, for example, simply to make a site subgrade trafficable, the proportions of additive needed may be very small. There can be problems with the even distribution of such small proportions of additive, so a dry 'inert' bulking medium such as pulverised fuel ash (PFA) can first be added.

(PFA is not inert and will also confer an additional cementitious element to the long-term strength.)

7.3.   The performance of treated soils
7.3.1   Soil modification
The addition of lime to a clay soil immediately tends to flatten the compaction curve, increase the optimum moisture content and reduce the maximum dry density for a given compactive effort. It then follows that acceptable fills will be found over a wider range of moisture content. The reduction in maximum dry density is more than compensated for by a gain in strength and stiffness.

These changes arise as the clay minerals flocculate, thereby effectively changing the grain size of the clay minerals.

7.3.2   Soil stabilisation
The above effects are not clearly seen with purely cement-treated soils. Soils treated with cement, or soils treated with higher proportions of lime than required for modification alone, undergo stabilisation in which cementitious products form within the soil. The process is much slower for lime- than for cement-treated soils.

The stabilisation process is marked by an increase in strength and stiffness with time.

The changes brought about by the initial soil modification usually render the treated soil frost susceptible. Lime-stabilised soil remains frost susceptible for around 3 months after placement, and frost action during that time would probably disrupt the cementitious bonds developed during the stabilisation process.

Cement stabilised soils are likely to be less frost susceptible than lime-stabilised, due both to the different grain size distribution of the original soil and to the more rapid development of strong cementitious bonds.

In stabilised soils, the lime can undergo an expansive chemical reaction with sulphate chemicals in the soil, potentially leading to heave of the treated soil. Heave magnitudes of 60% of treated layer thickness have been recorded. Such effects are the single main cause of failure of lime- or cement-treated earthworks. The reaction involves the formation of Ettringite and Thaumasite and is therefore directly equivalent to sulphate attack on concrete. The rapid oxidation of soil sulphides to sulphates during the lime mixing process makes it essential to determine both sulphide and sulphate contents of the soil to be treated during the planning stage.

Organic material in the soil interferes with the stabilisation reaction, tending to reduce the pH locally. An upper limit of 2% organic content for lime-treatable fills is often quoted (HA, 1991). Above this limit, lime addition is taken to be ineffective although it is recognised that the form of the organic matter is important; Oxford Clay with up to 10% disseminated bituminous content has been successfully treated.

Lime-treated soils can lose strength if inundated. Reductions of 30–50% in California bearing ratio (CBR) are quoted (HA, 1991), so it is important that treated materials are adequately protected and drained.

7.4. Testing

The proportion of additive (lime or cement) is expressed as a percentage of additive per unit dry weight of soil. Testing soil to establish the suitability of lime/cement treatment is very much dependent upon the end use of the treated product.

It is not appropriate to apply the results of testing of the original soil to the treated product. The nature of the soil is altered by treatment and new earthworks control criteria need to be derived. The Moisture Condition Value (MCV) test is recognised as being appropriate for the site control of treated soils.

Before the commencement of treatment on site, laboratory testing should be carried out in order to determine (for the treated soil) the following properties.

1   The sulphate, sulphide and organic contents of the soil to be treated (Longworth, 2004; HA, 2007). It is important to note that sulphides and sulphates are often leached out of the top metre or so of UK soils. Hence, if soils from deeper than this are to be treated, then it is important that they are adequately sampled and tested. Groundwater should also be tested for sulphates. A limit of 1% total sulphate is usually applied in UK highway works, but it is recognised that lower sulphate concentrations can still result in unacceptable swelling of treated materials and so site-specific testing (relating the sulphate content to heave in an inundation test) should be carried out where soil stabilisation is required (Perry *et al.*, 1996b).

2   The relationships between moisture content, MCV and dry density as well as (if applicable to end use) undrained strength and CBR for different proportions of added lime/cement. The Initial Consumption of Lime (ICL) is the quantity of lime required to bring the soil to a pH of 12.4, and marks the boundary between a soil modification effect and soil stabilisation. Where soil stabilisation is required (as opposed to simple modification), the ICL marks the lowest lime proportion that needs to be tested. Increments of 0.5% lime are usually tested until the optimum lime proportion is identified. It is important that if a resting period is to be used on site then a similar resting period is allowed in the laboratory (Perry *et al.*, 1996b).

3   Heave on inundation, carried out over 14–28 days on a compacted sample in a CBR mould, is important as an indicator of adverse sulphate reactions and should be carried out where soil stabilisation is required.

4   Frost susceptibility tests may be appropriate, but these are expensive tests requiring large samples and it may be more appropriate to ensure that treated soils are protected from frost or are not stabilised during the season when frost is a risk.

Quality control testing of the end-product is necessary. The testing undertaken would depend on the original intention of the stabilisation process. For example, if the intention is to produce a surface with a given traffickability, then plate-bearing tests or in situ CBR tests would be appropriate. The rate for such testing is commonly of the order of 1 test per 1000 m^2 of treated surface. If on the other hand the purpose was to produce a useable bulk fill, then compaction/density testing (to ensure the treated product could be readily compacted to achieve a given standard, for example, 95% Proctor maximum dry density) would be appropriate. A suitable testing rate in this case might be 1 test per 250 m^3 of treated fill.

7.5.   Plant

Lime/cement additives are usually mixed into the soil in situ, either for subsequent compaction in place or for subsequent excavation and placement/compaction elsewhere. There may be practical problems on site with dispersion through the soil of small proportions of lime/cement. In this situation, the additive can be bulked up by the addition of PFA to improve dispersion. This also imparts a cementitious component, leading to a further increase in strength with time.

In addition to storage facilities for the additive, the plant requirements comprise spreading and mixing equipment as well as the preliminary grading and subsequent compaction plant. On economic grounds, agricultural machinery (drag-bars, ploughs, rotovators, etc.) may be suitable for the spreading and mixing on minor works. For best results, however, and to ensure a uniformity of product, specialist spreading/soil pulverisation plant is required (Figure 7.3). More than one pass of the soil pulveriser may be required to produce uniform results. Wetting of the fill may be required in

Figure 7.3 Addition of lime using an integrated spreader and mixer unit and a simple mixer unit (working on pre-spread lime), both tractor drawn
Courtesy of Con-Form Contracting

order to achieve specification. Specialist soil pulverisation plant often incorporates a spray bar for this purpose. High mobilisation charges would generally apply to such plant.

A delay between mixing of the lime with the soil and the subsequent compaction allows the quicklime to slake and, depending on the delay, to migrate through and modify the clay soil, facilitating compaction. The duration of this delay, often between 1 hour and 72 hours depending on the soil and on site constraints, should be modelled during the original testing phase. Following compaction, the cementitious reactions are likely to lead to a gain in strength with time. The time over which the strength increases significantly is termed the 'curing' period.

7.6.   Health and safety

The reaction of quicklime with bodily fluids (in sweat, mucus membranes, eyes) is exothermic and the products are caustic. Burns are therefore a significant risk where lime is being handled and suitable protective clothing together with the intelligent imposition of exclusion zones on the site are necessary. Equipment and procedures for immediate treatment must be set up before work is allowed to start.

REFERENCES

Bell FG (1988) Stabilisation and treatment of clay soils with lime. Part 1 – Basic principles. *Ground Engineering* **21**(1): 10–15.

Christensen AP (1969) Cement modification of clay soils. RD002.01S. Portland Cement Association, Illinois. Available from the Association website.

HA (Highways Agency) (1991) HA44/91: Earthworks. Design and preparation of contract documents. Advice note published by the Highways Agency as part of the Design Manual for Roads and Bridges, Volume 4, Geotechnics and drainage, Section 1 Earthworks, Part 6. HMSO, London. (Amended 1995.)

HA (2007) HA74/07: Treatment of fill and capping materials using either lime or cement or both. Advice note published by the Highways Agency as part of the Design Manual for Roads and Bridges, Volume 4, Geotechnics and drainage, Section 1 Earthworks, Part 6. HMSO, London.

Longworth I (2004) Assessment of sulphate-bearing ground for soil stabilisation for built development. *Ground Engineering* **37**(5): 30–34.

Perry J, MacNeil D and Wilson P (1996a) The uses of lime in ground engineering: a review of work undertaken at the Transport Research Laboratory. In *Lime Stabilisation*. Thomas Telford Publishing, London.

Perry J, Snowdon R and Wilson P (1996b) Site investigation for lime stabilisation of highway works. In *Advances in Site Investigation Practice*. Thomas Telford Publishing, London.

FURTHER READING

BRE (British Research Establishment) (2005) BRE Special Digest 1: Concrete in aggressive ground. BRE, Watford.

BSI (2004) BS EN 13286 Parts 1–53 Testing stabilised materials. BSI, London. (This replaces BS 1924: 1990.)

BSI (2004) BS EN 13286-47: Unbound and hydraulically bound mixtures. Test method for the determination of California bearing ratio, immediate bearing index and linear swelling. BSI, London.

BSI (2004) BS EN 14227-1: Unbound and hydraulically bound mixtures. BSI, London.

Mitchell J and Jardine FM (2002) A guide to ground treatment. CIRIA, London.

Useful web addresses

British Lime Association: http://www.britishlime.org

British In situ Concrete Paving Association: http://www.soilstabilisation.org.uk

National Lime Association of the USA: http://www.lime.org

Portland Cement Association: http://www.cement.org

Temporary Works: Principles of Design and Construction
ISBN 978-0-7277-4177-6

ICE Publishing: All rights reserved
http://dx.doi.org/10.1680/twpdc.41776.101

Chapter 8
Jet grouting

John Hislam Director, Applied Geotechnical Engineering
Neil Smith Director, Applied Geotechnical Engineering

Jet grouting is a process of increasing the strength and/or decreasing the permeability of soil by wholly or partially eroding a volume of ground and replacing it with grout or a mixture of grout and the disturbed soil. The erosion and grout placement are both effected by high-pressure jetting from drillholes via a tube known as a 'monitor'. Zones of grout can either be cylinders created by full rotation of the monitor, segments of cylinders created by limited rotation or panels created without rotation. Closely spaced drillholes are used to make overlapping zones of treated ground to form the desired shape. Any shape is possible provided that the drillholes can be suitably oriented. A number of factors affect the strength of the treated ground, but unconfined compressive strengths of up to 8 MPa or 2 MPa are quite possible in coarse or fine soil, respectively, although a few weeks will be required for the maximum strength to be reached. The permeability of the treated ground can be reduced to 10^{-7} m/s or less. The technique can be used to form retaining structures around excavations or (with subhorizontal drillholes) arches above tunnels under construction or groundwater cut-offs. By treating only cylinders of limited height in a defined depth zone, bottom cut-offs or props between retaining walls can be created. On a small scale, tunnel to shaft break-ins or break-outs can be facilitated or leaky basements sealed.

8.1.   Introduction

Jet grouting is a method of ground improvement achieved by replacing the in situ soil with cement grout or by mixing soil and cement grout in situ. It can be used where permeation grouting (filling the voids between soil particles) would be impossible or ineffective. It is carried out from drillholes using radial fluid jets and forms generally cylindrical zones of cemented ground co-axial with the drillhole. High-pressure fluid is used to erode the soil and flush part or all of it to the surface. If only some of the soil is removed, that which remains must be thoroughly mixed with the grout.

Figure 8.1 shows the basic systems of single, double and triple fluids. The pipework which delivers the fluids into the ground is termed (confusingly) the 'monitor'. Figure 8.2 shows an example. The monitor is incorporated into the drillstring. During drilling, the drill flush is emitted through the bit. Usually the jet grout mixture is used as the flushing medium during drilling as this helps to stabilise the sides of the hole. As for the drillhole cuttings, the excess spoil generated during the jetting process is flushed to the surface via the annular gap between the monitor and the hole.

Figure 8.1 Jet grouting systems

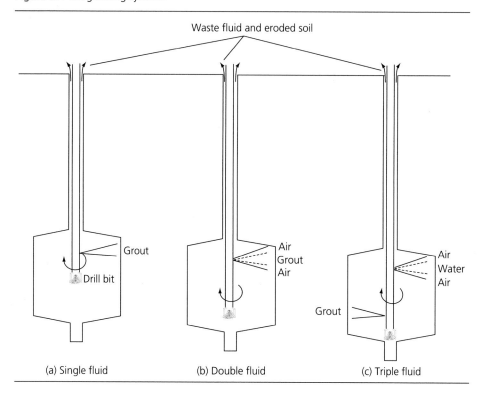

(a) Single fluid   (b) Double fluid   (c) Triple fluid

The technique is not restricted to the creation of vertical columns. It can be used from drillholes of any inclination. The treatment can be used over a limited section of a drill-hole to form a disc of improved ground. The treated ground has a relatively high compressive strength and a low permeability. It can, therefore, be used to form arches, gravity structures or tubes to create, for example

1   a water cut-off, either around the sides or below the floor of an excavation
2   a retaining structure to support the sides of an excavation
3   a horizontal low-level prop before excavation
4   a supporting arch to maintain ground stability during tunnel construction
5   on a small scale, it can be used to stop leakage through basement retaining walls
6   a region of low permeability ground to permit tunnel break-out from, or break-in to, shafts.

Coupland (2010) and Wit *et al.* (2007a) provide case histories of two interesting projects; many others can be found in the literature. Most applications entail the construction of cylinders of ground, since the jets are rotated throughout the process of erosion and filling. If rotation is limited or prevented, different geometric forms are possible. The work is covered by an 'execution of special geotechnical work' attachment to EC7 Part 1 (BSI, 2001).

Figure 8.2 Monitor and drill bit
Courtesy of Prof R Boulanger, University of California

Concentric pipes

Jetting nozzle

Drill bit

8.2.   Construction methods

There are three systems of jet grouting (see Figure 8.1). The first stage for all is to drill the monitor in to the full depth required. Grouting takes place as the monitor is withdrawn from the hole. The simplest grouting method is the single-fluid system, which uses grout both to erode the soil and to form the cylinder. The double-fluid system uses a combined grout and compressed air jet. The compressed air makes the combined jet much more aggressive. The triple-fluid system separates the erosion and the filling processes, using water instead of grout (plus air) to erode the soil with a grout jet at a lower level.

For the combined fluid jets, the compressed air is forced through an annular nozzle with the nozzle delivering the water or grout at its centre. The flow of air therefore surrounds the more viscous fluid as it leaves the jet. High jetting velocities are used (up to 300 m/s), requiring fluid pressures of the order of 20–60 MPa and compressed air pressures of c. 1.5 MPa. Triplex pumps are used to attain the high pressures required. Extreme care must be observed when the monitor is above ground level as the jets, especially because they carry particulate matter, can cause damage and injury.

The size of the cylinder which can be treated with this method depends to a significant extent on the nature of the soil, as well as the method adopted. While jet grouting can treat virtually all soils (and some very weakly cemented rocks), some materials are more resistant to erosion than others so that the size can vary between strata. Stiff clay is much more resistant than silt or fine sand. Very coarse soil particles require more force to move them than fine grains. The drillhole would typically be about 150 mm diameter. Grouted column diameters from 0.75 m (for the single-fluid method) to 2 m are commonly quoted and up to 5 m diameter has been claimed. Cylinders for temporary works would normally be used in groups and the selection of the spacing between drillholes must therefore ensure sufficient overlap of adjacent cylinders. In theory, the depth which can be treated is not limited but in practice the method has been used to about 50 m below ground.

If the mixing process is not properly effective, lumps of unmixed soil can be trapped within the column (see Stark *et al.*, 2009).

The treatment is generally terminated a short distance below ground level because of the risk of the jetted fluids breaking through to the surface. While the plant used does not need to be large (so that restricted access working is possible), columns may have to be constructed in stages where there is a height constraint. If this is the case, it is obviously important to ensure good overlap between adjacent sections.

8.3. Design principles

8.3.1 Material properties

The principal properties of the treated ground needed for design are its strength and permeability.

The strength varies with the construction technique, for example, the proportion of the in situ soil which is mixed with the grout, how well it is mixed and the nature of the soil itself. Time is also a factor which may influence the design if the work is on the critical path. Figure 8.3 gives an indication of the strength values which may be achieved, depending on soil type and time after mixing. It can be seen that the full strength of the mixture will take several weeks or more to be reached.

Permeabilities of 10^{-7} m/s and lower have been reported from various sites. Preliminary testing for strength and/or permeability is necessary to ensure that the design and the achieved properties are compatible. Generally, samples of the treated ground are recovered in cored drillholes and tested in the laboratory. Piezometers can be installed in these holes to permit measurement of the in situ permeability.

8.3.2 Design of the treated mass

There are two aspects to design. The requirements for the overall shape and dimensions of the treated ground can be determined using conventional analysis techniques, for example, by treating a jet-grouted retaining structure as a gravity structure and using normal earth pressure calculations. Where the strength of the grouted mass and the programme time are both critical, due attention must be given to the slow development of strength in some soils. Where a cut-off is required, conventional groundwater flow analysis can be used.

Figure 8.3 Typical strengths of jet grout-soil mixtures

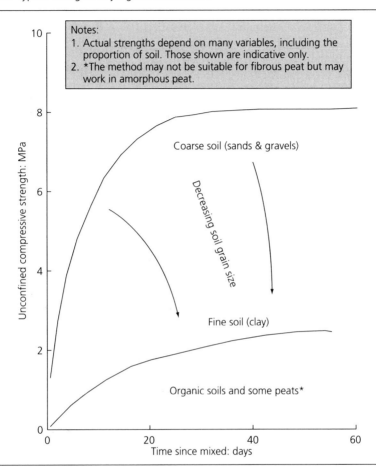

The second aspect of design involves the selection of the construction method, the determination of the column diameter and grout mix requirements and the monitor rotation and lifting speeds. All of these are empirical; they depend partially on the particular equipment and should therefore be the province of the specialist contractor.

8.3.3 Design verification
Any design of a jet-grouted mass of ground must be verified. Trials are needed in the actual ground conditions. The dimensions of the treated zone require checking; samples need to be taken (by rotary coring methods) for strength and laboratory permeability testing as appropriate. It may also be wise to install piezometers in the cored holes to test the in situ permeability of the mass.

8.4. Monitoring and validation
It is necessary both to monitor the construction process and to validate the adequacy of the treated ground (see de Wit *et al.*, 2007b).

If the location is critical, it may be appropriate to survey long drillholes before grouting. Parameters to be monitored during construction should include the grout density, the fluid pressures and flow rates, the rate of rotation and withdrawal. When a column has just been completed, its diameter can be checked using callipers. Conventional instrumentation such as inclinometers can be used to monitor the performance of retaining structures. It may be prudent to deploy precise survey techniques and borehole extensometer systems during the grouting process to measure and control heave or settlement.

Preliminary trials can be used to verify the condition of the treated ground by exhumation (for example, see Stark *et al.*, 2009). Treated ground can be drilled to recover cores for testing strength and permeability. Piezometers can be installed within or around treated ground to confirm its effectiveness in controlling groundwater flow.

8.5. Secondary and side effects

8.5.1 Ground heave and hydrofracture

There is a risk that the process may produce heave of the surface in the area around the treated ground. There are two potential mechanisms. In high plasticity clays, heave may be caused by swelling resulting from the availability of large quantities of water. Alternatively, excessive fluid pressures may cause hydrofracture, especially if the flushed material is prevented or restricted from escaping directly back up the drillhole to the surface. The restriction can cause a sudden increase of the fluid pressure in the bore. If the fluid pressure becomes higher than the lowest normal pressure in the soil, a fracture in the drillhole wall can occur which results in an escape of fluid, forcing the ground aside and bringing about surface heave. Some recovery may occur if the pressure is released but this is likely to be uneven and is almost certain to be incomplete.

When used to stabilise very soft clay (having a consistency similar to toothpaste) for a 1 km length of tunnel for the Singapore Mass Rapid Transit scheme, heave of up to 550 mm was recorded (Berry *et al.*, 1987). Average heave above the westbound tunnel (at 15–25 m depth) was 140 mm and above the eastbound tunnel (at 10–15 m depth) was 70 mm.

8.5.2 Reaction with the ground

The setting cement increases the ground temperature and this can cause the alkaline cement to react with organic material in the soil to produce ammonia. This can be of particular concern where the treated ground surrounds a confined space such as a tunnel. If the groundwater is acidic, for example, in peaty or contaminated ground, the grout mix will need special consideration.

8.5.3 Spoil disposal

The process produces large volumes of waste in the form of slurry consisting of a mixture of water, soil and grout, the largest component of which is water. The volume discharged may be three times the volume of the treated ground. It demands considerable care in collecting the waste at the surface of the drillhole and then directing it to a suitable point for disposal from the site. The consequences of poor control of the waste are a dirty and potentially unsafe site. Control issues regarding drillhole location become important. Off-site disposal of this effluent adds a significant cost to the process.

REFERENCES

Berry GL, Shirlaw JN, Hayata K and Tan SH (1987) A review of grouting techniques used for bored tunnelling with emphasis on the jet grouting method. *Proceedings of the Singapore Mass Rapid Transport Conference*, Institution of Engineers, Singapore.

BSI (2001) BS EN 12671: Execution of special geotechnical works: Jet grouting. BSI, London.

Coupland J (2010) New York's Fulton Street Transit Centre – Dey Street Structural Box. *Proceedings of the DFI/EFFC Conference on Geotechnical Challenges in Urban Regeneration*, London.

de Wit JCM, Bogaards PJ, Langhorst OS, Schat BJ, Essler RD, Maertens J, Obladen BKJ, Bosma CF, Sleuwaegen JJ and Dekker J (2007a) Design and construction of a metro station in Amsterdam, challenging the limits of jet grouting. *Proceedings of 14th European Conference on Soil Mechanics and Geotechnical Engineering*, 24–27 September 2007, Madrid: 1061–1066.

de Wit JCM, Bogaards PJ, Langhorst OS, Schat BJ, Essler RD, Maertens J, Obladen BKJ, Bosma CF, Sleuwaegen JJ and Dekker H (2007b) Design and validation of jet grouting for the Central Station, Amsterdam. *Proceedings of 14th European Conference on Soil Mechanics and Geotechnical Engineering*, 24–27 September 2007, Madrid: 1299–1305.

Stark TD, Axtell PJ, Lewis JR, Dillon JC, Empson WB, Topi JE and Walberg FC (2009) Soil inclusions in jet grout columns. *DFI Journal* **3**(1): 33–44.

FURTHER READING

Bell AL (ed.) (1994) *Grouting in the Ground*. Thomas Telford Limited, London.

Temporary Works: Principles of Design and Construction
ISBN 978-0-7277-4177-6

ICE Publishing: All rights reserved
http://dx.doi.org/10.1680/twpdc.41776.109

Chapter 9
Artificial ground freezing

Neil Smith Director, Applied Geotechnical Engineering

Artificial ground freezing (AGF) is a method for temporarily increasing the strength and decreasing the permeability of ground. Since AGF works in all ground types, it is particularly useful in highly variable water-bearing ground and for deep shaft sinking. The ground is frozen by passing a cold fluid through pipes buried in the ground. The system creates overlapping cylinders to form a freeze-wall to stabilise the void and exclude groundwater. The moisture content of the soil must normally be above 10% and the rate of flow of groundwater less than about 2 m/day if brine is the coolant or 20 m/day for nitrogen. The shape of the frozen ground is limited only by the ability to orientate the freeze tubes. Several weeks are required for the frozen ground to be ready for use if using brine, but nitrogen is much quicker. The system design needs specialist knowledge of the complex properties of frozen ground. The structural design of vertical freeze-wall cylinders can be based on empirical formulae. For other applications, conventional analyses can be used to determine the required strength and dimensions of the frozen ground. Numerical thermal modelling is required to predict freeze-wall growth. Monitoring of the work throughout the entire process is essential.

9.1. Introduction

It is well known to everyone who lives in a climate where freezing temperatures occur that, when frozen, the soil near the surface is generally stronger than when unfrozen. It is also obvious that water ceases to flow when it is frozen. From these two facts, the principal benefits of ground freezing are clear: the soil is strengthened and groundwater flow is prevented. Artificial ground freezing (AGF) is therefore a specialist process which is used for temporarily preventing groundwater ingress into excavations and, where the ground is unstable, assists in strengthening the ground. Its use is not widespread due to the relatively small number of opportunities where the process may be required and, as a result of this, there are few organisations with real competence in its use. General opinion appears to balk at the up-front cost of employing the process but experience has shown that, in a number of cases, if a value, risk and cost-effectiveness exercise had been carried out first, the adoption of AGF would have brought savings. The fact that AGF operates by modifying the water within the soil pores means that it is much less affected by variations in soil type than, for example, dewatering or grouting and hence there is less chance that treatment will be ineffective.

The basis of ground freezing is to pass a cold fluid through a pipe buried in the ground and thereby freeze the pore water. This solidifies a column of ground approximately centred on the pipe. By combinations of suitably closely spaced pipes, it follows that the shape of a mass of frozen ground is limited only by the ability to orientate boreholes. It is, therefore, a very flexible technique of ground stabilisation. Provided the soil has a sufficient moisture content and groundwater is not flowing too quickly, any soil can be frozen so that heterogeneous mixtures of sand/clay layers or glacial clay with gravel lenses can be treated effectively.

In normal circumstances, a zone of frozen ground is created around the volume of ground in which construction is required. An array of boreholes is drilled and pipework installed to carry the refrigerating fluid, which can be either brine (slow-freeze fluid circulation) or liquid nitrogen (fast-freeze gas exhaust). The spacing between the bore-holes is close enough to ensure that the cylinders of frozen ground around each pipe will touch and overlap within a reasonable time to stop groundwater flow and create a thick enough wall to provide the necessary strength.

When construction has been completed, the fluid circulation or gas exhaust is stopped and the ground begins to thaw. The ground does not necessarily return to its previous condition.

9.2. Construction principles
9.2.1   Methods of ground freezing

The oldest method of freezing the ground uses a solution of chilled brine. Conventional refrigeration plants, normally using ammonia, can reduce the temperature of the brine to as low as $-40°C$, although a temperature of $-25°C$ is likely to be suitable in most circumstances. The cooling fluid is then pumped around the circuit to freeze the ground surrounding the buried pipes. The process requires various components of plant, including: compressor; condenser; evaporator; pump; and distribution pipes.

Considerable time is required for a brine-based system to bring the ground to a condition in which it is sufficiently frozen for work to begin. The stages are drilling boreholes and installation of pipework, chilling the brine and building the freeze-wall. This process may take up to four months.

The distribution system would typically consist of a header pipe (or ring main) and freeze tubes within the ground. The freeze tubes can be connected to the header in series or in parallel but, for risk reduction, it is normal that there should be at least two parallel circuits to ensure that if a pipe leaks the whole system does not have to be shut down. Adjacent freeze tubes should be connected to different parallel circuits to ensure that the worst spacing between pipes is double the installed spacing. This needs to be considered in the design factor of safety.

More recently, the ability to deliver liquid nitrogen to site in reasonably large quantities and to store it in vacuum-insulated tanks has provided an alternative to brine. The system does not require refrigeration plant or pumps to circulate the fluid. The nitrogen vaporises at $-196°C$ at a pressure sufficient to drive the fluid through the circuit without the aid of pumps. At the end of the process, it is vented to the atmosphere rather than re-circulated. The very low temperature of the fluid reduces the freeze-wall formation

Figure 9.1 Schematic diagram of brine system

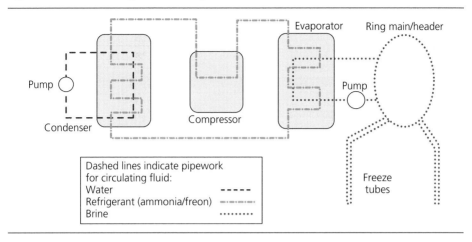

time from several weeks to a few days. The high temperature differentials make it more appropriate to connect the freeze tubes in parallel rather than in series.

The loss of product and consequent maintenance costs may make the use of nitrogen uneconomic if the ground must be kept frozen for an extended period. It is, however, possible to use nitrogen initially to produce the freeze-wall rapidly, and then to replace it with a brine system for longer-term freezing.

Schematic diagrams of the two systems are shown in Figures 9.1 and 9.2. Figure 9.3 shows a system installed in preparation for shaft construction.

9.2.2   Advantages and disadvantages
In variable ground, freezing will be effective on nearly all soils although the rate of freezing will differ between, for example, clay (slower) and gravel (quicker). Another

Figure 9.2 Schematic diagram of liquid nitrogen system

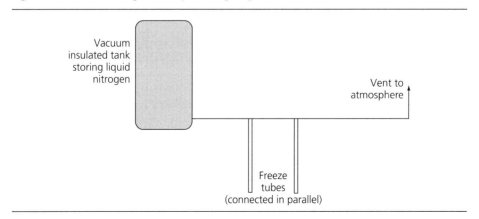

Figure 9.3 Freezing system for shaft construction through 30 m of superficial deposits to bedrock at Belmont, NSW
Courtesy of the British Drilling and Freezing Company Limited

significant advantage of freezing is that, given suitable conditions, the frozen ground will encircle service pipes, making it possible to reduce the disruption and re-routing of services often required by other forms of ground treatment. It is possible to use the technique on a small scale, for example, to plug leaks in basements while a permanent seal is formed.

However, there may be problems in achieving freeze-wall formation if the groundwater is saline or contains other dissolved salts or if the ground is contaminated with hydro-carbons. Below a moisture content of about 10%, there may be insufficient ice in the body of the ground to form a competent retaining structure. Flowing groundwater can also prevent freeze-wall formation and ground may heave during freezing; movements can be as much as 100 mm. Consolidation occurring on thawing can exceed the heave movement. The structure of peat or organic soil may be broken down by freezing.

9.3.   Design principles
9.3.1   Introduction
There are two principal aspects to the design of a ground freezing scheme, as follows.

■ Calculations of the thermal behaviour of the ground are needed to ensure that the columns of frozen ground around each freeze tube meet to provide a continuous freeze-wall which is sufficiently thick. This is a specialist subject which requires the knowledge and experience of the specialist contractor's staff. The text in the following section is therefore limited to describing the main parameters involved and some aspects of the behaviour of frozen soil.

- The structural design of the freeze-wall must ensure that it has sufficient strength to support the ground around the intended excavation and that its deformation will be tolerable; frozen ground exhibits significant creep characteristics.

Time is a further factor to be considered in design. If the time available for freeze-wall formation is short, then nitrogen may be preferred to brine or the spacing between freeze tubes may be reduced. Over-capacity should be built into the design as a protection against the malfunction of any elements of the system, or simply a less effective system than anticipated.

9.3.2 Thermal behaviour
9.3.2.1 Thermal parameters

There are similarities between the flow of heat through the ground and the flow of water. In the latter case flow is governed by the permeability and the head gradient, whereas for heat flow the parameters are thermal conductivity (K) and temperature gradient. The thermal conductivity is the amount of heat per unit time flowing through a unit area under a unit temperature gradient. The temperature is usually expressed in degrees Kelvin, resulting in the slightly confusing situation that the units of thermal conductivity (K) are W/mK where the second 'K' refers to the temperature (degrees Kelvin). The range of thermal conductivity values for different soil types is far less than the range of permeability. Organic soil has a K value of about 0.25 W/mK; other soils range between about 0.6 and 4 W/mK; values for rocks range up to about 7 W/mK. For comparison, the K value of wood is c. 0.1–0.2 W/mK and that of iron is 80 W/mK. Thermal conductivity is not constant with temperature, however. It increases with reducing temperature and this effect may need to be considered for nitrogen freezing.

For thermal design, the heat capacity is measured per unit volume (not mass) of material and is the quantity of heat transfer required for a unit change in temperature of a unit volume of the ground. It is denoted by C and has units of J/m^3K where K is degrees Kelvin. The range of C is also small for a range of soils, roughly from 1.8 to 2.5 MJ/m^3K. It decreases with decreasing temperature, tending towards zero at a temperature of absolute zero.

The thermal diffusivity (α) is the ratio K/C and is the equivalent in heat flow to the coefficient of consolidation in water flow and has the same units (L^2/T). It relates to the rate at which the temperature of the material can change. A high value of α implies a high rate of change of temperature. When water changes to ice, its α value increases roughly eightfold from 1.45×10^{-7} to 11.5×10^{-7} m^2/sec. Hence, if other factors are unchanged, the rate of temperature drop increases when the soil becomes frozen.

9.3.2.2 Engineering properties of frozen soil

The enhanced strength and stiffness of frozen (compared to unfrozen) soil is largely due to the strength of the ice. However, frozen soil is not simply a combination of ice and soil particles. It also contains unfrozen water and air so the composite material is very complex, as is its behaviour. Ice itself exhibits significant creep characteristics at low shear stress levels; this is manifested in the flow of glacier ice. In soil, the creep of the ice transfers stress to the intergranular (effective) stress between particles; if this eventually exceeds the frictional capacity of the soil, failure will occur.

As examples of the variability of the strength of frozen soil, low strain peak shear strengths of frozen Ottawa sand have been found to range from c. 5 to 8 MPa, increasing with confining pressures which ranged from about 1.4 to 6.9 MPa. Strength is also heavily dependent on strain rate, however. The strength of frozen silt has been shown to vary by a factor of 3 for strain rates varying from 10^{-6} to 10^{-3} s^{-1}. While the variations in strength can be seen to be very significant, it is also clear that the strength of the frozen material is very much higher than strength values associated with unfrozen soil.

The two aspects of design must proceed in tandem. The engineer designing the freezing system must be provided with the strength and stiffness requirements for the frozen ground. It is also important that the designer knows the duration for which the ground is to retain its enhanced strength and stiffness.

9.3.3   Structural design

Many applications of ground freezing are for the construction of shafts. Regardless of the plan shape of the shaft, it is normal to form a circular freeze-wall which envelopes the shaft. The use of a circular wall ensures a uniform compressive stress in the horizontal plane. The required freeze-wall thickness may be determined using empirical formulae (Harris, 1995) or complex finite element programs (Haasnoot, 2010).

Other applications include the construction of temporary arch supports for tunnel construction in unstable ground and stabilisation of localised zones for tunnel break-in to (or break-out from) shafts. A relatively frequent application of the technique is to 'rescue' tunnelling projects which have run into difficulty. Freezing has been used in instances where dewatering and/or grouting has been ineffective. Another infrequent use is to form a temporarily strengthened roadway for heavy plant to cross weak ground. In uses other than to facilitate shaft construction, the project engineer may use a conventional analytical approach to determine the required properties and dimensions of the frozen zone. This then provides the criteria for the design of the freezing system and freeze tube layout.

9.4.   The effects of freezing and thawing

It is important to realise that the soil will not necessarily return to its previous state after it has been subjected to a cycle of freezing and thawing. The structure of some clays can be disrupted by the freezing process, generating fissures and causing an increase in the permeability (Harris, 1995). The ratio of post- to pre-frozen permeability may be as much as two orders of magnitude.

When water freezes and turns to ice, its volume increases by approximately 9%. In some soils, however, especially low plasticity clays and silts, much larger ground movements may be caused by frost heave. This occurs when lenses of frozen water are formed by water which migrates in response to suctions which occur in the ground during freezing. The localised increases in volume can also cause significant increases in pressure on adjacent structures such as foundations or retaining walls.

Ground settlement or deformation can occur on thawing, with the potential to create voids around the newly completed structure. In such circumstances, it may be necessary to use compensation or 'back-wall' grouting to fill the voids and ensure the long-term integrity of the structure.

Various researchers have investigated the effect of the freeze-thaw cycle on soil strength. Some have found that the strength of clay increases following the cycle, where other studies report a decrease in strength. If the post-freezing strength of the soil is a matter of concern, it is advisable to carry out testing in advance of the works.

The thickness of the freeze-wall will continue to increase until the rate of heat extraction is balanced by the supply from the ground. The void excavated within the freeze-wall will generally be maintained at a temperature in which men and machines can work effectively. There will therefore be some water generated in the void by melting. In addition, where the void has to be ventilated and the air drawn from the surface is warm and humid, substantial condensation can take place.

9.5.   Monitoring

It may be necessary to survey the drilled holes prior to installation of the freeze tubes. Significant deviations from the design hole location may result in gaps in a freeze-wall. Accurate hole-drilling is especially important for deep shafts and when precision is required (e.g. the rescue of a tunnelling machine).

Once the freezing process has been started, the ground temperature should be monitored at suitable locations throughout the length of dedicated freeze tubes to ensure that the plant is functioning correctly and to check that the ground is freezing as predicted. Temperature monitoring must continue through the whole period of freezing until the ground has thawed.

Ground levels must be monitored to check for heave and post-thaw settlement. For schemes where the frozen zone is required to control groundwater, piezometers are required to measure groundwater conditions.

REFERENCES

Haasnoot J (2010) Large scale ground freezing in the Netherlands. *Proceedings of the DFI/ EFFC Conference on Geotechnical Challenges in Urban Regeneration*, London

Harris JS (1995) *Ground Freezing in Practice*. Thomas Telford Publishing Limited, London

FURTHER READING

BTS/ICE (British Tunnelling Society and Institution of Civil Engineers) (2000) *Specification for Tunnelling*. Section 4 Ground stabilisation processes. Thomas Telford Ltd, London: 116–118.

BGFS (British Ground Freezing Society) (1995) Technical Memoranda on the Ground Freezing Process. BGFS, Nottingham. (TM1 Harris JS, Wills AJ: Introduction to artificial ground freezing; TM2 Harris JS: AGF processes; TM3 Harris JS: Site investigation for AGF works; TM4 Jones RH: Control of ground movements in AGF works; TM5 Harvey SJ, Wills AJ: Value, risk and cost effectiveness in AGF works; TM6 Harris JS, Bell MJ: Shaft freezing; TM7 Harris JS: Tunnel freezing; TM8 Auld FA: Casting concrete against frozen ground.)

Useful web addresses

For information on contractors and consultants specialising in ground freezing, visit http://www.tunnels-directory.co.uk

Temporary Works: Principles of Design and Construction
ISBN 978-0-7277-4177-6

Chapter 10
Slope stability in temporary excavations

Neil Smith Director, Applied Geotechnical Engineering

Most construction sites require excavation and the stability of the sides must be considered in relation to safety and economy. Where possible, it is usually most economic to form excavations in open cut. The essence is to determine the steepest practicable slope. Several factors influence slope behaviour: (1) the nature and variability of the soil; (2) groundwater conditions; (3) loading close to the crest; (4) the time the excavation will remain open; and (5) the consequences of failure. Factors (1) and (2) require adequate information from site investigation. Factors (3–5) need good liaison with the construction planning team. Construction is generally straightforward, although it must be coordinated with other processes (especially groundwater control). Slopes in rock require similar considerations, but the behaviour of rock slopes tends to be dominated by the discontinuities since the blocks of intact rock are comparatively strong. The important characteristics of rock slope discontinuities are: inclination relative to the cut slope (noting that there may be more than one set of discontinuities); frequency; persistence; openness; and smoothness. Safety is a paramount consideration: unsupported trenches are examples of steep cut slopes and collapses are a major cause of accidents on construction sites.

10.1. Introduction

This chapter gives guidance on the design and construction of temporary slopes for excavations on construction sites. Construction of below-ground works within an unsupported excavation has generally been viewed as the cheapest option. However, the use of battered (as opposed to vertical) slopes requires excavation of significantly larger amounts of material and the extra excavation can bring substantial additional cost if the material has to be taken off site, especially if any of it is contaminated. The use of sloping sides may also affect the choice of plant, for example, if cranes have to be sited outside the excavation and so need a longer reach. Figure 10.1 is a decision diagram showing the steps involved in determining whether excavating to a batter is a viable option for the project.

Provided that the safety and financial risks associated with slope movement are properly controlled, relatively simple approaches to the design of temporary slopes on construction sites can be acceptable. For large temporary slopes, sophisticated investigation, analysis and monitoring may be appropriate (Kovacevic *et al.*, 2007).

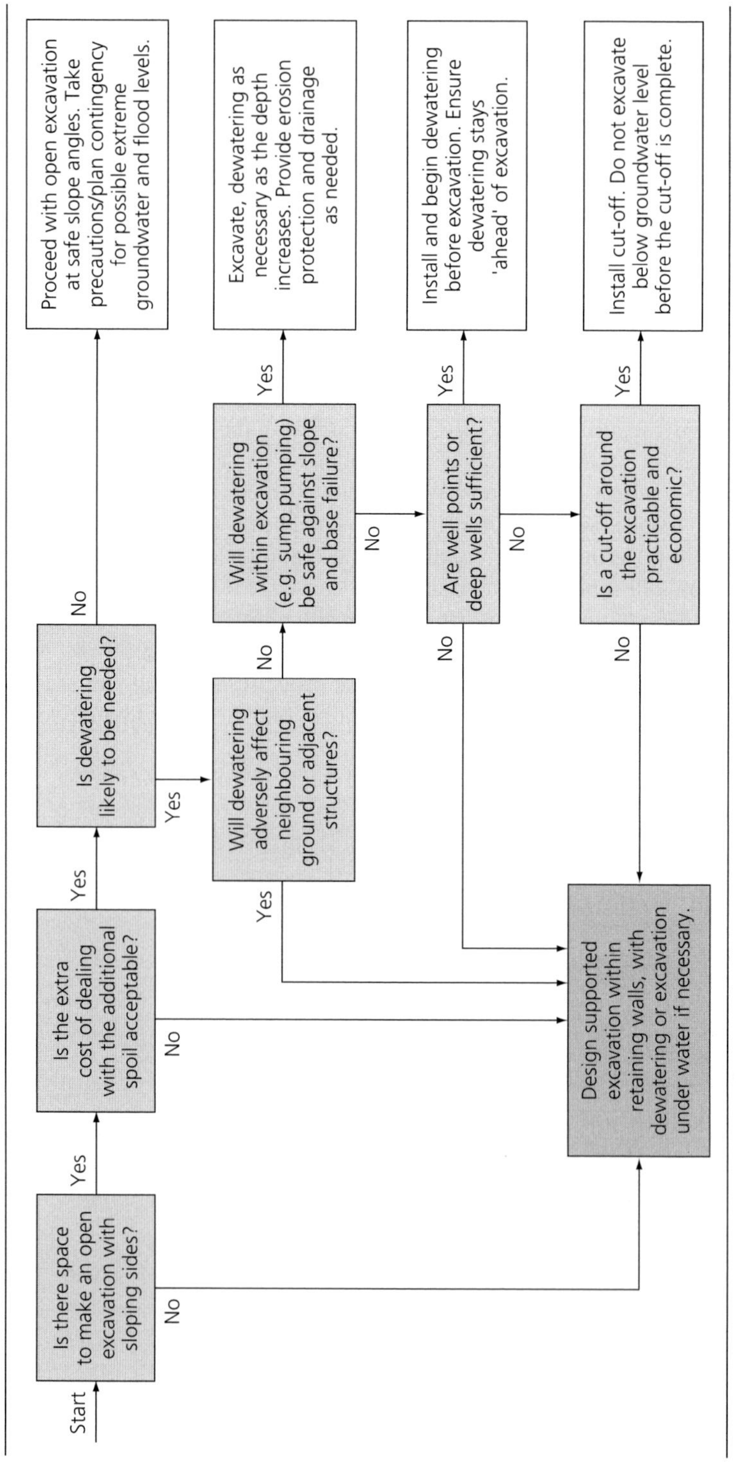

Figure 10.1 Decision diagram for open excavation
Relates also to Chapters 6, 11, 12, 13 and 14

In addition to the nature of the ground and the groundwater regime, time is an important parameter for temporary slope design; the shorter the design life of the slope, the better. The design must also take account of the consequences of movement occurring. In this regard, it must be remembered that soil can tolerate much larger pre-failure strains than most buildings or hard-paved surfaces. Failure of adjacent structures may therefore take place before the slope itself fails.

Eurocode 7 (EC7; BSI, 1997) gives general guidance on slope design in Section 11. Clause 2.2(1)P requires that both short-term and long-term design situations shall be considered. In this context, the distinction between short and long term depends on the nature of the ground as well as the design life of the slope. In coarse soil, long-term conditions are established quickly and there is generally no requirement to consider short-term conditions. In fine soil, initial stability is governed by undrained parameters; an indefinitely long period is required for fully drained (long-term) conditions to be established. Tomlinson (2001) presents information from a number of excavations in London Clay; the period prior to slippage ranged from 1 day to no failure after four months. The design life of temporary slopes in clay lies somewhere between fully undrained and fully drained conditions.

10.2. The consequences of failure

In most circumstances, if it is possible to carry out an excavation within open cut slopes, it is also possible to arrange construction in order to minimise both the chance of failure and the consequences, should ground movement occur. The following relatively simple matters need to be considered at an early stage of project planning.

1 Try to keep excavations away from the site property boundary to avoid a risk to neighbours or the public (and party wall problems).
2 Ensure there are no critical services close to the crest or toe of the slope.
3 Plan drainage or surface-covering measures to minimise rainwater infiltration to the ground beneath the slope, including the elimination of ponded water close behind the crest.
4 Avoid routing haul roads or locating heavy plant just above the crest of a slope.
5 Avoid stockpiling spoil near the crest.
6 Where relatively steep slopes are needed, make an initial cut to a flat angle and then cut to the steepest slope in short lengths (as short as practicable and less than the slope height). Do the work then reinstate the slope to a flat angle before excavating the next bay. Consider constructing in 'hit and miss' bays.
7 Keep the period for which the slope is open down to a minimum, for example, by using a two-stage approach as in (6) above.

10.3. Construction principles

The excavation of temporary slopes in soil is a straightforward process. For excavation in rock, it is necessary to determine whether the rock can be ripped or whether blasting will be required. The assessment of 'excavatability' (also referred to as 'rippability') has been examined by a number of authors, for example, Pettifer and Fookes (1994). Monitoring of the slope after excavation is an essential part of the process.

10.4. Some simple fundamentals
10.4.1 The nature of fine- and coarse-grained soil

It is widely appreciated in the construction industry that excavated slopes in fine-grained (clay) soils may stand for a considerable period at a steep angle, even vertical, but that slopes in coarse soil (sand and gravel) will quickly ravel to an 'angle of repose'. This difference in behaviour is not the result of any fundamental clay property which is different from sand but derives from the surface tension of the pore water which creates high capillary (suction) pressures within the pores of fine-grained clay soil. Due to the difference in grain size (and therefore also pore size), clay can support suction pressures of the order of 1000 times that of gravel. (These suction pressures allow a clay to remain saturated at levels tens of metres above the level at which the hydrostatic pressure is zero – the phreatic surface, or 'water table'.)

When an excavation is cut into clay, the surrounding ground experiences lateral and vertical stress relief. In simple terms, this produces a tendency for the soil to expand and hence generates a corresponding suction in the pore water while the effective (intergranular) stress between the soil particles, which controls strength, remains largely unaffected. An example of the extent of suction within a clay slope is given in Figure 10.2, which is a prediction by Kovacevic *et al.* (2007) for a major excavation at Heathrow Terminal 5. Over time, groundwater flows towards the zones of high pore suction and an equilibration process takes place which reduces the suction and decreases the stability of the clay slope. In a homogeneous clay of low permeability, this process is slow, so that a relatively steep slope may remain stable for a substantial time (months or years).

The suction pressure which can be maintained in a clean gravel is negligible and equilibration is rapid so that, on excavation, the effective stress (and thereby the shear strength) within the soil reduces; a steeply cut slope will quickly degrade to the angle of repose of the soil.

Figure 10.2 Predicted contours of pore pressure within the London Clay at Heathrow Terminal 5. Note the extent of the suction zone and the high suction pressures
Reproduced from Kovacevic *et al.* (2007)

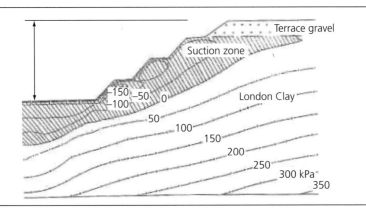

In real soils, gravels and sands will generally contain some fine grains which may be sufficient to allow small suctions to be maintained for short periods. This leads to slopes which may stand longer than expected at steeper angles than the angle of repose, but this additional stability may only persist for a short time. Another possible factor which may maintain a steep slope in coarse soil is the deposition of salts at grain contacts when groundwater evaporates. Reliance on these factors is risky unless supported by good local experience.

On the other hand, real clays (especially glacially deposited clays) contain discontinuities such as fissures or thin bands, pockets or ribbons of coarser soils. The discontinuities or occurrences of coarser soil allow suction pressures to fall more rapidly and the result is that the slope is likely to be less safe than predicted (or safe for a shorter time) and there may be a higher risk of small failures within a larger slope (see Kovacevic *et al.*, 2007).

10.4.2 Effects of groundwater

If groundwater is introduced into a previously dry soil, its principal effect is to reduce the effective stress between the soil particles. Where the groundwater is static, the effective stress in coarse-grained soil can reduce to as little as around half the dry value. In clay soils initially supporting high suctions, far greater reductions are possible. If groundwater is flowing in an unfavourable direction (e.g. towards the surface of a cut slope), the water can reduce the effective stress further still. The unit weight of the saturated soil is also higher due to the replacement of air by water in the soil voids. Both of these effects reduce the stability of a soil slope.

In silts, sands and more permeable soils, flows can be established quickly such that excavation side slopes can be rapidly eroded by groundwater issuing into the excavation. This leads to severe problems on site. The answer is (a) to ensure that the groundwater regime is properly known from investigation and monitoring prior to the design of temporary works, and (b) to install suitable groundwater control measures before excavation starts (see Chapter 6 on control of groundwater).

In rocks, adverse groundwater conditions reduce the stress across discontinuities and hence the friction available to resist movement. They also impose lateral forces on steeply inclined discontinuity planes.

10.4.3 Geotechnical categories

While not specifically stated, EC7 (BSI, 1997) is principally directed to ensuring that failure does not occur. In some circumstances of temporary slope design, it may, however, be accepted that there is a relatively high possibility of a failure.

EC7 Clause 2.1(14–21) defines three geotechnical categories (1, 2 and 3) as described in the following sections.

10.4.3.1 Category 1

Clause 2.1(8)P of EC7 states that 'small earthworks [shall be identified] for which it is possible to ensure that the minimum requirements [see National Annex (BSI, 2007)] will be satisfied by experience and qualitative geotechnical investigations, with negligible risk'. Referring to this clause, Table NA.1 of the UK National Annex states that 'Minimum requirements are not given in this National Annex and should be agreed where appropriate with the client and other relevant authorities'.

10.4.3.2 Category 2
Clause 2.1(17) of EC7 defines Category 2 works as having 'no exceptional risk or difficult soil or loading conditions'. Most temporary slopes on construction sites would fall into this category, but if the consequences of failure can be reduced sufficiently they could be treated as Category 1.

10.4.3.3 Category 3
Clause 2.1(20) states that this category includes slopes which fall outside the other two categories. Clause 2.1(21) states that this category 'should normally include alternative provisions and rules to those in this [EC7] standard'. The notes to this clause give the examples of 'unusual or exceptionally difficult ground or loading conditions'.

Temporary slopes classified as Category 3 are outside the scope of this guidance, and specialist advice should be sought at an early stage in the planning of the project.

10.4.3.4 Categorisation example
Figure 10.3 is a photograph of a small slip which occurred approximately two weeks after the toe of an existing cutting was removed to give access for construction work. A steep (c. 80°) slope about 1.5 m high (visible at the right-hand side of the photograph) was cut

Figure 10.3 Small slip caused by temporary removal of the toe of a 100 year old cutting in stiff clay. Some fill has been placed in front of the slip to stabilise the ground and to re-establish the access road on which the men are standing

into a stiff clay to make an access road on which the two men are standing. At the time of the photograph, fill had been placed in front of the slipped mass to restrain further movement and to re-establish the access road. The slipped clay was subsequently replaced with coarse granular fill. The slip that occurred could be considered a Category 1 event, since the consequences of the failure were trivial and easily accommodated by the contractor within a contingency.

However, the boundary of the site was very close to the slope crest (at the fence in Figure 10.3) and the designer's main concern was to avoid any ground movement which would affect the neighbouring property. The risk of such a failure classifies as a Category 2 event. It would therefore be possible in principle for the designer to accept a lower factor of safety against a small failure such as the one which did occur, but to require a higher factor against any failure which would reach the crest of the slope. This example indicates that it is possible for the same slope to have more than one category.

10.4.4 Design for soil slopes of 'small' size

Figure 10.4 provides suggested temporary cut slope angles for different materials. Here the designer should ensure that all interested parties understand and accept the risks involved in the selected slope angle(s). Simple slip surface analyses as referred to in Section 10.4.5.2 may be used in support of the designer's judgement.

10.4.5 Design for soil slopes of 'medium' size
10.4.5.1 Coarse-grained soil

In coarse-grained soil, if the groundwater level is above the excavation bottom, digging should not be started until groundwater control measures have been put in place either to cut off the supply of groundwater to the excavation or to reduce its level to below the proposed excavation surface. (In deep excavations, it may be possible to dewater and dig in stages; see Chapter 6.) Stable slopes can then be formed at the angle of repose, less a margin for a factor of safety. If the consequences of a failure are trivial then a contractor may opt to take a risk and cut the slope to a steeper angle, having made contingencies for the disruption and cost of a failure. Table 10.1 is adapted from BS 8002 (BSI, 1994) and lists critical friction angles (ϕ'_{crit}) for sands and gravels formed of silica. (Most common sands are siliceous, but it should be remembered that different friction angles would apply to sands of different mineralogy, e.g. carbonate or mica.)

As an example, ϕ'_{crit} of a well-graded sub-angular sand and gravel may be taken as 36°. The factor of safety to be used on slopes cut into coarse-grained soil will depend on the circumstances. Where the consequences of slope movement are small (Category 1), $F = 1.0$ may be acceptable provided that the value of ϕ'_{crit} is reasonably conservative. For longer-term slopes or where failure is to be avoided (Category 2), then $F = 1.25$ may be prudent. The factor of safety is applied to $\tan(\phi'_{crit})$; if the slope angle is β, then

$$F = \frac{\tan(\phi'_{crit})}{\tan\beta}$$

Hence, for $\phi'_{crit} = 36°$, $F = 1.25$ would give a slope (β) of 30° (1:1.73).

Figure 10.4 Suggested temporary cut slope gradients for different materials

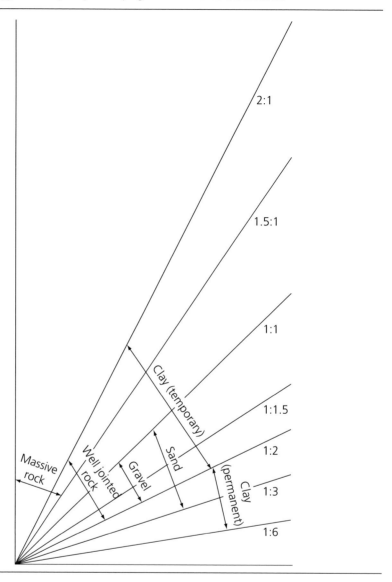

It may of course be possible to cut slopes to angles steeper than ϕ'_{crit}, provided that some failures can be accepted. Factors such as the presence of some fine soil combined with slight cementing of the soil grains can give a considerable increase in the stable slope angle over that which theory would predict.

For the case with the water table at the ground surface, stable angles are approximately half that of dry slopes.

Table 10.1 Critical angle of friction $\phi'_{crit} = 30° + A + B$ for siliceous sand and gravels

Data taken from BS8002: 1994 Earth Retaining Structures

A – Angularity[1]	A: °
Rounded	0
Subangular	2
Angular	4

B – Grading of soil[2]	B: °
Uniform	0
Moderate grading	2
Well graded	4

[1] Angularity is estimated from a visual description of the soil.
[2] Grading can be determined from grading curve by use of: Uniformity coefficient $= D_{60}/D_{10}$ where D_{10} and D_{60} are particle sizes such that in the sample, 10 % of the material is finer than D_{10} and 60 % is finer than D_{60}.

Grading	Uniformity coefficient
Uniform	<2
Moderate grading	2 to 6
Well graded	>6

A step-graded soil should be treated as uniform or moderately graded soil according to the grading of the finer fraction.

Intermediate values of A and B may be obtained by interpolation.

10.4.5.2 Fine-grained soil

The analysis of temporary slopes in fine-grained soil is much more complex. Despite the use of sophisticated methods to back-analyse two failed temporary slopes, Kovacevic et al. (2004) found that 'actual times to failure are still difficult to predict'. The presence of undetected inhomogeneities in the ground can hasten the loss of suction and cause failure within a few days of cutting the slope and sometimes during excavation. The designer of a temporary slope in fine-grained soil on all but very major projects is likely to have to work with incomplete information about the stratigraphy and relatively poor-quality data on soil properties. The design must therefore start by minimising the consequences of ground movement.

Conventional limit equilibrium analyses may be used to analyse slopes. A problem with these analyses is that the failure mechanism must be assumed (or guessed) in order to perform the analysis. If the mechanism is wrong, the analysis is likely to give misleading results. A recent development which can help with the determination of the critical ultimate limit state mechanism is discontinuity layout optimisation (Smith and Gilbert, 2007). However, the early approaches of Bishop (1954) (circular surfaces) and Janbu (1954) (general surfaces) are still in wide use. An advantage of the assumption of a circular plane of sliding is that a family of potential surfaces can be defined in terms of a grid of centres and a range of radii. The most critical of these can then be found.

In uniform clay soil, the critical slip surface is likely to be moderately deep and to emerge somewhere close to or a little beyond the toe of the slope. Where a weak layer is present, the most critical surface found in a circular analysis will be tangential to the weak layer, but a distinctly non-circular surface will probably be the most critical. In some cases, non-circular surfaces can be simplified to an active wedge at the upslope side, a passive wedge at the downslope side and a polygon sliding on the weak layer between the two wedges.

In view of the uncertainties involved, the analysis is best viewed as a tool to guide the judgement of the designer in the selection of the most appropriate slope to adopt. Whatever method is used, sensitivity analyses are essential to give an appreciation of the possible effects of differences in shear strength. It is normal to use undrained soil parameters in the analysis of the short-term stability of clay slopes, but to allow for some loss of strength dependent on the design life of the slope and the nature of the material. A range of strength values should be used to examine the effects of softening (loss of suction) on stability.

10.4.6   Design of rock slopes

Rock slopes of Category 1 or 2 will generally be designed using relatively simple kinematic considerations. The process essentially involves determining whether there are discontinuities or combinations of discontinuities that can delimit a block of rock able to slide or topple into the excavation. If there are no such discontinuities, then the chance of failure at this scale of project will be very small since failure must occur through the intact rock. If blocks with the potential to fail do exist, then the friction on the discontinuities must be assessed and the factor of safety for the block must be calculated. If weak discontinuities slope into the excavation, then it may be necessary to cut the slope at the same angle as (or flatter than) the discontinuities.

If the factor of safety is insufficient, it may be improved by installing rock bolts to increase the restraint. If the friction is reduced because of the groundwater conditions, then dewatering will enhance the factor of safety.

10.5.   Monitoring

There are two principal principles in the construction of temporary slopes. As mentioned in Sections 10.2 and 10.3, one is to minimise the angle, length and open period of the slope and the other is to monitor the slope. Monitoring systems must be properly designed, bearing in mind that it is no use gathering data which cannot be analysed and interpreted. It is possible to acquire so much information that important trends cannot easily be discerned.

All monitoring systems should include regular visual inspection of the slopes, especially the areas just behind the slope crest and at the toe. Substantial slope movements can be preceded by smaller movements which are manifested in cracking behind the crest (tension cracks) or bulging of the ground near the toe. If such movement is seen, there is often time to carry out some stabilisation work such as placing backfill at the toe before a major failure takes place. The ground should also be checked for indications of ground-water emerging from the slope; this may simply be dampness or softening, rather than flowing water.

A wide range of monitoring systems is available, from very simple to very sophisticated. At the simple end of the spectrum, a row or rows of ranging poles arranged in straight lines along and above the slope can be visually monitored on a daily basis. It should be noted, however, that the predominant component of movement of the ground at the top of a slipping mass will be vertical, so level measurement is important. Targets fixed to pegs can be surveyed precisely, either manually or by automated instruments. In-ground instrumentation can take the form of slip indicators, inclinometers or piezometers.

Slip indicators are essentially simple tubes installed in boreholes drilled through the zone of likely movement into stable ground below. Slippage is evidenced by a closure of the tube at the surface of shearing; however, these instruments do not provide information on the amount of movement.

There are two types of inclinometer. The early instruments consisted of tubes grouted into boreholes (taking care to try to match the stiffness of the installation to that of the ground). Like slip indicators, these must extend into fully stable ground at depth in order to provide a datum for lateral movement. A 'torpedo' is lowered down the tube, using locating grooves to orient readings of the tilt of the torpedo at (normally) 0.5 m intervals down the tube. In that way, a continuous profile of the tube is obtained from each monitoring visit. More recently, inclinometers have been developed to measure the tilt of devices which are permanently installed in the ground. This allows remote reading and the distribution of data through the internet.

Piezometers measure the pressure in the groundwater at a particular point. If the instrument is not located suitably, it will not give useful information and could mislead. Some types are capable of measuring negative (below atmospheric) pressure and can therefore measure suction in the soil mass. Measurement of suction in a temporary slope would normally only be used on Category 3 slopes.

Note that it is generally less practicable to install instruments at or close to the toe of the slope since this is the main area of construction activity.

Finally, the contractor and designer (and any other concerned parties) must agree trigger levels and contingencies to stabilise a moving slope. The simplest and quickest approach to movement is often to place new fill in front of the slipped or slipping mass (see Figure 10.3). This may be only an emergency measure to arrest movement and to allow work on re-design of the slope. Careful excavation of failed fine-grained soil and replacement by coarse granular material such as hardcore can be a sufficient remedy. A further alternative may be the installation of soil nails, which is effectively a way of reinforcing the soil mass. Nails are usually drilled and grouted in place although driven nails can be used. Unlike ground anchors, they are not pre-tensioned and require further movement of the ground to develop tensile resistance. While costlier than replacement, they may allow the reinstatement of a steep slope required for construction.

REFERENCES

Bishop AW (1954) The use of the slip circle in the stability analysis of slopes. *European Conference on the Stability of Earth Slopes*, Vol. I, Stockholm.

BSI (1994) BS 8002: Earth Retaining Structures. BSI, London.

BSI (1997) BS EN 1997-1: Eurocode 7 Geotechnical design. BSI, London

BSI (2007) UK National Annex to Eurocode 7 Part 1. NA to BS EN 1997-1. BSI, London.

Janbu N (1954) Application of composite slip surfaces for stability analyses. *European Conference on the Stability of Earth Slopes*, Discussion Vol III, Stockholm.

Kovacevic N, Hight DW and Potts DM (2004) Temporary slope stability in London Clay – back analyses of two case histories. Advances in Geotechnical Engineering. *Proceedings of the Skempton Conference*, London, 3: 1–14.

Kovacevic N, Hight DW and Potts DM (2007) Predicting the stand-up time of temporary London Clay slopes at Terminal 5, Heathrow Airport. *Géotechnique* **57**(1): 63–74.

Pettifer GS and Fookes PG (1994) A revision of the graphical method for assessing the excavatability of rock. *Quarterly Journal of Engineering Geology* **27**(2): 145–164.

Smith CC and Gilbert M (2007) Application of discontinuity layout optimization to plane plasticity problems. *Proceedings of the Royal Society A: Mathematical, Physical and Engineering Sciences* **463**(2086): 2461–2484.

Tomlinson MJ (2001) *Foundation Design and Construction*. Seventh edition. Pearson Education, London.

FURTHER READING

Bromhead E (1992) *The Stability of Slopes*, 2nd edition. Taylor & Francis, London.

Hoek E and Bray JW (1981) *Rock Slope Engineering*. E & F N Spon, London.

Useful web addresses

www.ggsd.com provides a comprehensive listing of available geotechnical programs. The categories include both soil slope stability and rock slope stability.

Temporary Works: Principles of Design and Construction
ISBN 978-0-7277-4177-6

ICE Publishing: All rights reserved
http://dx.doi.org/10.1680/twpdc.41776.129

Chapter 11
Sheet piling

Ray Filip Temporary works consultant and training provider – RKF Consult Ltd

Interlocking steel sheet piles are profiled steel sections which are installed vertically into the ground by a variety of methods to support the ground and exclude water when excavating or to carry applied loads. They are used in temporary works to support the ground and to exclude water while a structure or service is installed below ground level. They are generally extracted to be re-used; however, they may be incorporated into the permanent works such as sealed basement walls where they may also be used to carry vertical loads from the building or structure. Sheet piles can also be used as anchorages and in conjunction with other types of retaining walls. They may be used with tubular or I-section piles to form a high modulus combination wall. 'Cofferdam' is a term given to a closed sheet pile 'box' used for deep retention schemes and which may include provisions for excluding water. Isolated steel I or H sections or steel tubes can be driven into the ground to form bearing piles. The design concept of sheet piling is unusual in that it utilises the shear strength of the ground to support itself; the element being supported is therefore also part of the supporting mechanism.

11.1. Major alternatives
Alternatives to sheet piling include the following

■ contiguous or secant piling can be used in place of sheets to form temporary and permanent retaining walls or cofferdams
■ diaphragm walling can form very substantial temporary and permanent retaining walls
■ concrete caissons are an alternative to cofferdams
■ concrete bearing piles (driven pre-cast or augured and cast in situ) which can carry compressive, tensile and horizontal loads
■ post and plank, trench boxes are appropriate for minor retaining structures (see Chapter 12 on trenching)
■ 'top down' is an alternative to traditional basement construction using temporary frames.

11.2. Types of steel sheet piling
The main types of steel sheet piles are: straight web, U profile, Z profile and combination wall (see Figure 11.1) and each individual element interlocks with adjacent elements (whereas the majority of lighter trench sheets overlap rather than interlock). Straight web sheets are intended for the construction of circular structures where they work in hoop tension. U- and Z-profile hot-rolled sheets are the most common and can be

Figure 11.1 Examples of U profile, Z profile, combination wall, straight web and box pile

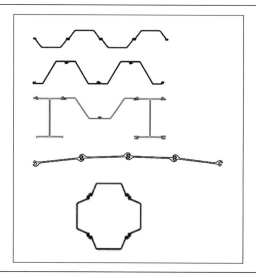

used in straight lines or can also be installed to a gentle radius. Combination walls are for high modulus work (e.g. for marine work) and comprise steel I beams or large diameter steel tubes with U- or Z-profile sheets between. Where a line of piles is required to turn a corner or form a junction, special corner sections are available (see Figure 11.2).

Sheet piles are available as hot-rolled sections with standard steel grades varying from grades S240GP–S460GP to EN 10248 (BSI, 1996a) and cold formed sections with standard steel grades from S235JRC to S355JRC to EN 10249 (BSI, 1996b). From grade 270 to 355 the increase in stress is 30% but the increase in procurement cost is approximately 2% (also improved driveability). Specialist products such as marine grade steels are also available. For further information on the available range of products, rolling tolerances, corrosion protection and achievable radii, see the Arcelor Mittal *Piling Handbook* (2008) or similar information from other manufacturers.

11.3. Installing sheet piles

Piles can be installed individually (pitch and drive) or installed progressively using panel technique (panel driving) in combination with piling gates for improved installation accuracy, driveability and stability. With combination walls, the heavier element (I section or tube) is installed first using piling gates, with double Z sheets or triple U sheets filling the gap between to allow for installation tolerances. A number of common installation techniques are used.

11.3.1 Open trench

Relatively short and light sheet piles (and trench sheets) may be installed by placing them into a pre-excavated trench then backfilling, or by pushing them into relatively soft ground with an excavator bucket.

Figure 11.2 Examples of corner sections
Reproduced from ArcelorMittal *Piling Handbook* (2008), courtesy of ArcelorMittal Ltd

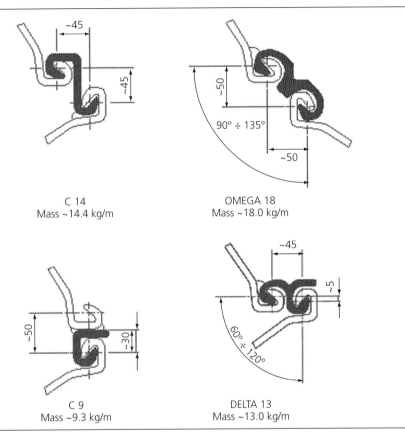

11.3.2 Dig and push

Sheets are progressively pushed into the ground using an excavator bucket as the excavation progresses. The sheets will not be significantly 'toed' in, hence multiple frames are required. This technique is generally utilised in soft ground conditions and accuracy is poor unless guides are used.

11.3.3 Vibrators

Vibrators are suitable for use in predominantly granular soils and soft to firm silts or clays. Small versions known as excavator-mounted vibrators are attached to a standard site excavator, whereas larger (more powerful) versions are attached to a piling rig or freely suspended from a crane. Spinning eccentric weights generate the vibration (spin in opposite direction to cancel out the horizontal components leaving the vertical component) which is used to liquefy the soil and reduce resistance rather than drive the pile. With rig-mounted vibrators, a crowding force is often provided to concurrently push the piles and the self-weight of the vibrator is utilised for crane-suspended versions. Vibrators are not very suitable in stiff clay.

11.3.4 Percussive or impact hammers

These are suitable for most soil types and can often work where hard driving or subsurface obstructions are likely to be encountered. Most are suspended by cranes, and a weight is dropped onto the top of the pile. The most basic form of impact is known as a drop hammer; the weight is dropped onto the top of the pile and must then be lifted for next blow. Although drop hammers are still used, impact force is today provided by compression of diesel, air and (most efficiently) by hydraulic impulse (75–95% efficiency compared to 40–60% for diesel).

Hammers can be single-acting (where the power is used to lift the drop weight so it can fall under gravity) or double-acting (using the impulse to accelerate the drop weight downwards as well as lift it back up for the next blow). Double-acting hammers provide a much faster impact rate (120 blows per minute), but single-acting have their place in highly cohesive or tough ground conditions. Hammers generate significant noise (even when acoustically shrouded) and develop vibration in hard driving conditions.

Noise and vibration are significant issues and local authorities can set limits under the 1974 Control of Pollution Act (see Figure 11.3).

11.3.5 Hydraulic pushing

Hydraulic pushing (commonly known as 'silent piling') is used in cohesive soils. Piles are pushed into the ground using a steady pushing force from powerful hydraulic jacks. Equipment with jacking forces of 2000 kN is available. Reaction to the pushing force is achieved by pulling on adjacent piles which utilise the skin friction of the soils. A key element to the process is installing the first few piles, which can be achieved by using a reaction frame with kentledge or self weight and crowd force of a rig. These methods are vibration-free and quiet (the principal noise is from the engines), hence they are suitable in built-up or sensitive areas. In rock, a pilot drill precedes the pushing process (see Figure 11.3).

11.3.6 Driving aids

Methods are available to aid the installation process, as described in the following sections.

11.3.6.1 Pre-augering

A small auger is screwed into the ground at the sheet pile clutch interlock positions. This loosens the dense ground locally and probes for buried obstructions. For retention schemes, pre-augering below formation level should be avoided as it reduces passive resistance.

11.3.6.2 Water jetting

A lance is connected to the pile and water is forced under pressure to the toe of the sheet. The water softens clay or loosens gravel as the pile is forced downwards. Water jetting should be used with care to prevent fines being washed out around the installation area or pressure build-up in the vicinity causing heave to adjacent foundations or services. Jetting to the bottom of the pile wall may form a scour pathway.

Figure 11.3 Examples of hydraulic pusher and hydraulic impact hammer
Courtesy of Dawson Construction Plant Ltd

(a)

(b)

Piles are often installed by tracked machines such as leader rigs or with piling equipment suspended from crawler cranes. Consideration must be given to the working platform beneath the machinery (see Chapter 5 on site roadways and working platforms).

11.3.7   Water control

Clutched sheet pile walls become less permeable with time as fines will fill the interlocks. Some water seepage is inevitable through the clutches and minor seepage can be controlled with internal sump pumping. Sealants can be applied into the clutches to aid with water control. The type of proprietary product to be used is dependent on the degree of moisture penetration permitted. These include

- bituminous sealants: applied pre-driving and mainly used for temporary sheet piling
- hydrophilic or resin-based sealants: applied pre-driving, more effective than bituminous sealants and mostly suitable for permanent works but can be damaged during installation particularly by heat generated by hard vibratory installation
- seam welding clutches: applied after installation and provides the highest degree of water tightness; predominantly used for permanent sealed basements.

See also Chapter 6 on control of groundwater.

11.3.8   Extracting piles

Piles can be extracted by a vibrator, which can be rig-mounted or crane-suspended. When crane-suspended, a significant line pull will be necessary as the vibrator will only loosen the soil and the crane must pull the pile out. If the sheet piles have been in the ground for some time or have been driven into hard ground, some blows with an impact hammer may be necessary to break interlock or ground friction. 'Silent' piling equipment can also extract piles. Purpose-made hydraulic extractors are available which use spreader beams on the ground for reaction to the jacking force. Extractors up to 10 000 kN capacity are available, which exceeds the tensile strength of most sheet piles.

11.3.9   Cofferdams

Cofferdams are essentially a sheet pile 'box' formed to support the ground and possibly to exclude water from the excavation (Figure 11.4). Cofferdams are conventionally single skin but, for very deep excavations, double-skin walls are used which are formed from two parallel lines of piles filled with rock and tied together with tie rods. These are generally designed as a gravity-retaining structure. Corner sections (see Figure 11.2) are used to form a continuous wall in square or rectangular cofferdams. Circular cofferdams are generally installed using circular piling gates by the panel-driving method though leader rigs can also be used.

For all cofferdams (and retaining walls in general), internal framing or external anchorage can be used. The design and detailing of a cofferdam and its framing or anchorage requires careful consideration by a competent designer with experience of the construction process that will occur within the cofferdam. The sequence of installation and removal must be considered in the design to identify the critical loads. It is not unusual for the critical load case to be during the removal process rather than installation.

It is difficult and generally not economic to exclude 100% of the water, hence sump pumps are used to pump water out of the cofferdam. Dewatering can be used to

Figure 11.4 Sheet pile excavation with heavy duty proprietary framing
Courtesy of Groundforce Shorco Ltd

control water ingress but can be expensive and has significant risks associated with it (see Chapter 6 on control of groundwater). Water may also enter the cofferdam over the top of sheet piles (when positioned in a river or sea) or from beneath. Care should be taken to avoid base failure by piping or heave. The sheet piles can be driven to a greater depth to penetrate an impervious soil layer (cohesive material) as a cut-off typically around 2 m. If it is not possible to utilise a cut-off, an underwater concrete plug can be formed in the base of the cofferdam and the water pumped out once the concrete has hardened.

The supports to cofferdams can be provided by ground ties and anchorage, fabricated steel internal framing or heavy-duty proprietary hydraulic framing (hydraulic struts with capacities of 2500 kN and more are available). Further information is available in CIRIA SP95 (2003a).

11.4. Eurocode 7

A variety of design methodology and guidance documents have been developed such as: Arcelor Mittal (2008), CIRIA 104 (1995), CIRIA C580 (2003b) and CIRIA SP95 (2003a). The most recent code is EC7 (BSI, 2004a) and EC3 (BSI, 1990) and the UK National Annexes. EC7 is a comprehensive limit state design code based on the use of partial factors with three design approaches (geotechnical application classification categories 1, 2 and 3) in terms of increasing perceived risk with design procedures altered accordingly. In the basis of design, loads (known as actions by Eurocodes) and load combinations should be taken from EC0 (BSI, 2004b) and EC1 (BSI, 2004c). Section 2.4.2 of EC7 (BSI, 2004a) lists the items that should be considered in geotechnical design with consideration being given to actions occurring jointly and time effects. The code requires that: 'for each geotechnical design situation it shall be verified that no relevant limit state, as defined in EC0 (BSI, 2004b), is exceeded'.

Limit states should be verified by one of the following methods

- use of calculation
- adoption of prescriptive measures such as the use of conservative rules, attention to specification and control of materials, workmanship, protection and maintenance procedures
- experimental models and load tests
- observational methods.

Section 2.2 of EC7 requires that both short- and long-term design situations are considered. Typical ultimate limit states from section 2.4.7.1 of EC7 are

- loss of equilibrium (EQU) of the structure or ground, considered as a rigid (this limit state is often critical to sizing structural elements)
- internal structural failure or excessive deformation (STR)
- failure or excessive deformation of the ground (GEO)
- loss of equilibrium due to uplift (buoyancy) by water pressure or other vertical actions (UPL)
- hydraulic heave, internal erosion and piping caused by hydraulic gradients (HYD).

Partial factors are defined in Annex A of EC7 with the factors being increased for abnormal risk situations or reduced for less severe cases, temporary structures or transient design situations. A partial factor of 1.0 should be used for accidental situations.

Section 2.4.7.3.4 of EC7 provides details of three design approaches for the various limit states. Section 4 of EC7 states that: 'to ensure the safety and quality of a structure, the following shall be undertaken, as appropriate'.

- The construction processes and workmanship shall be supervised; this would include identifying differences in the actual ground and water conditions compared to those assumed in the design. Any differences in the method of construction from those assumed in the design, should be reported.
- The performance of the structure shall be monitored during and after construction to validate assumptions made in the design.
- The structure shall be adequately maintained to ensure safety and serviceability.

For flexible retaining walls supported by anchors or struts, the magnitude and distribution of earth pressures, internal structural forces and bending moments depend to a great extent on the relative stiffness of the structure and the stiffness, stress and strength of the ground. For problems of ground–structure interaction, analyses should use stress–strain relationships for ground and structural materials and stress states in the ground that are sufficiently representative, for the limit state considered, to give a safe result.

Sections 7–9 of EC7 provide guidance on the design of piled foundations, anchorages and retaining structures (where diagrams of modes of failure are shown). EC7 (BSI, 2004a) does not provide specific guidance to the supervision, monitoring and maintenance of retaining structures. This specific guidance can be found in EN 12063 (BSI, 1999) for sheet pile walls and EN 12699 (BSI, 2001) for displacement piles. Specifiers may use *ICE Specification for Embedded Retaining Walls* (2007) for guidance.

Issues in EC7 (BSI, 2004a) that remain to be resolved include tie bar and 'dead-man' anchorage systems and factoring water pressures.

11.5. Design

The first and perhaps the most important stage in design process is to interpret the site investigation information and establish a geotechnical model for analysis. Most site investigations are commissioned for the permanent structure and it is not uncommon for additional investigation to be required to aid the temporary works design. EC7 Part 2 (BSI, 2004a) now gives guidance and rules for the extent of the site investigation required for embedded retaining walls and bearing piles.

There are two philosophies of design so that we can utilise the inherent shear strength of the soil to help the sheet piling support it, namely

1   soil–structure interaction (SSI) which requires the elastic properties of both to provide the stresses by iterative analysis
2   limit-equilibrium (LE) which sizes the elements and penetration such that the whole is in equilibrium when maximum stresses are mobilised.

Although SSI is a very precise analysis, it uses the elastic properties of soil which can only be determined to a very imprecise level. Historically, LE has therefore been the common method of calculation. It permits very simple pile designs to be carried out manually; whether the use of SSI or LE provides the best solution is best determined by use of specialist software.

A design should aim to be both safe and economical and the structure classification should determine the expertise employed in the design. Codes and standards that should be followed have recently changed; British Standards were effectively withdrawn and ceased to be maintained on 31 March 2010, to be replaced by Eurocodes. There are associated European Standards effectively in place to be used by the designer in conjunction with Eurocodes, but the designer should be aware that, although limit state methods and analysis are common to present and former Codes of Practice, application and values of partial factors and resulting Factors of Safety are different.

The design of sheet pile walls, cofferdams, etc. and their supports need to consider the elements described in the following sections.

11.5.1 Stresses due to applied loads

Bending and axial stresses generated by lateral earth and water pressures surcharges, applied loads (e.g. impact) and vertical loads should be checked against the stress in the steel in accordance with EC3 (BSI, 2003). Pressures can be different if the wall is retaining an excavation or if backfilling is being compacted behind the wall. Variations in soil profile and properties should be considered. When using U-profile sheets in cantilever, the designer should be satisfied that clutch interlock and ground cohesion/friction is sufficient to overcome the possibility of 'neutral axis clutch slip' or apply a factor of 0.8 to the modulus (see Section 11.5.16 and National Annexe to EC3; BSI, 2003). As a general rule, clutch interlock and ground cohesion/friction in typical UK soils are usually sufficient to overcome neutral axis clutch.

Timescale should also be considered in cohesive materials; in short-term usage un-drained (total stress) and, in the medium–longer terms, drained (effective stress) design are appropriate. The pressures on the retaining wall will generally increase with time.

11.5.2 Limit equilibrium methodology

This considers overall stability to prevent rotation of the wall or forward displacement (sliding). Destabilising forces are due to lateral earth, water and surcharge pressures (known as active pressures). Stabilising forces are due to the embedment of the wall in the soil (known as passive resistance) and restraint by framing or anchorage. Note that passive resistance, being a reactive force, can act in any direction to provide a stabilising mechanism. The sheets should sufficiently penetrate below formation level to maintain stability, even if multiple levels of framing or anchorage are provided. The stability of the surrounding soil must also be considered to ensure there is no possibility of slip failures forming. Stability due to heave, piping or excessive ingress of water must also be considered.

11.5.3 The installation and removal sequence

This should be carefully considered to identify the critical design case. It is not unusual for the critical stresses in the sheets, framing or anchors to occur during the backfilling and removal process, rather than during installation and excavation. The most onerous water table conditions should be considered.

11.5.4 Deflection

Deflection should be limited to prevent damage to surrounding, roads, buildings or services caused by settlement or ground movement. Deflection limits should be established and a monitoring regime established if necessary. Readings should be taken on a regular basis during excavation and also once excavation is completed. Trigger levels should be established, such as

- green: low movement; continue taking readings
- amber: increased movement; increase frequency of readings
- red (maximum designed deflection): significant movement; thorough investigation of the causes and remedial measures to be considered.

Deflections as well as the required penetration of cantilevered sheet pile walls can be significant for retained heights over c. 4.0 m (unless very heavy piles are used).

11.5.5   Corrosion protection

Corrosion protection is mainly a consideration for permanent works and not temporary works. Cathodic systems are sometimes required for marine applications.

11.5.6   Workmanship, construction tolerances

Accidental over-dig at formation level (maximum of 0.5 m or 10% of retained height), softening of the formation in cohesive soils (usually top 1 m of formation on the passive side) and accidental impact should be considered. Cofferdams in water should include flooding valves and measures taken if water ingress becomes excessive.

11.5.7   Framing and anchor support loads

These are affected by the stiffness of the structural members involved (stiffer members attract load) and the soil–structure interaction (SSI design can give loads as high as 85% higher than LE). Timber, steel tubes or steel structural sections are common materials for framing and occasionally reinforced concrete for walings. Useful guidance and detailing is shown in CIRIA SP95 (2003a). Design should be undertaken by a site-experienced engineer. Steelwork wallings tend to be I sections, sometimes as battened pairs, with tubular or UC struts. The struts can rake down onto concrete thrust blocks. Long horizontal struts (where the effective length and self weight bending are significant) can be supported by king posts. Web stiffeners should be used at waler/ strut junctions and are installed at points of concentrated load; shear plates or welded/bolted connections are used to carry shearing components of reactions from raking members or corner braces.

Torsion on the waling beam should be considered due to the vertical reaction imposed from raking props, unless the vertical reaction can be carried by corbels. Self-weight bending and impact loading (in the least favourable position) should be allowed for. Prevention of progressive collapse from impact is usually achieved by back-analysing assuming any one strut is removed and limit state conditions. The design of steel framing was developed from BS 449 (BSI, 1989), BS 5950 (BSI, 1990) and EC3 Part 5 (BSI, 2003), with all three methodologies currently in use.

11.5.8   Tension cracks

Allowance should be made for tension cracks in clay behind the wall filling with water.

11.5.9   Thermal effects

These can be significant in large struts and should be considered in the design.

11.5.10 Releasing strut and anchor loads
These should be released gently by incorporating sand boxes, hydraulic jacks or striking packs.

11.5.11 Circular cell structures
Circular steel or reinforced concrete walings are designed for hoop-stresses.

11.5.12 Twin-wall cofferdams and other gravity structures
Well-drained granular fill is essential and the bearing resistance of the ground should be considered (soft soil formations should be avoided). A width/height ratio of >0.8 is required to prevent shear-failure of the filling.

11.5.13 Site constraints
On confined sites, horizontal framing can be designed to carry live loading such as plant and material storage.

11.5.14 Driveability
Drivability refers to the ability of sheets to be installed into the ground without buckling, damage or end-resistance or wall-adhesion preventing penetration. It should be noted that, in all soils other than those of low strength, the calculated structural requirements of the sheet piles will almost invariably be less onerous than the strength needed for driveability. The Piling Handbook (Arcelor Mittal, 2008) provides the calculation method for suitable sections relative to items such as Standard Penetration Test (SPT) N values and soil descriptions, length and steel grade of pile and installation methods, but tends to give overly optimistic findings for drivability. Generous factors are advised in the calculations.

11.5.15 Design sequence
The design of a sheet pile wall for LE analysis should follow the sequence of steps as follows.

- Cross-sections of the soil profile should be established and moderately conservative soil parameters established from available data such as the site investigation report or from guidance values given in documents such as CIRIA SP95 (2003a) or CIRIA C580 (2003b). Groundwater, river levels and tidal ranges should be considered (generally worst-case scenarios). A certain degree of engineering judgement may be necessary in regard to the reliability of drainage behind the wall.
- A decision should be taken if skin friction and skin adhesion are to be considered. If there is any doubt, they should be ignored.
- Consider timescale and if total stress or effective stress conditions apply to each stratum.
- Partial factors of safety are applied to the previously determined moderately conservative soil parameters to derive design parameters.
- Establish the coefficients of active (Ka) and passive (Kp) earth pressure loading together with water pressure on both sides of the wall.

- Use coefficients and the Rankine formula to develop active and passive pressure diagrams. Over-dig, tension cracks filling with water on the active side and soil softening on the passive side should be considered. The active and passive pressure diagrams should then be combined to give a design analysis model.
- Supports may be introduced at appropriate levels using a framing/anchorage arrangement to allow the work to be carried out as easily as possible and limit deflections.
- Forces and moments are resolved to test equilibrium of the total pressure diagram in the ultimate limit condition. This is the maximum load situation and will give the required penetration (adding a length to permit reverse passive reaction). Partial factors are applied to variable and applied loads in accordance with EC7 (BSI, 2004a); the worst case for Design Approach 1 (UK National Annexe) combinations 1 or 2 determines the required pile length with the design effect moment and forces.
- The depth of penetration determines the length of pile required.
- The maximum moment multiplied by a factor plus the yield strength of the pile steel will give the minimum required pile section modulus and therefore the pile section designation for structural adequacy. The pile section modulus may need to be increased to account for 'driveability' (see Section 11.5.14). After checking driveability, the chosen section is verified for structural adequacy in accordance with EC5 and the National Annexe after taking into account effects of corrosion on the section properties including the check on section classification and the effects of that. Piles can be verified for bending strength using plastic section properties if remaining in Class 2 but, if the section drops to Class 4, then buckling and shear may determine the section. It is best to adopt sections remaining in Class 3 or higher for structural walls.
- Multiply the forces put into the supports by a factor F_T if using the limit equilibrium (LEQ) method to allow for the interaction of the soil and piles. This gives the design forces for anchors or frames.
- Back-analyse the frames to test for any one strut or tie accidentally removed for the serviceability limit state, to check that progressive collapse will not occur.
- Maximum potential deflections and ground settlements may be estimated using SSI or Finite Element methods of analysis. Alternatively, the appendix to CIRIA C580 (2003b) shows deflections and settlements from extensive site studies for use with LEQ.

11.5.16 Partial factors which may be considered for use in sheet piling design

Refer to EC7 (2004a) and the National Annexe for the factors given therein. The following have been found to be appropriate for use in limit state design to date, but do not mix factors from more than one source.

- $F_s = 1.2$ divider applied to the tangent of moderately conservative (MC) angle of friction and MC drained cohesion values to give design $\tan \phi'$ and C' when soil is under effective conditions (NB 1.25 in National Annexe).

- $F_s = 1.5$ divider applied to MC un-drained cohesion values to give design cohesion when soil is under total conditions (1.4 in National Annexe)
- $F_{pen} = 1.2$ multiplier to calculated depth of net pressure diagram, from point of zero net pressure to the bottom of pile, to add a finite length for F3 (stabilising passive force at bottom of pile). Applicable only to cantilever or fixed earth configuration, and only to find actual length of pile to be driven.
- $F_m = 1.2$ multiplier to calculated moment in all steel members and piles to compensate for the difference in design stresses between old factored yield and new yield stress, with partial factors as in this list.
- $F_T = 1.85$ multiplier to calculate loads from sheet piles onto all rigid frame members to compensate for the difference between LE results and those from SSI results.
- $F_\beta = 0.8$ divider applied to required bending capacity of U piles to compensate for the clutches being on neutral axis. (Note that there are research results which appear to disprove this reduction as necessary in practice.)

11.5.17 Other allowances suggested in design

- Accidental over-dig: design rules are given in EC7 (BSI, 2004a). Consider 10% of the retained height or 0.5 m, whichever is the lesser.
- Softening of the top 1 m of ground after excavation: applies only in cohesive soil on the passive side of the pile. Usually taken as zero cohesion at formation level to full cohesion at 1 m depth.

11.6. Inspection and maintenance

Excavations and cofferdams should be inspected as per the requirements of the Construction (Design and Management) Regulations (HSE, 2007; clauses 31–33). Many excavations and cofferdams are in use for a significant period of time and a regular maintenance regime should be established. This may include checking and replacing timber wedges, remedial measures to seal interlocks, adequate means of access/ egress and adequate edge protection. For management issues, refer to Chapter 2 and BS 5975 (BSI, 2011).

REFERENCES

Arcelor Mittal (2008) *Piling Handbook*, 8th edition. Arcelor Mittal.
BSI (1989) BS 449: Specification for the use of structural steel in building. BSI, London.
BSI (1990) BS 5950: Structural use of steelwork in building. BSI, London.
BSI (1996a) BS EN 10248: Hot rolled sheet piling of non-alloy steels. Technical delivery conditions. BSI, London.
BSI (1996b) BS EN 10249: Cold formed sheet piling of non alloy steels. Technical delivery conditions. BSI, London.
BSI (1999) BS EN 12063: 1999, Execution of special geotechnical work, sheet pile walls. BSI, London.
BSI (2001) BS EN 12699: Execution of special geotechnical work, displacement piles. BSI, London.
BSI (2003) BS EN 1993: Eurocode 3, Design of steel structures. BSI, London.
BSI (2004a) BS EN 1997: Eurocode 7, Geotechnical design. BSI, London.

BSI (2004b) BS EN 1990: Eurocode 0, Basis of structural design. BSI, London.

BSI (2004c) BS EN 1991: Eurocode 1, General actions on structures. BSI, London.

BSI (2011) BS 5975: 2008 + A1: 2011 Code of practice for temporary works procedures and the permissible stress design of falsework. BSI, London.

CIRIA (Construction Industry Research & Information Association) (1995) Remedial Treatment for Contaminated Land. Special Publication 104. CIRIA, London.

CIRIA (2003a) The Design and Construction of Sheet-Piled Cofferdams. Special Publication 95, CIRIA, London.

CIRIA (2003b) Embedded Retaining Wall – Guidance for Economic Design. Report C580. CIRIA, London.

Control of Pollution Act (1974) Control of Pollution Act. HMSO, London.

HSE (Health & Safety Executive) (2007) Construction (Design and Management) Regulations. HMSO, London.

ICE (Institution of Civil Engineers) (2007) *ICE Specification for Piling and Embedded Retaining Walls*, 2nd edition. Thomas Telford Publishing, London.

FURTHER READING

BSI (British Standards Institution) (1984) BS 8002: Code of practice for earth retaining structures. BSI, London.

Byfield M and Mawer R (2001) The development of section modulus in Larssen U-shaped sheet piles. University of Cranfield, Cranfield.

CIRIA (Construction Industry Research & Information Association) (1984) Design of retaining walls embedded in stiff clay. Report 104. CIRIA, London.

CIRIA (2008) EC7 implications for UK practice. Report C641. CIRIA, London.

Dawson R (2001) Steel to replace concrete. Proceeding of the Institution of Civil Engineers, *Geotechnical Engineering* **149**(4): 205–207.

Day RA and Potts DH (1989) Comparison of design methods for propped sheet pile walls. SCI Publication 077.

Filip RK (2004) Recent advances in quiet and vibration-less steel pile installation. *Proceedings of Conference of Deep Foundations Institute*, Chicago: 1–11.

ICE (Institution of Civil Engineers) (1996) *The Observational Method in Geotechnical Engineering*. Thomas Telford Publishing, London.

Packshaw S (1962) Cofferdams. *Proceedings of Institution of Civil Engineers* **21**: paper Number 6588.

Rowe PW (1955) A theoretical and experimental analysis of sheet pile walls. *Proceedings of ICE* **4**(1): 32–69.

Rowe PW (1957) Sheet pile walls in clay. *Proceedings of ICE* **7**(3): 629–654.

Symons IF, Little JA, McNulty TA, Carder DR and Williams SGO (1987) Behaviour of a temporary anchored sheet pile wall on A1(M) at Hatfield. TRRL Research Report 99, TRL, London.

Yau JHW and McNicholl DP (1990) Failure of a temporary sheet pile wall: case study. In: *Proceedings of the Seminar on Failures in Geotechnical Engineering*, University of Hong Kong.

Useful Websites

ArcelorMittal Ltd, www.arcelormittal.com

Dawson Construction Plant Ltd, www.dcpuk.com
Groundforce Shorco Ltd, www.groundforceuk.com
Mabey Hire Ltd, www.mabeyhire.co.uk
MGF Ltd, www.mgf.co.uk

Temporary Works: Principles of Design and Construction
ISBN 978-0-7277-4177-6

ICE Publishing: All rights reserved
http://dx.doi.org/10.1680/twpdc.41776.145

Chapter 12
Trenching

Ray Filip Temporary works consultant and training provider – RKF Consult Ltd

A trench is defined as an excavation whose length greatly exceeds its width and depth. It is generally considered that a shallow excavation is less than 6 m deep (most trenches) and a deep excavation is greater than 6 m deep (specialist advice should be sought). Trenches can be excavated by hand or mechanical digger to allow a service, pipeline or foundation to be installed or, when backfilled with granular fill, used to improve drainage. A trench may have battered sides when site circumstances allow, or temporary shoring may be installed (traditional timbering, sheets and frames, proprietary trench boxes) to protect workers entering the trench. Controlling water ingress into a trench is often a major issue (see Chapter 6 on control of groundwater). A safe system of work and adequate planning is necessary, especially when workers are required to enter a trench, and the trenching operation can also have a detrimental effect on the surroundings when appropriate management control measures are not provided or inappropriate solutions used. Good health and safety practice is critical to trenching operations.

12.1. Introduction
12.1.1 Major alternatives
Trenchless techniques (to minimise surface disruption) include methods such as micro-tunnelling, auger/thrust boring, pipe ramming, impact moling, directional drilling, mole ploughing and rock boring. Trenchless techniques might not be possible or practical because soils are unsuitable or very large diameter or very long lengths of pipework are to be installed, or due to cost limitations, site-specific restrictions and the non-availability of specialist machinery and labour (CIRIA, 1987).

Other alternatives to trenching include traditional timber headings or tunnelling techniques for larger diameter services; the installation of services above ground to avoid having to excavate a trench; and specialist techniques such as soil nailing or ground freezing

12.1.2 Soils
Soils can be classified by particle size (broadly cohesion-less or cohesive), compactness and structure with a separate classification for organic soils (soil classifications are provided in various documents such as BS 5975 (BSI, 2011; table 18) and BS 8002 (BSI, 1994). Accurate soil descriptions are essential to allow soil design parameters to be determined. Designers will summarise and approximate actual soil conditions to

form an idealised model for design and these approximations have to be confirmed by monitoring the soils being excavated.

Granular soils are sands and gravels which have an angle of repose. This angle is dependent on particle shape, particle roughness, compaction and grading. A well-graded material has a variety of sized particles and these tend to pack together, giving higher angles of repose. Poorly graded materials have a predominance of a single-size soil and tend to have lower angles of repose. Granular soils have high permeability and close sheeting will generally be required for deeper trenches or when a high water table is encountered to prevent collapse, significant ground movement and fine materials being washed out. If the groundwater pressure is not relieved (de-watering) or released through any gaps in the support scheme, there will be a large increase in the pressure on the support scheme.

Cohesive soils are bound together due to the effects of water between the fine particles in clays and silts (this is known as cohesion). When excavated, clay soils can stand near vertical without support for a period of time. The cohesion in silts will vary with moisture content and they are less stable than clays. The permeability is low (particularly in clays) and drainage occurs over a significant time period, hence extensive dewatering is often not required in cohesive soils (sump pumping is often adequate) unless bands of sands or coarse silts (known as partings) are present or the soil is heavily fissured. Even though these soils can be relatively stable in the short term, a risk assessment should determine whether support is necessary (considering fissures, surcharges, adjacent works, timescale, etc.).

Rock has cemented particles and even though the rock mass itself may be very strong, inclined bedding planes and fractures can lead to instability of blocks. Heavily weathered rock may need to be considered as a very dense cohesionless material. Excavating rock can require heavy machinery or specialist techniques.

When groundwater is encountered, the following items should be observed: the level at which the water was encountered, the rate of inflow and rise of water and the final level which the water reaches.

12.1.3 Battering trenches

Any vertically sided trench is rarely totally acceptable for any appreciable length of time. Collapse has to be avoided which means battering or benching the sides to a safe slope, or supports should be provided. An appropriate risk assessment or stability analysis (see Chapter 10 on slope stability) is required to ensure a batter allows a safe system of work to be provided. A battered trench (which may be stepped) should consider the actual site conditions of surcharges, groundwater, excavated depth, space available, possible deterioration of the soil with exposure and timescale. Virtually all soils can be excavated to a safe angle, but the presence of water will detrimentally affect the safe angle and dewatering is likely to be required to improve stability. Additional protective measures such as netting or fencing may be used to prevent any loose material falling on operatives. Blinding or sheeting may be used as protection from weathering, and berms and ditches dug to cut off surface water. In layered soils, different batter angles may be appropriate for each of the strata.

Regular checks should be carried out looking for potential signs of instability or degradation. Warning signs of rotational slip failures are: bulging at the toe and tension cracks appearing at the top of the batter. If these signs are noted then the batter can be re-graded, weight added to the toe of the slope or the drainage of the batter improved.

In dry conditions over a short duration, granular soils have an internal angle of friction (φ) which will typically range c. 25–50° and batters may be safely cut at an angle slightly less than φ. When groundwater is present, the safe angle will be reduced. In the longer term (months), the angle will need to be less than the effective internal angle of friction (φ'). Cohesive soils can be cut near vertical in the very short term (up to a week), but drainage occurs and collapse will inevitably follow. Where men are required to work in a confined excavation, then the sides will need to be safely battered or sheeting and propping or boxes used. Safe batter angles are listed in many publications (e.g. CIRIA, 1983).

12.1.4   Risks, planning and construction

Designers must carry out an appropriate risk assessment and design out risk where possible (principle of prevention); any residual risks should be communicated so they can be managed on site effectively. Risk assessments and method statements are required on site. Some common considerations for planning and designing of a trenching operation include the following.

- Knowledge of the site: history, topography, previous slippage, voids, flooding, location of existing services, foundations, existing soil and groundwater conditions.
- Can the trench be battered, or is shoring required and which type of shoring is suitable? If supports are required, is the necessary equipment readily available on site or will it be hired (delivery and lead-in times need to be considered).
- Reasons for trench: the item to be installed will determine depth, width (including working space) and equipment to be used.
- Soil, water and surcharge pressures must be considered on any shoring to prevent collapse and overloading of shoring equipment. These pressures will vary depending on the type of soil, depth of trench, head of water and magnitude of surcharge. Soil pressures (particularly in cohesive soils) will also vary with time. Out-of-balance pressures should be considered on sloping ground or when high surcharges exist on one side of the trench. Allowance should be made for variations in the soil and groundwater conditions (or tidal variations).
- Limit deflections and ground movements to an acceptable amount (note adjacent structures and services); is heave of the base likely?
- Consider the installation and removal sequence and allow for construction tolerances.
- Allow for accidental impact on structural members (in particular props), accidental over-dig and provision for softening of formation level.

- Is groundwater a problem and might pumping be required? Dewatering may draw in fines and cause boiling and settlement in the vicinity.
- Access, egress, edge protection (plus stop logs for plant and vehicles) and confined spaces measures must be provided.
- Consider undermining of adjacent structures or ground movement, which may damage services.
- For permanent schemes or very-long-term temporary schemes, an allowance for deterioration of structural members (e.g. corrosion of steel) should be made.
- Can the excavated material be used as backfill?

Thermal and seismic effects are generally not considered.

Some common considerations for constructing and monitoring a trenching operation include the following.

- Operatives and supervision should be briefed, trained, competent and follow a safe pre-instructed method of work. Emergency procedures should be communicated and correct personal protective equipment (PPE) worn.
- Ground and water conditions should be monitored and any changes from the design assumptions should be communicated to the designer.
- Shoring equipment should be inspected and damaged or faulty items disregarded. Once installed, measures should be taken to prevent damage due to accidental impact (e.g. from excavator bucket).
- Existing services should be located by hand digging or vacuum excavation (avoid using mechanical diggers).
- How will the trench be protected from the possible inrush of surface runoff (sandbags, bunds or ditches may be considered)?
- Monitor the trench carefully if excessive vibration is generated from nearby operations, or large surcharges are positioned near the trench, as well as during periods of bad weather.
- Trenches should be inspected as per the requirements of the Construction (Design and Management) Regulations (HSE, 2007; clause 31). Some contractors and clients (e.g. National Grid) are introducing an 'excavation tag', similar to the 'scaffold tag' system that has been in existence for many years.
- How is the trench backfilled and compacted to prevent settlement?
- How will the support system be removed? A detailed removal sequence should be provided and followed on site; simply stating removal is the reverse of installation is not adequate.

Some contractors and utility companies have standard solutions for relatively shallow low-risk trenching operations. These pre-designed solutions indicate sizes for trench sheets, walers, struts, traffic clearances and surcharge limitations. Appropriate risk assessments and method statements are provided by a competent person and operatives must have been appropriately trained. Such solutions are very useful for short duration or repetitive 'reactive maintenance' contracts (repairing a damaged service).

12.2. Techniques

Over a very short period of time and for a relatively shallow depth most soils will stand near vertical, allowing sufficient time for certain shoring systems to be installed. If the sides do need to be supported (as a result of a risk assessment being carried out) due to the nature of the soil, longer-term use, sensitive surroundings or for deeper trenches, then a trench support scheme will be required. A competent person should make the decision (by risk assessment and consideration of site-specific conditions) if any of the below types of equipment are suitable and which type to use. Work should not be permitted outside the protected area. All equipment should be assembled and used as per the manufacturers' instructions and consideration should be given to a safe method of installation and a safe method of removal.

12.2.1 Traditional timbering

'Timbering' is the term given to traditional support techniques using timbers. In the 1970s, regulations were introduced which forbad operatives entering inadequately supported trenches. As a result, many traditional methods of timbering trenching became impractical and hydraulic support systems were developed. These traditional timbering techniques have, however, been developed and are still in use, particularly in the utility sector. Many of these solutions are for relatively low-risk narrow trenches, shafts and headings. These methods are versatile and the equipment easily handled, but they are labour-intensive and rely on good workmanship. Many companies have standardised solutions for use in a variety of circumstances, and these have been designed to satisfy a range of conditions likely to be experienced on site. The design principals rely on soil arching (the full overburden pressure can be reduced) and have been proved satisfactory by experience. The Timber Research and Development Association (TRADA) publication *Timber in Excavations* (1990) provides design examples. The third edition, however, dates from 1990, and the examples require updating to current design standards. The recommendation is that timber quality should be at least SC4 (C24).

12.2.2 Trench/drag boxes

Trench/drag boxes (see Figures 12.1 and 12.2) are generally considered to be suitable as a shield for low-risk situations in relatively stable dry ground (capable of standing near vertical for a short period of time) or rock. A trench box can be placed into a pre-excavated trench and moved either by raising it or moving it forward by excavator. A drag box can be dragged along a wider pre-dug trench by an excavator. Both versions require at least two struts for stability and there are limitations to the maximum diameter of pipe that can be installed (maximum distance from the toe of the box to the bottom strut).

Drag boxes are suitable for relatively shallow trenches (up to about 4 m depth). Trench boxes can be assembled in lifts to achieve significant depths (over 6 m is not uncommon). Trench sheets can be placed at the ends of the boxes to provide additional protection to the open ends. With both versions the pre-excavated trench is wider than the box to allow the box to be installed and moved; they do not support the sides of the excavation, but act as a shield to protect the workforce (even when backfill is placed

Figure 12.1 Diagrammatic trench boxes
Courtesy of Groundforce Shorco Ltd

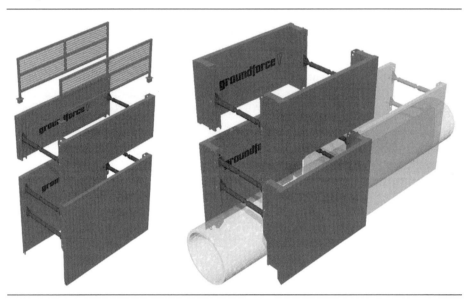

between the box and the surrounding ground there is a period of time when the ground has to be self-supporting). There is a risk of the ground collapsing onto the box affecting operatives, plant and services on the surface around the box, whereas those inside the box are shielded.

Excavation should not be permitted beneath the box (known as 'flying' a box) as friction between the box and the surrounding ground cannot be relied upon to support the box. An alternative installation method for a trench box known as 'dig and push' exists (see Figure 12.3). With this method the soil is supported throughout installation; although this reduces the risk of significant ground movement, it will be slower.

12.2.3 Vertical shores

Vertical shores are an intermittent system comprising a pair of vertical aluminium rails and a pair of hydraulic struts. They are installed into a pre-dug trench in dry stable ground, which can stand unsupported vertically for a period of time. They are suitable for relatively narrow and shallow trenches. The spacing of the rails is determined by the ground conditions, typically between 1.2 m and 0.5 m. They are hinged and designed to be manually installed from outside the trench, being activated by a hand pump to a working pressure indicated by a gauge. Only small-diameter pipes can be installed below the bottom strut, which is typically c. 0.5 m from the base of the trench. Vertical shores can be used between services, but there is a risk of ground collapse between the shores. For this reason, vertical shores are limited in their application.

Figure 12.2 Trench box on site (edge protection not installed). Note backfilling between the box and ground, dewatering and excavated spoil kept away from edge of trench
Courtesy of Groundforce Shorco Ltd

Figure 12.3 'Dig and push' sequence for installing a trench box
Courtesy of Groundforce Shorco Ltd

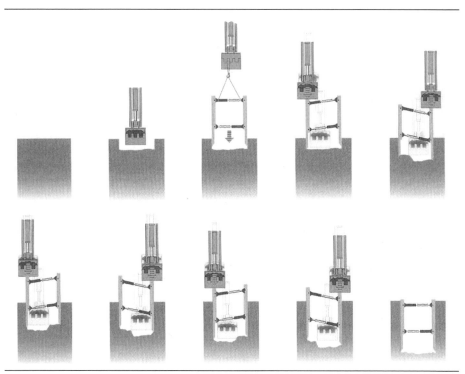

12.2.4 Trench sheets and hydraulic waling frames

Trench sheets and hydraulic waling frames (Figure 12.4) are the most adaptable of systems and hence the most widely used. They are generally used in poorer ground, for deeper trenches where surcharges are higher or where ground movement may need to be limited and some design is likely. The trench sheets (or light sheet piles) provide continuous support and may rely on penetration below the formation level for passive resistance. The sheets can be pushed in by an excavator or driven using an excavator-mounted vibrator or small piling rig (driving method depends on length of sheet, ground conditions and site limitations).

A simple guide system (baulk timbers or steel beams) should be used to ensure the sheets are driven near vertical and to maintain a straight line. When site conditions allow, the sheets can be partially installed into a pre-excavated 'lead trench' which is then back-filled. Multiple levels of horizontal waling beams with hydraulic, adjustable struts (or timber walings and struts) are used with the spacing of the struts suiting the pipe lengths to be installed. The trench depth is limited by the length of sheets that can be installed by light machinery, especially with interlocking (rather than overlapping) sheets which require additional height for 'clutching' the sheets together. The slenderness of the sheet can also preclude driving into dense or stiff soils. These systems can also be installed using the 'dig and push' method.

Figure 12.4 Sheets with steel waling beams and props
Courtesy of Groundforce Shorco Ltd

Small gaps can be left in the sheeted wall to allow for services crossing the trench and, if relatively stable ground is encountered, then intermittent sheeting can be used. This is the principal reason why the horizontal waling system is so adaptable and popular. Similarly, manholes can be constructed in a square- or rectangular-sheeted excavation using proprietary hydraulic supports known as manhole braces, whereby all four walers in a frame are hydraulically driven off a common manifold (timbers can also be used). Gaps can be left in the sheets or some sheets left above formation level to allow pipework to be installed.

12.2.5 Post and plank vertical H-sections

Post and plank (Figure 12.5) vertical steel H-sections are pre-driven by an excavator, piling rig or installed into augured holes at c. 1–3 m centres with horizontal planks

Figure 12.5 (a) Post and plank excavation and (b) side rail system trench
Courtesy of Groundforce Shorco Ltd

(a)

(b)

(timber, precast concrete, in situ concrete or steel sheets) which span between the flanges of the vertical H-section. When placed into augured holes, the bottom of the H-section is often held in concrete. The planks are installed and wedged in position, one beneath the other, as the excavation progresses downwards. When using timber, steel or precast planks, the soil behind the planks has to be excavated slightly larger to accommodate the planks, with sand backfill placed behind the planks to fill the gap, but some ground movement is inevitable. In situ concrete planks accommodate construction tolerances and are cast against the excavated face; backfilling is, therefore, not required. This method has the advantages that the main structural supports are installed prior to excavation, can be easily altered and gaps can be left to accommodate services. However, it can be time-consuming, labour-intensive and some ground movement is possible.

A variant uses light steel sections spanning horizontally between the flanges of the posts with trench sheets pushed down progressively, and this dramatically reduces the labour content. A proprietary version is known as a 'side rail system' which comprises posts, sliding panels (each c. 1.5–2.5 m deep) and struts, which form a continuous ground support and are installed by excavator. They can be used for widths up to 7 m and depths in excess of 7 m. The equipment is relatively large and heavy and requires heavy excavators for installation. For deeper trenches with large diameter pipes, an in situ concrete blinding is cast at the base and lower levels of struts can be moved upwards or removed. Additional support such as trench sheets may be required to provide additional support at each end.

Proprietary equipment is designed for the most robust loadings envisaged, and in all but obviously excessive conditions the need for detailed calculations is unlikely. Where it is felt wise to calculate, empirical methods as given in the following section may suffice.

12.3. Design to CIRIA 97 trenching practice

The CIRIA publication (1983) *Trenching Practice* was last revised in 1992; however, it is still an authoritative guide to this type of work even though some items require revision to current standards (e.g. 'obligatory support at deeper than 1.2 m' rule is still quoted). The calculation of earth pressures is still relatively empirical as soils are a naturally variable material.

Supports for trenches often have several levels of supports; for such cases traditional soil mechanics theory such as the triangular Coulomb pressure diagram have been found not to apply (because these support systems are relatively flexible and there is a degree of soil arching and displacement which leads to a redistribution of pressures). From full-scale tests, Terzaghi and Peck (1996) derived empirical trapezoidal pressure diagrams for calculating maximum strut loads. From further experience, these pressure diagrams were developed to incorporate rules for the design of walings and sheets. These are incorporated into simple charts in the CIRIA 97 (1983) guide, which was prepared assuming the following conditions.

■ Dry conditions (assumes water is dealt with by dewatering) as water pressure has
    a great effect on soil behaviour.
■ Up to 6 m in depth with supports (walings and struts). Experience has shown that
    in a wide range of soils the strut loads are similar up to this depth; specialist
    advice must be sought and an experienced person must design the trench support
    scheme for trenches of depth greater than 6 m.

- Short-, medium- and long-term trenches in granular soils and mixed soils but only short–medium-term in clays. Pressure increases with time in clays, so different parameters are used in long-term trenches in clay.
- Steel sheets with a minimum section modulus z of 35 cm³/m (or timber poling boards of 32 mm thickness) which can be driven using non-specialist driving techniques are assumed. There is no minimum 'toe in' of the sheets quoted and the maximum cantilever of the sheeting should not exceed 500 mm.
- Timbers are a minimum grade of SC4 (C24) and steel walers are a minimum grade S275 to BSEN 10025 (previously grade 43A). Adjustable props meet regulations as described by BS 4074 (BSI, 2000).
- The slope across the trench does not exceed 1:4.
- Surcharge limited to 10 kN/m² and deflection is not considered a major problem.
- Not to be used in soft clays (un-drained cohesion <30 kN/m²) and saturated silt.
- There is no heave or boiling at the base of the trench.
- The supports should be installed tight against the sides of the trench to ensure soil arching takes place and the load on the waling is relieved.

The effective depth of a trench is the actual depth, but an adjacent batter is considered to increase the effective depth. Timber waling and trench sheets are designed for loads equivalent to 50% of the pressure diagram to allow for arching. Steel walings, being stiffer, are designed for the full pressure diagram.

The chart in Figure 12.6 is for use in granular soils, mixed soils and short-term trenches in clay. It uses a rectangular pressure diagram and the pressure is calculated as:

$3.07\,H + 1.76\,(kN/m^2)$.

A second case is provided for medium-term trenches in clay as the earth pressure increases with time. Unless the water table is lowered by dewatering, then the full hydrostatic pressure diagram should be used. The pressure due to soil and due to surcharge are calculated as follows:

Pressure due to soil $= 0.65 \times Ka \times \gamma \times H = 0.65 \times 0.27 \times 17.5 \times H = 3.07\,H$

Pressure due to surcharge $= 0.65 \times Ka \times S = 0.65 \times 0.27 \times 10 = 1.76$

where $\gamma = 17.5\,kN/m^3$ is the density of soil, $\emptyset = 35°$ is the soil friction angle, H is effective depth of excavation (m) and $S = 10\,kN/m^2$ is surcharge. The coefficient of active earth pressure is defined $Ka = 1 - \sin\emptyset$, where $Ka = 0.65$ approximates maximum triangular pressure to rectangular pressure.

For medium-term trenches in clay, an alternative chart is provided based on similar principles to those mentioned above. The formula for the uppermost 1 m is as above; below this depth it increases to:

$6.56\,H + 3.75\,(kN/m^2)$

Figure 12.6 Example design chart from CIRIA97
Reproduced courtesy of CIRIA

Calculating waling loads as per CIRIA report 97 charts

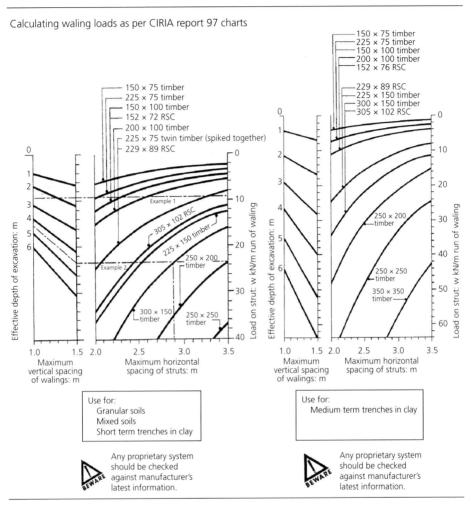

12.4.   Controlling water

Water can enter a trench from a number of sources: ingress of groundwater when excavating below the water table, surface runoff, excavating through land drains or ditches, damage to nearby water mains or artesian water pressure. Water control measures are necessary to keep the base of the excavation dry and prevent excessive soil softening (by blinding) so work can progress safely and efficiently and to avoid the base of excavations in sandy soils boiling during dewatering from inside a sheeted trench.

Some of the associated risks in trenching are

■   lowering the water table may lead to fine soils being drawn out of the soil, leading to settlement and possible damage to surrounding buildings, services and roads

- reduction in near-surface bearing pressures due to high water table
- difficult to achieve compaction densities if soils are too wet
- fine soils exhibit short- and long-term characteristics as drainage occurs
- heavy rain can cause high surface-runoff rates
- when excavating above artesian water pressure (where an impervious soil overlies a granular soil containing pressurised water), the weight of the remaining impervious soil may not be sufficient to resist the upward water pressure and this can cause the base of the trench to heave
- contamination of rivers, streams and other water courses needs to be considered (bunds and silt busters) and discharge licences may be required
- battered trenches become increasingly unstable when water inflow occurs.

Site investigation data should be studied to determine the groundwater level and if artesian water pressure may be encountered. The permeability of the soils should also be estimated to determine the rate at which groundwater will flow into the trench. Trial holes can be a simple way of crudely estimating inflow rates and the stability of soils. It should also be noted that soils tend to be laid down in layers; vertical and horizontal permeability will therefore differ.

When determining dewatering techniques, professional advice should be sought. For further details, see Chapter 6 on control of groundwater.

REFERENCES

BSI (1994) BS 8002: Code of practice for earth retaining structures. BSI, London (replaced by BS EN 1997-1, 2004).

BSI (2000) BS 4074: Specification for steel trench struts. BSI, London.

BSI (2011) BS 5975: 2008 + A1: 2011 Code of practice for temporary works procedures and the permissible stress design of falsework. BSI, London.

CIRIA (Construction Industry Research & Information Association) (1983) *Trenching practice*, 2nd edition. Report 97. CIRIA, London.

CIRIA (1987) Trenchless construction for underground services. Technical Note 127. CIRIA, London.

HSE (Health & Safety Executive) (2007) The Construction (Design and Management) Regulations. HSE, London.

Terzaghi K and Peck R (1996) *Soil Mechanics in Engineering Practice*. John Wiley & Sons, London.

TRADA (Timber Research and Development Association) (1990) *Timber in Excavations*, 3rd edition. Thomas Telford Publishing, London.

FURTHER READING

Arcelor Mittal (2008) *Piling Handbook*, 8th edition. Arcelor Mittal, London.

BSI (2002) BS EN 13331-1: Trench lining systems. BSI, London.

CIRIA (Construction Industry Research & Information Association) (1986) Proprietary trench support systems. Technical Note 95. CIRIA, London.

CIRIA (1986) Control of groundwater for temporary works. Report 113. CIRIA, London.

CIRIA (2001) Control of groundwater. Report R515. CIRIA, London.

CPA (Construction Plant-hire Association) (2001) Selection of proprietary shoring equipment and the use of chains to support shoring equipment. Guidance STIG0201. CPA, London.

CPA (2004) Risk assessments for shoring and piling operations. Guidance STIG0403. CPA, London.

HSE (Health & Safety Executive) (1997) Avoidance of danger from overhead electric power lines. Guidance GS6. HSE, London.

HSE (1997) Safe work in confined spaces. Guidance INDG258. HSE, London.

HSE (1997) Safety in Excavations. Guidance CIS8 (Revision 1). HSE, London.

HSE (1999) Health & safety in excavations. Guidance HSG185. HSE, London.

HSE (2000) Avoiding danger from underground services. Guidance HSG47. HSE, London.

HSE (2009) ACoP Safe work in confined spaces. Guidance L101. HSE, London.

New Road and Street Works Act (1991) New Road and Streetworks Act. HMSO, London.

Safety at Street Works and Road Works (2000) Safety at Street Works and Road Works. Stationery Office, London.

Useful web addresses

CIRIA: www.ciria.org

Contractors Plant Association: www.cpa.uk.net

Dawson Construction Plant Ltd: www.dcpuk.com

Groundforce Shorco Ltd: www.groundforceuk.com

Mabey Hire Ltd: www.mabeyhire.co.uk

MGF Ltd: www.mgf.co.uk

Temporary Works: Principles of Design and Construction
ISBN 978-0-7277-4177-6

ICE Publishing: All rights reserved
http://dx.doi.org/10.1680/twpdc.41776.161

Chapter 13
Diaphragm walls

Chris Robinson Technical Manager, Cementation Skanska Limited
Andrew Bell Chief Engineer, Cementation Skanska Limited

Diaphragm walls (also known as slurry walls) can be used to form cofferdams, quay walls, foundation elements and embedded retaining walls (e.g. to construct tanks, shafts, basement excavations or cut and cover tunnels). Their use is becoming more prevalent in congested urban environments where construction below ground is becoming ever more common; this is due to the availability of development land and associated high land prices and to the development of deep urban infrastructure. The economics of diaphragm wall use become increasingly attractive when they can be used to form part of the permanent works. This chapter will describe common uses of diaphragm walls, their method of construction (including aspects of additional temporary works required to facilitate construction), a summary of typical construction details which can aid construction of a high-quality finished product and a description of the most significant design considerations.

13.1.　Introduction
Diaphragm walling refers to the in situ construction of vertical walls by means of deep trenches. Stability of the trench excavation is maintained by the use of a support fluid; this is most commonly a bentonite suspension, although polymer support fluids can also be used. Diaphragm walls are constructed in discrete panels typically ranging in length from 2.8 m to 7.0 m using purpose-built grabs or milling machines. The panels are constructed in the required sequence (discussed in Section 13.3.1) abutting each other to form a continuous structural wall. T-shaped panels or counterforts can be constructed where very high bending capacity elements are required, typically to minimise propping requirements. A variety of details are available to form the ends (stop ends) of each panel which will generally incorporate a water bar, and can include details to facilitate the transfer of shear forces between panels.

13.2.　Applications
Although an expensive form of temporary works, generally used where other forms of temporary ground support are not practical, diaphragm walls become very economical when they can be used to form part of the permanent works.

In addition to providing ground support and water exclusion, diaphragm walls can also be utilised to carry vertical loads. Where the magnitude of vertical loading exceeds the available wall capacity (based on an embedment length required to maintain wall stability), the panels can be taken deeper to carry the vertical load. Discrete isolated panels known as barrettes can be constructed to carry vertical loads alone. These might be adopted where diaphragm walls are being constructed elsewhere on a scheme and it would be uneconomic or impractical to mobilise additional plant to construct conventional bearing piles, or where the founding level is so deep as to preclude these from being adopted.

13.3. Construction methods and plant

13.3.1 Planning

The construction methods and plant selected will depend on the characteristics of each project. These will include consideration of ground conditions (including groundwater chemistry which may impact upon support fluid performance), depth of walls to be constructed, access restrictions, headroom restriction, any working time restrictions, party wall issues (which may impact upon panel dimensions), panel trench stability, etc.

Figure 13.1 depicts the typical sequence of operations for diaphragm wall construction. Upon construction of the first diaphragm wall panel (opening panel), further panels are constructed to suit the specific site conditions and constraints. Panel sequencing is typically ordered such that a minimal number of stop-ends (peel off/re-usable type stop ends) are in the ground at any one time. This is not a constraint where non-reusable stop ends (e.g. pre-cast concrete stop ends) are used.

As well as diaphragm walls being a temporary works solution in their own right, their construction can require some significant additional temporary works to ensure successful execution. These include guide walls, temporary anchorages and/or temporary props, jet-grouted props at depth, working platforms for tracked plant (see Chapter 5), slope stability assessment (see Chapter 10), temporary screening to protect public and personnel, protection of water courses and adjacent services, and foundations for wet and dry silos (for support fluid).

Where ground movements are critical, additional precautionary measures may be adopted which can vary from limiting panel lengths to preliminary underpinning of particularly sensitive adjacent structures.

As noted by Fernie *et al.* (2001), ancillary works (broadly speaking all operations prior to bulk basement excavation) can cause a significant proportion (up to around 80%) of recorded settlements of adjacent structures. Caution should therefore be taken to ensure that any precautionary measures do not cause more problems than they are intended to mitigate.

13.3.2 Site preparation

Demolition works may be needed in advance of the commencement of diaphragm walling operations. Often this will entail excavation or grubbing-out of existing foundations. Where this occurs along the line of the wall, it is good practice to ensure the backfill to these areas is selected not only to give adequate support to tracked plant, but also to

Figure 13.1 Typical construction sequence
Courtesy of Cementation Skanska Limited

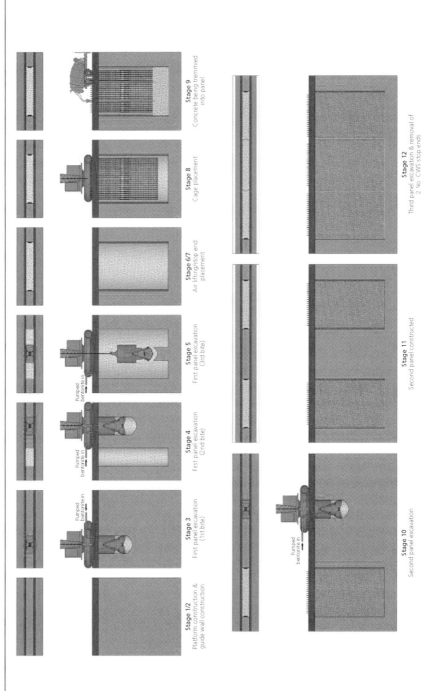

Stage 1/2
Platform construction &
guide wall construction

Stage 3
First panel excavation
(1st bite)

Stage 4
First panel excavation
(2nd bite)

Stage 5
First panel excavation
(3rd bite)

Stage 6/7
Air lifting/stop end
placement

Stage 8
Cage placement

Stage 9
Concrete being tremmied
into panel

Stage 10
Second panel excavation

Stage 11
Second panel constructed

Stage 12
Third panel excavation & removal of
2 No. CWS stop ends

Pumped
bentonite in

avoid high overbreak occurring. This would adversely affect the finished surface of the diaphragm wall, which may require trimming back if the overbreak is in excess of the specification limits. Suitable backfill materials often used are stiff clays or clay-bound hogging. Properly placed and compacted, these materials will give a relatively smooth finish to the wall over the backfill depth and potentially aid wall verticality.

13.3.3 Working platforms
As with any other site where tracked plant (predominantly piling rigs and cranes) is to be employed, a suitable working platform should be provided. Reference should be made to Chapter 5 for full details of working platform design. As well as supporting the tracked plant, the platform may be required to support significant loads from support fluid silos and tanks.

13.3.4 Guide walls
Guide wall construction will usually follow on from construction of the working platform. The guide wall is required to undertake two main functions: it facilitates provision of tighter tolerances and dimensional control of the diaphragm wall panel excavation at commencement level, and also enables the bentonite support fluid to be controlled. The guide wall will also need to provide support for keying off stop ends and the panel reinforcement cages via trapping beams.

Care should be taken to ensure that the guide wall itself remains stable with the diaphragm walling plant operating in close proximity to it. This may be achieved through provision of suitable backfill or strutting. Once the panel has been constructed and cured for a day or so, it will provide the required support to the guide wall in lieu of the original backfill.

A trench stability calculation should be undertaken to ensure the panel excavation is sufficiently stable. The method described by Huder (1972) is often adopted for this analysis.

It may be necessary or prudent to design the guide wall to span laterally while supporting vertical loads, for example, trapping off the panel reinforcement, in the event that the ground beneath it collapses during panel construction.

13.3.5 Support fluid
The most common support fluid used for diaphragm wall construction is a bentonite suspension. Most commercially available bentonite powders tend to be a blend of bentonite and polymers. The exact properties and combinations will depend upon the required properties. Most support fluid properties can be adjusted with addition of the right polymer or other chemical additives. Detailed discussions with suppliers are important prior to commencement of diaphragm walling works, to ensure that the correct materials are procured for the methods to be employed.

In principle, there is no reason why polymers cannot be used alone without bentonite minerals. There is quite a large body of experience of polymer support for diaphragm

Table 13.1 Bentonite support fluid compliance testing
Courtesy of Cementation Skanska Ltd and Federation of Piling Specialists

Property	Equipment	Typical compliance values		
		Freshly mixed	Ready for re-use	Prior to concreting
Density	Mud balance	<1.10 g/ml	<1.25 g/ml	<1.15 g/ml
Viscosity	Marsh cone (946 ml)	32–50 s	32–60 s	32–50 s
pH	Electrical pH meter (to BS 3445) or pH strips (colour matching)	7–11	7–12	N/A
Gel strength	Fann rheometer	3–10 N/m^2	3–20 N/m^2	N/A
Fluid loss	Filter press (30 min)	<30 ml	<50 ml	N/A
Sand content	Sand content apparatus	N/A	N/A	<4%

wall construction in North America and Asia, but very limited experience within the UK.

The support fluid will require cleaning or de-sanding throughout the construction process to ensure that the required properties are maintained.

Prior to commencing panel excavation, it is normal practice to undertake compliance testing of the fresh bentonite to ensure it has the required properties as defined by the contractor's method statement and/or the project specification. Table 13.1 lists typical compliance values.

During panel excavation, compliance testing is then undertaken at a regular pre-defined frequency. Further compliance testing should be undertaken upon completion of panel excavation and prior to concreting the panel. It is particularly important to ensure the bentonite within the panel is sufficiently de-sanded prior to placing concrete.

The size of the bentonite farm (the area required for mixing, cleaning and storing the support fluid) will depend on the scope of the works, number of rigs used, the maximum panel volume and the nature of the ground supported.

Deep panels in fine granular materials will require far more fluid cleaning than for stiff cohesive ground.

It should be noted that one of the major costs of diaphragm walls is the establishment and removal of the bentonite farm. Diaphragm walling, therefore, tends to be less economic for small areas of wall compared to alternative solutions. There are, however, certain circumstances which will preclude the adoption of alternatives, for example, secant piled walls. These might be factors such as the depth of excavation required and watertightness.

A suitable area of the site should be identified for location of the bentonite farm (or other support fluid mixing and storage area). The bentonite farm will occupy a relatively large proportion of a typical site; Figure 13.2 depicts a typical set-up.

A check should be undertaken to ensure that the bearing capacity of the materials forming the foundations for the dry and wet silos is adequate. It is common for a reinforced concrete slab to be provided to ensure sufficient stability of the bentonite farm components, which may require to be bolted down to withstand wind loading when empty.

13.3.6 Reinforcement cages

Reinforcement cages for diaphragm wall construction can be supplied pre-fabricated or site fixed. Site fixing of cages has certain advantages (if sufficient space is available) since cages can be fabricated to fit the excavated panel widths, typically up to around 7 m. The maximum cage width that can easily be transported by road in the UK is 2.8 m. Multiple cages can be provided within a wide panel, but this may not work where full reinforcement continuity is required within a panel.

Lifting of diaphragm wall reinforcement cages will almost certainly require a tandem lift (see Figure 13.3) to ensure that the cage is not damaged when lifting from the horizontal to the vertical plane. This is classified as a complex lift and requires greater consideration than more conventional lifting operations. Refer to Chapter 20 for further guidance on lifting operations.

Where cage sections are to be spliced, the splice detail should ensure that the reinforcement configuration is as free from bar congestion as possible. This will assist construction of a high-quality finished product. Reinforcement bar congestion is often the primary cause of poor-quality concrete, particularly at the near face of the panel. The splice should ensure that operatives are not required to place their hands within the cage where serious injury could be incurred should the cage sections move relative to each other.

Careful checking of diaphragm wall cages is required, particularly when there are a large number of relatively complex details, for example, box-outs for pull-out bars (such as Kwikastip® or Startabox®), starter couplers, etc. BS EN 1538 (BSI, 2010) specifies tolerances for reinforcing elements (including couplers) both in the plane of and perpendicular to the plane of wall. Failure to address these areas sufficiently can lead to support fluid inclusions remaining within the completed panel.

13.3.7 Concreting

Diaphragm wall panels are concreted in an identical manner to bored piles constructed under support fluid or which have groundwater in the bore. Sectional tremmie pipes are employed which typically have a diameter of between 200 mm and 300 mm. The diameter of tremmie pipe will depend on individual contractors' equipment and the depth of tremmie pipe required (i.e. the depth of panel or barrette to be concreted).

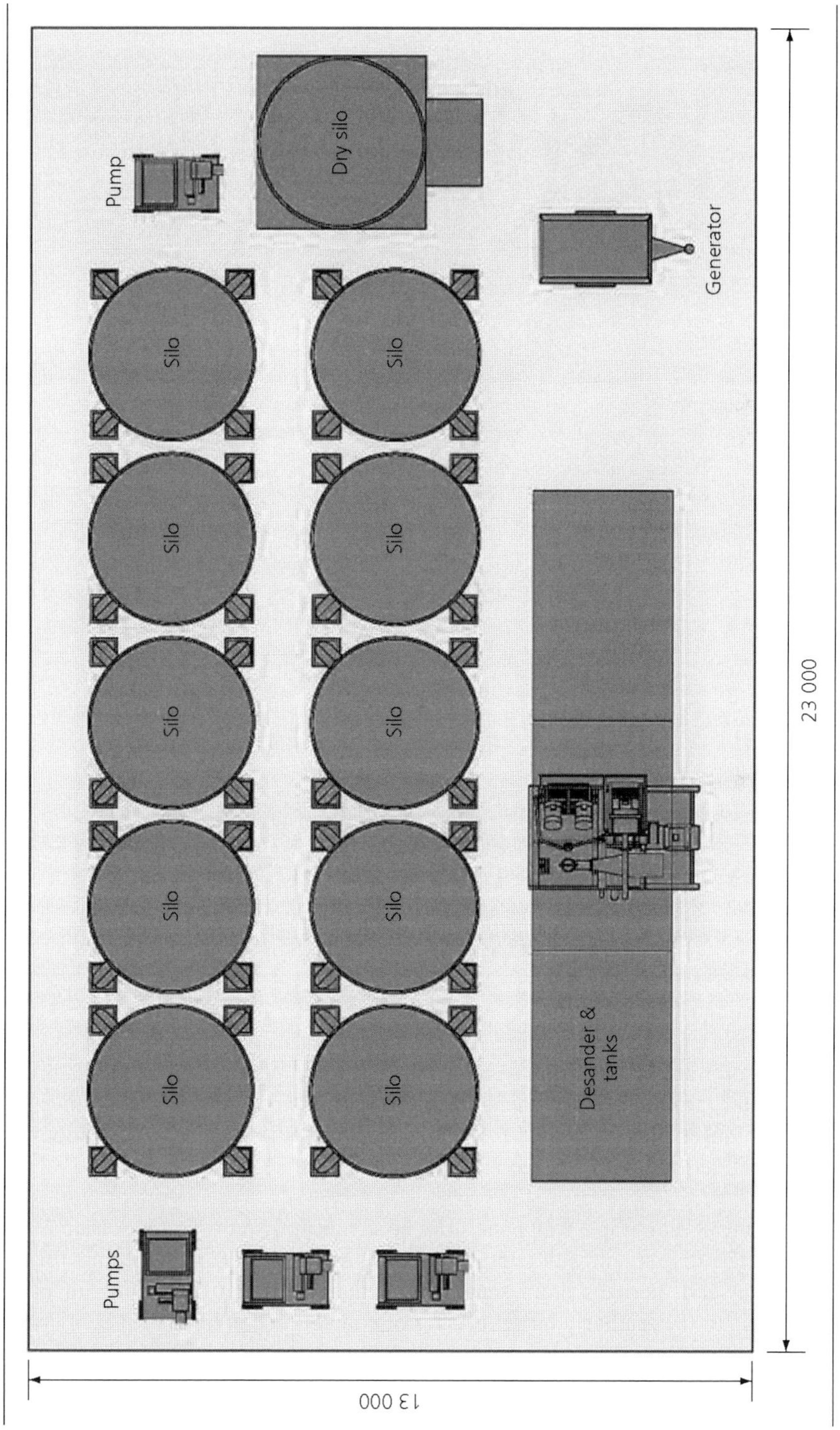

Figure 13.2 Typical diaphragm wall bentonite farm set-up
Courtesy of Cementation Skanska Limited

167

Figure 13.3 Tandem lift of reinforcement cage
Courtesy of Cementation Skanska Limited

The reinforcement cage detailing should fit the dimensions of pipe to be used and the number of tremmie positions required to ensure a high-quality finished product. A short panel (around 2.8–4.5 m length) would typically require a single tremmie location, whereas longer panels (around 6.5–7.5 m length) would require two positions. Corner panels will require particular consideration.

Concreting of diaphragm wall panels can be significantly more complex than for bearing piles. Single diaphragm wall panels may have multiple tremmie locations for concrete placement and, perhaps more significantly, the concreting operation can take many hours due to the relatively large volumes of concrete required to be placed. When very large concrete pours are required, a prudent measure is to ensure that the concrete supplier has a standby batching plant available. To comply with the ICE specifications (2007), tremmie pipes must be maintained at levels to ensure that they have a maximum

Figure 13.4 Rope grab
Courtesy of Cementation Skanska Limited

Figure 13.4 Rope grab
Courtesy of Cementation Skanska Limited

penetration of 6 m and a minimum penetration of 3 m. The tremmie pipe must not be withdrawn from the panel concrete until the concreting operation has been completed. Additionally, sufficient head of concrete within the tremmie pipe must be maintained to ensure that this exceeds the support fluid pressure.

To attain the highest possible quality finished product, it is essential that panel construction is completed in the shortest practicable time without unnecessary delays.

13.3.8 Grabs (rope and hydraulic)

Generally moderately deep diaphragm wall panels (up to around 40–50 m depth) will be excavated using a conventional grab. Grabs can take the form of either traditional rope grabs or, more recently, hydraulic grabs (see Figures 13.4 and 13.5).

Rope grabs are more basic than the more modern hydraulic grabs. They consist of a short body, at the base of which is a clamshell bucket. The grab has one set of ropes

Figure 13.5 Hydraulic grab
Courtesy of Cementation Skanska Limited

to carry the weight of the grab (and spoil when the clamshell bucket is full) and a second set to close the clamshell bucket and cut the panel. The grab is generally supported by a crawler crane. While rope grabs are old technology, they still have a place in modern construction. For example, since a conventional crawler crane is used in conjunction with the rope grab, the system lends itself to low-headroom scenarios where a short jib crawler crane is required. Alternative low-headroom hydraulic systems are commercially available, but these may be significantly more costly. However, as with consideration of all alternative systems, the system to be adopted also needs to be compatible with the site-specific ground and project conditions such as programme requirements, etc.

Hydraulic grabs have a much higher closing force than rope grabs which can improve production rates or enable them to be used to excavate panels in stronger ground. The grab can be supported on a kelly bar or, more recently, a rotator itself supported by a modified crawler crane unit. Rotators are available for 180° and 360° plan movement. The rotator allows a high degree of flexibility of panel orientation, which is particularly

Figure 13.6 Hydromill
Courtesy of Cementation Skanska Limited

Figure 13.6 Hydromill
Courtesy of Cementation Skanska Limited

important on tight sites and at corner panel locations. The use of a rotator in conjunction with steering teeth on the grab clamshell bucket allows the grab to be steered according to ground conditions to maintain the panel verticality within tight specification tolerances. Hydraulic grabs are also fitted with electronic inclinometers which enable the grab operator to see a graphical representation of panel geometry and verticality in real time. The data enables the grab operator to react quickly to maintain panel verticality.

13.3.9 Hydrofraise/hydromill/trenchcutter

For diaphragm walls constructed within relatively strong strata, or for deep diaphragm walls, the use of hydromills becomes necessary (see Figure 13.6).

A hydromill is essentially a reverse circulation trench cutter. This cuts the panel rather than digging it (as is done with grabs). Hydromills can have counter-rotating cutting wheels or cutting chains, depending upon the manufacturer and the ground conditions.

Deeper diaphragm wall panels require a longer cycle time to lower a grab into the panel, take a bite from the base of the panel, be lifted from the panel and deposit the spoil. Reverse circulation hydromills, on the other hand, continuously cut the ground which then goes into suspension within the support slurry. This is circulated from the panel through de-sanding equipment and returned into the panel. The hydromill thereby negates the requirement for the cutting tool to be continuously lowered and lifted from the panel. The use of hydromills is costlier than the use of grabs; however, they will usually be employed where grabs cannot be used to progress panel excavation due to the strength of the ground or where the greater production rates outweigh the greater plant costs.

As stated, the adoption of particular plant or techniques needs to be compatible with the ground conditions. The use of hydromills within cohesive materials can be problematic in clays with a relatively high plasticity, such as London Clay. The mills can become blocked by the clay and their efficiency dramatically reduced. One solution would be to employ a hydraulic grab to excavate the upper section of a panel (e.g. to the base of London Clay) and then employ a hydromill to continue panel excavation to final depth.

As with hydraulic grabs, hydromills are fitted with electronic instrumentation to enable the panel excavation to be undertaken to achieve the required tolerances.

13.3.10 Panel joints (stop ends)
Stop ends are used to perform two principal functions: to temporarily house a water bar and to provide a profiled end to the diaphragm wall panels to facilitate shear transfer between adjacent panels.

Stop ends most often used in modern practice take the form of either re-usable 'peel off' profiled steel plate (e.g. CWS (Continuous Water Stop) stop ends; see Figure 13.7) or precast concrete profiles.

When using a hydromill it may be possible to grind a slotted profile into the end(s) of the adjacent panel(s) to provide both a shear key and a significantly more tortuous path for groundwater.

If water ingress is not critical, then stop ends may be entirely omitted.

13.4.   Design
13.4.1   Scope
This section on design is not intended to provide full guidance on how to design embedded retaining walls. This subject is covered in detail within the various codes of practice and best practice guides referenced listed at the end of this chapter and the next. In particular, the reader is referred to CIRIA Report C580 (2003), BS 8002 (BSI, 1994) and BS EN 1997-1 (2004).

The intention for this section is to provide commentary on those aspects specific to the design of diaphragm walls.

13.4.2   Geotechnical model
Prior to undertaking any stability analyses for embedded retaining wall design, it is

imperative that a representative ground model can be produced. As a general rule of thumb, the site investigation should ideally extend to a depth of around 50% greater than the deepest part of the temporary works structure.

The appropriateness of specific investigation techniques should be assessed in the light of guidance given by geotechnical design codes of practice. Reference should be made to BS EN 1997-1 (2004) for the derivation of geotechnical data for site characterisation and design purposes.

The site investigation should also provide the designer with other relevant information which may have an impact upon the design, including

- adjacent structures, magnitude and level of permanent and variable surcharge loading
- adjacent structures, any limitations on ground-borne vibrations which may influence the construction technique(s) to be adopted

- adjacent highways, magnitude of variable surcharge loading
- information on adjacent services, for example, potential for water main rupture, magnitude of tolerable ground-borne vibrations, etc.
- buried infrastructure and impact of ground movements (e.g. London Underground Ltd (LUL) assets).

During construction of the embedded retaining wall, any significant variation in ground/groundwater conditions should be communicated to the design team without delay. It is imperative that the contracting organisation has a sufficient understanding of the design to decide what constitutes a significant variation. The wall designer should provide a wall manual in accordance with the ICE specifications (2007). Depending upon the design route adopted for the contract, the intention of the ICE specifications (2007) is to provide sufficient information to facilitate communication of pertinent design and construction information between parties.

13.4.3 Embedded retaining wall design

Most embedded retaining wall design in current practice is undertaken adopting the Factor on Strength method described in BS 8002 (1994) and BS EN 1997-1 (2004). In certain circumstances practitioners may prefer to adopt alternative design methods, for example, Potts and Burland's (1983) method based on specific experience of embedded retaining wall design in stiff clays, where this is not precluded by the project specification.

The design of embedded retaining walls will often involve both undrained (total stress) and drained (effective stress) design. This of course will depend upon the geological materials present at the particular site under consideration. Where the retaining wall is required to provide ground support/groundwater exclusion for a longer time than undrained behaviour can be assumed, effective stress analysis will be necessary.

Most practitioners adopt a limit state design approach when designing embedded retaining walls. The limit states considered are ultimate limit state (ULS) and serviceability limit state (SLS). ULS involves consideration of the safety of people and safety of the structure itself, for example, instability of the structure, failure by rupture of the structure or any part of it or excessive deformation of the structure such that adjacent structures reach their ultimate limit state. SLS describes the consideration of conditions relating to the performance of the structure under normal operating conditions, for example, deformation of the structure or deformation of the ground supported by the structure.

Two sets of analysis calculations are generally performed when considering the ULS design of embedded retaining walls. The first ULS analysis assesses the required wall toe depth to maintain stability for the relevant earth pressures, applied loads and specified factors of safety (partial factors on resistances, actions, soil mobilisation, etc.). The second set of calculations determines the reinforcement requirements based upon the ULS bending moments and shear forces derived from the first analysis.

Project specifications (as well as design codes/guidance documents) usually require the design of the retaining wall to allow for unplanned excavation, usually 10% of the retained height up to a maximum of 0.5 m. While this can be considered to be best practice in most circumstances, it may be possible to make some economies to the design by gaining the agreement of all relevant parties that this design requirement be removed; sufficient control measures must be implemented during the bulk excavation operations and this design constraint must be clearly communicated to all parties. Most design analyses are generally undertaken using some form of soil–structure interaction (SSI) analysis. SSI analyses can be further divided into subgrade reaction/pseudo finite element methods and finite element/finite difference methods. When considering SLS calculations, these preclude the use of limit equilibrium methods and will require some form of SSI to be undertaken.

The selection of analysis method should be compatible with the problem and the available design input information. There is clearly little point opting for the more complex SSI analysis method where there is little accurate information on design soil parameters. Modern complex analyses can appear deceptively easy to run and can lull the uninitiated into a false sense of security regarding the appropriateness of their analyses.

The relative size of the embedded retaining wall element is generally governed by the magnitude of the ULS bending moment which it is required to resist. SLS considerations are often involved in determining the temporary support requirements (e.g. propping/waling beam stiffnesses and locations) rather than in consideration of the wall element size.

Fernie and Suckling (1996) report that embedded retaining walls in stiff UK soils will generally exhibit excavation-induced lateral movements of around 0.15% of the retained height. The relationship with wall stiffness is reported as being more relevant to cantilever and single-propped systems than for multiple-propped embedded retaining walls.

Bolton *et al.* (2010) further postulated that wall displacements are unavoidable regardless of the embedded retaining wall element constructed (within the bounds of conventional element sizes and stiffnesses). The wall displacements are controlled to a much greater degree by the wall support system adopted (temporary propping and bottom-up construction versus top-down construction using permanent floor slabs, and even the construction of propping/lateral support elements by pre-excavation techniques).

13.4.4   Vertical capacity of walls

As described in Section 13.2 of this chapter, embedded retaining walls can also be required to carry vertical loads. The embedded retaining wall can be constructed to a deeper toe than required for wall stability alone. Any additional depth of wall can be constructed from plain concrete, i.e. constructed unreinforced, subject to the net vertical loading being compressive in nature. Clearly the additional depth would need to be suitably reinforced to carry any tensile loads (e.g. hydrostatic uplift forces). Due to the high stiffness of diaphragm walls, both active and passive faces below dredge level will contribute to the vertical capacity of the wall (note this may not be possible with significantly more flexible walls such as sheet piles).

Where temporary support to the diaphragm wall is provided through ground anchorages, the vertical stability of the wall due to the increased vertical loading on the wall from the anchorages should be checked. In most cases, the increased vertical load will not require any increase in wall embedment, but the design must demonstrate sufficient vertical capacity of the wall.

13.4.5 Reinforcement design

Reinforcement requirements should be determined by adopting analysis methods compatible with the stability analysis, for example, EC2 for EC7 geotechnical design.

Depending on the nature of the diaphragm wall, there may be an opportunity to refine the reinforcement design according to the distribution of bending moment and shear force magnitude with depth. Bars can potentially be curtailed or bar sizes changed across splice zones to provide the most economic reinforcement configuration.

The detailed design of diaphragm wall reinforcement cages must consider the potential impact of cage congestion. BS EN 1538 (2010) requires that the horizontal clear space between single vertical bars or groups of vertical bars parallel to the face of the panel should be at least 100 mm. For horizontal shear reinforcement, BS EN 1538 recommends a minimum vertical spacing of 200 mm.

The detailed design of the reinforcement cages should also consider how the cages are to be fabricated. For example, such detailed design should consider if closed or open shear links will facilitate easier (and potentially safer) fabrication. While it may seem that such considerations are going to the extremes of detail, they can have a significant impact on the overall quality of the wall, particularly where the reinforcement cages have a large number of complex details (coupled box outs, pull-out starter bars, etc.).

13.4.6 Watertightness and wall toe level for groundwater cut-off

The client's expectations with regard to water tightness must be suitably managed throughout the design and procurement process. If the wall is to remain as a permanent structure, a useful reference is the ICE document *Reducing the Risk of Leaking Substructures* (2009) for risk-based guidance on basement waterproofing.

Where water-bearing strata are retained by the embedded retaining wall, it is often a requirement to take the toe of the retaining wall to a depth where it will provide a vertical cut-off by effectively sealing in to a low permeability strata. This relies on the presence of such a suitable stratum within a sensible depth of the toe level, which is designed for wall stability.

Where a low permeability stratum is not present within a depth considered to be economically or practically viable, the required toe level of the wall can be assessed by undertaking a flow net analysis in conjunction with an assessment of flow rates into the excavation which are considered to be tolerable. A sensitivity analysis should be undertaken to assess the likely envelope of inflow rates based on potential permeability variations (both vertical and horizontal) which in turn depend upon the degree of anisotropy of the soil. Greater guidance on ground water control is given in Chapter 6.

13.4.7 Observation method

Where the embedded retaining wall is governed by temporary works considerations, it may be appropriate to adopt a risk-based design approach (i.e. the observational approach) to realise savings to the project. It is imperative that the project is set up from a very early stage to accommodate all the requirements such an approach requires if it is to be successfully executed. The adoption of the observational approach requires sufficient instrumentation to be in place which is actively monitored, together with an agreed set of trigger/action levels and a comprehensive suite of contingency and emergency plans.

Regardless of whether the observational method is to be adopted, sufficient appropriate instrumentation should be deployed and monitoring undertaken to ensure that design assumptions and construction details can be validated and risk managed appropriately. Further discussion relating to instrumentation can be found within Chapter 14, Section 14.4.3.

Often savings through adoption of the observational approach arise from a reduced construction programme through revised propping requirements and excavation sequencing.

Reference should be made to CIRIA Report 185 (1999) for comprehensive guidance on the subject of the observational approach.

REFERENCES

Bolton M, Lam SY and Vardanega PJ (2010) Predicting and controlling ground movements around deep excavations. In Mair RJ and Taylor RN (eds) *Geotechnical Aspects of Underground Construction in Soft Ground*. Balkema, Rotterdam.

BSI (1994) BS 8002: Code of practice for earth-retaining structures. BSI, London.

BSI (2004) BS EN 1997-1: Eurocode 7: Geotechnical Design: Part 1 General Rules. BSI, London.

BSI (2010) BS EN 1538: Execution of special geotechnical works – Diaphragm walls. BSI, London.

CIRIA (Construction Industry Research & Information Association) (1999) The observational method in ground engineering: principles and applications. Report 185. CIRIA, London.

CIRIA (2003) Embedded retaining walls – guidance for economic design. Report C580. CIRIA, London.

Fernie R and Suckling T (1996) Simplified approach for estimating lateral wall movement of embedded walls in UK ground. In Mair RJ and Taylor RN (eds) *Geotechnical Aspects of Underground Construction in Soft Ground*. Balkema, Rotterdam.

Fernie R, Shaw SM, Dickson RA *et al.* (2001) Movement and deep basement provision at Knightsbridge Crown Court, Harrods, London. Conference on response of buildings to excavation induced ground movements, CIRIA, SP199, July 2001.

Huder H (1972) Stability of bentonite slurry trenches with some experience in Swiss practice. *Proceedings of 5th European Conference on Soil Mechanics and Foundation Engineering*, Madrid, 517–522.

ICE (Institution of Civil Engineers) (2007) *ICE Specification for Piling and Embedded Retaining Walls*, 2nd edition. Thomas Telford, London.

ICE R&D (Institution of Civil Engineers Research & Development Enabling Fund) (2009) *Reducing the Risk of Leaking Substructure: A Clients' Guide*. ICE, London.

Potts DM and Burland JB (1983) *A parametric study of the stability of embedded earth retaining structures*, Transport and Road Research Laboratory, Supplementary Report 813.

FURTHER READING

BSI (1986) BS 8004: Code of practice for foundations. BSI, London.

BSI (1997) BS 8110-1: Structural use of concrete – Part 1: Code of practice for design and construction. BSI, London.

BSI (2004) BS EN 1992-1-1: Eurocode 2: Design of concrete structures. Part 1-1 General rules and rules for buildings. BSI, London.

BSI (2009) BS 8102: Code of practice for protection of below ground structures against water from the ground. BSI, London.

CIRIA (Construction Industry Research & Information Association) (1999) Temporary propping of deep excavations – guidance on design. Report C517. CIRIA, London.

CIRIA (2000) Prop loads in large braced excavations. Project Report 77. CIRIA, London.

Puller MJ (1994) The watertightness of structural diaphragm walls. *Proceedings of Institution of Civil Engineers* **107**: 47–57.

Puller MJ (2003) *Deep Excavations: A Practical Manual*, 2nd edition. Thomas Telford Publishing, London.

Useful web addresses

Federation of Piling Specialists: www.fps.org.uk

European Federation of Foundation Contractors: www.effc.org

Deep Foundations Institute: www.dfi.org

Temporary Works: Principles of Design and Construction
ISBN 978-0-7277-4177-6

ICE Publishing: All rights reserved
http://dx.doi.org/10.1680/twpdc.41776.179

Chapter 14
Contiguous and secant piled walls

Chris Robinson Technical Manager, Cementation Skanska Limited
Andrew Bell Chief Engineer, Cementation Skanska Limited

Contiguous and secant piled walls can be used to form embedded retaining walls, for example, to construct tanks, shafts, tunnel portals, road/rail cuttings, basement excavations, cut and cover tunnels and other forms of underground structures. They are commonly adopted where alternative methods cannot be successfully implemented because of the nature of the ground or performance requirements. In common with diaphragm walls, the economics of contiguous and secant piled walls become increasingly attractive when they form part of the permanent works. This chapter includes a description of common uses of contiguous and secant walls and their method of construction (including aspects of additional temporary works required to facilitate construction), a summary of typical construction details which can aid construction of a high-quality finished product and a description of common design approaches and design considerations.

14.1. Introduction

Contiguous and secant piled walls are two common forms of embedded retaining walls. The most significant difference between these two forms of retaining wall is that contiguous piles are designed to be totally independent reinforced elements with, typically, 150 mm between adjacent pile elements at commencing level, whereas secant piles are designed to form an interlocking wall. Secant piles can therefore retain both ground and groundwater (subject to construction tolerances as discussed in Section 14.3).

14.1.1 Contiguous pile wall

Contiguous piled walls are suitable where the groundwater table is below excavation level since groundwater is free to flow through the interstices between pile elements. Permanent works applications for contiguous piled walls therefore require an additional reinforced concrete lining to secure exposed soil and resist long-term groundwater pressures. Figure 14.1 depicts a typical contiguous piled wall.

14.1.2 Secant pile wall: hard/soft or hard/firm

Where short-term water retention is required, this system offers the most cost-effective and rapid solution and consists of interlocking bored piles. Female (or primary) piles are constructed first using a 'soft' cement-bentonite mix (commonly $1 N/mm^2$) or 'firm' concrete (commonly $10 N/mm^2$). Male (or secondary) piles, formed in structural reinforced concrete, are then installed between (and cutting into) the female piles with a typical interlock of 150–250 mm. These walls may need a reinforced concrete lining

Figure 14.1 Contiguous piled wall
Courtesy of Cementation Skanska Limited

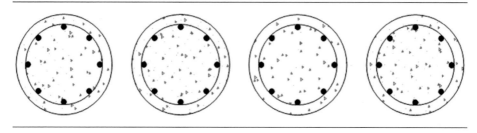

Figure 14.2 Hard/soft or hard/firm secant piled wall
Courtesy of Cementation Skanska Limited

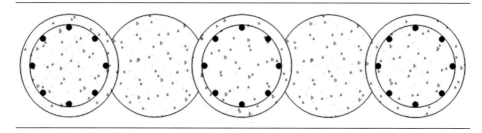

for permanent works applications, depending on the particular watertightness requirements of the project. An illustration of a typical hard/soft or hard/firm secant piled wall is provided in Figure 14.2.

14.1.3   Secant wall: hard/hard

Hard/hard wall construction is very similar to a hard/firm wall except that the primary piles are constructed in higher-strength concrete and may be reinforced by reinforcement cages or steel beam/column sections. Heavy-duty rotary piling rigs, using tools fitted with specially designed cutting heads, are necessary to cut the secondary piles. Since structural concrete is used throughout, there may be no need to provide a lining wall. The end product provides a fully concreted face and can be an effective alternative to diaphragm wall construction. Figure 14.3 depicts a typical hard/hard secant piled wall.

Figure 14.3 Hard/hard secant piled wall
Courtesy of Cementation Skanska Limited

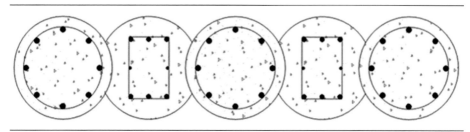

14.2. Applications

Contiguous and secant piled walls can be adopted to provide solutions to a variety of constructed situations. They tend to be adopted where the general site conditions, depth of excavation, ground conditions or watertightnesss requirements (note: secant piled walls only) preclude the adoption of alternative (potentially cheaper) methods, for example, construction in open-cut excavations, king post walls or sheet piling (see Chapter 11).

In addition to providing ground support (and a groundwater exclusion function in the case of secant piling), contiguous and secant piled walls can also be utilised to carry vertical loads (temporary and/or permanent vertical loads). Where the magnitude of vertical loading exceeds the available wall capacity (based on an embedment length required to maintain wall stability), the wall piles can be constructed to a greater depth than required by consideration of wall stability alone in order to satisfy design criteria relating to factors of safety. This additional depth of pile can be constructed from plain unreinforced concrete, subject to the superstructure loading being compressive in nature. The additional depth of excavation would clearly need to be suitably reinforced to carry any tensile loads (e.g. hydrostatic uplift forces). When designing embedded retaining walls to withstand applied vertical loads, it is usual to consider only that part of the wall below the deepest excavation level.

Where particularly onerous ground conditions are present, for example, very loose fine sands, a secant piled retaining wall may represent the preferred solution even if groundwater is not present above excavation level. The nature of such ground may pose an unacceptable risk of ground loss through insufficient arching capability of the ground, which may in turn pose a risk to the stability and serviceability of adjacent structures, services or ground to be supported.

14.3. Construction methods and plant

14.3.1 General considerations

Most forms of replacement piling can be employed to construct contiguous and secant walls. The plant employed will have certain constraints or limitations to the physical dimensions of piles which can be constructed. As discussed in Chapter 13 on diaphragm walls, the construction methods and plant employed needs to be determined through consideration of each individual project's particular characteristics. This will include consideration of aspects such as site-specific ground conditions, length of wall piles to be constructed, watertightness requirements, access restrictions, headroom restriction, any working time restrictions and party wall issues.

The drawing sequence presented in Figures 14.4 and 14.5 shows the typical sequence of site operations for contiguous pile wall and secant pile wall construction, respectively. Pile construction needs to be sequenced to ensure that construction of any pile does not adversely affect any previously constructed piles. For secant walls, the sequence needs also to take account of the strength gain of the female pile concrete (female pile concrete can potentially crack when male piles are cut into them if the concrete is too strong, which may have a significant impact on the wall watertightness).

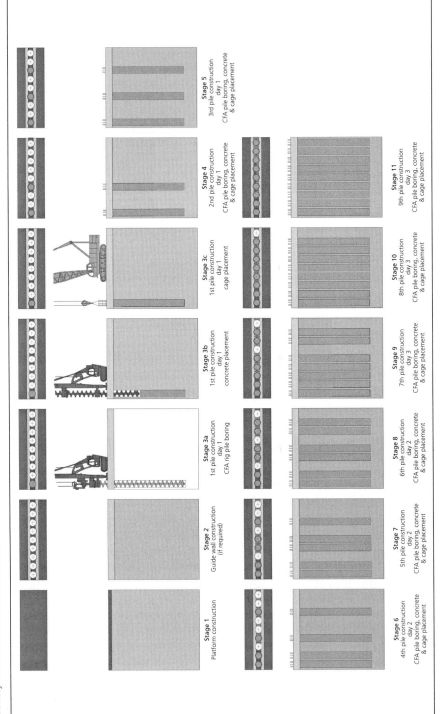

Figure 14.4 Contiguous piled wall and indicative sequence of construction
Courtesy of Cementation Skanska Limited

Stage 1
Platform construction

Stage 2
Guide wall construction
(if required)

Stage 3a
1st pile construction
day 1
CFA rig pile boring

Stage 3b
1st pile construction
day 1
concrete placement

Stage 3c
1st pile construction
day 1
cage placement

Stage 4
2nd pile construction
day 1
CFA pile boring, concrete
& cage placement

Stage 5
3rd pile construction
day 1
CFA pile boring, concrete
& cage placement

Stage 6
4th pile construction
day 2
CFA pile boring, concrete
& cage placement

Stage 7
5th pile construction
day 2
CFA pile boring, concrete
& cage placement

Stage 8
6th pile construction
day 2
CFA pile boring, concrete
& cage placement

Stage 9
7th pile construction
day 3
CFA pile boring, concrete
& cage placement

Stage 10
8th pile construction
day 3
CFA pile boring, concrete
& cage placement

Stage 11
9th pile construction
day 3
CFA pile boring, concrete
& cage placement

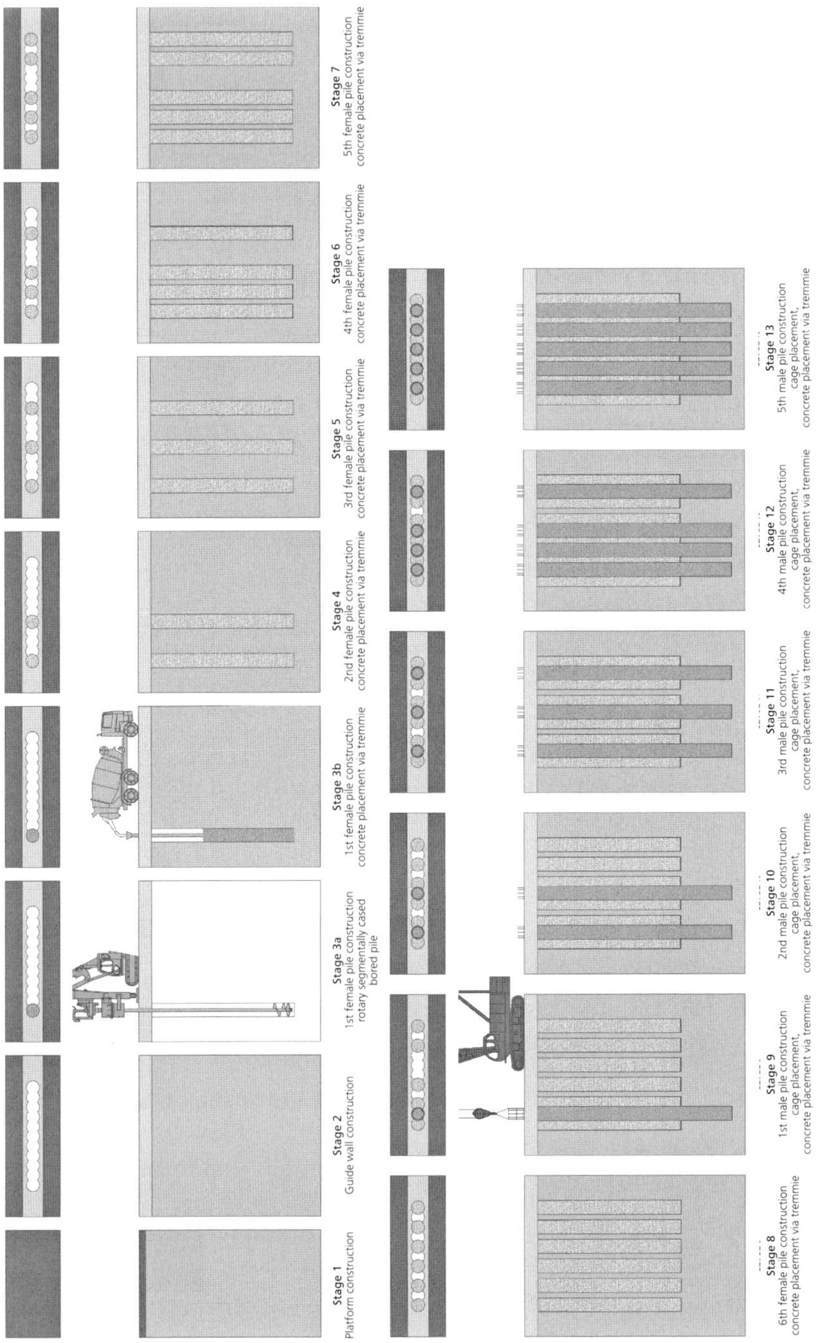

Figure 14.5 Secant piled wall and indicative sequence of construction
Courtesy of Cementation Skanska Limited

As well as being a temporary works solution in their own right, both contiguous and secant pile wall construction can require some considerable elements of additional temporary works for their successful execution. As described in Chapter 13 on diaphragm walls, these include aspects such as guide walls, temporary anchorages and/or temporary props, working platforms for tracked plant (Chapters 5 and 7), consideration of slope stability (Chapter 10), temporary screening to protect public and personnel, protection of water courses and protection of adjacent services.

Precautionary measures may be adopted such as using long temporary casings, limiting the number of piles constructed along sensitive elevations within one shift or underpinning of particularly sensitive adjacent structures.

14.3.2 Site preparation
Many sites require demolition works to be undertaken in advance of wall construction operations; this will often entail excavation or grubbing out of existing foundations. Where this occurs along the line of the wall it is good practice to ensure the backfill to these areas is selected not only to give adequate support to tracked plant, but also to mitigate against high overbreak occurring and adversely affecting the finished surface of the piled wall. This may require trimming back if the overbreak is in excess of the specification limits. Suitable backfill materials often used are stiff clays or clay-bound hogging. These materials, properly placed and compacted, will give a relatively smooth high-quality finish to the wall over the backfill depth and can aid wall verticality.

14.3.3 Working platforms
As with any other site where tracked plant (predominantly piling rigs and cranes) is to be employed, a suitable working platform should be provided to ensure that an adequate factor of safety against platform failure is maintained under the range of loading which will be applied by the plant operating on it. Refer to Chapter 5 for full details of working platform design.

14.3.4 Guide walls
Guide wall construction will usually follow on from construction of the working platform, although this is not always the case. It is usual for guide walls to be constructed in advance of secant piled wall construction to enable greater dimensional control at the commencing level to be achieved. Generally a maximum tolerance of ±25 mm at commencement level can be achieved through the use of a guide wall.

When constructing contiguous piled walls, guide walls tend to be used less often since the verticality tolerance is usually less critical (contiguous piled walls are not designed for groundwater exclusion and therefore do not have any watertightness performance criteria to satisfy). Without a guide wall, a tolerance limit of ±75 mm is typically specified.

Unlike contiguous piled wall construction, secant pile wall construction will almost invariably require a scalloped guide wall to be constructed in advance of piling operations. The very nature of secant piled walls requires the piles to interlock, usually for watertightness.

14.3.5 Pile construction techniques

Different pile construction techniques will have different limits to attainable verticality. Most rotary piling techniques will typically have a verticality limit of 1:75. Stiff double-walled continuous flight auger (CFA) strings may be able to achieve verticality limits of the order 1:100 to 1:150, whereas cased CFA and large diameter segmentally cased piled wall may be able to achieve pile verticality of the order 1:200. Specific guidance should be sought from specialist contractors on a case-by-case basis.

A large range of piling techniques can be adopted for construction of contiguous and secant walls, although practical considerations may limit the use of some of these for constructing interlocking secant walls.

A non-exhaustive list of applicable piling techniques includes: continuous flight auger (CFA); cased CFA; segmental flight auger (SFA); large-diameter rotary bored piling with conventional slip casings; large-diameter rotary bore piling with segmental casing; mini piled case/auger; and drilled pile systems (e.g. Symmetrix).

Some of the above piling techniques (e.g. rotary bore piling/case and auger piling, etc.) can be employed adopting a short length of temporary casing (although care needs to be taken when assessing pile spacing for cased/uncased diameters) where the ground is self-supporting. Others may require full-length casing in unstable ground or the use of a bore support fluid, while CFA/SFA provide full bore support without the need for temporary casings or support fluid.

14.3.6 Reinforcement cages

Reinforcement cages for wall piles are typically fabricated using at least 6 bar cages. There are exceptions to this general rule, but the design must take account of the potential for unfavourable cage orientation within the pile bore.

The number of longitudinal reinforcing bars forming the pile cage needs to be compatible with the pile diameter and minimum reinforcement requirements. In most instances, the reinforcement requirements of wall piles will satisfy minimum reinforcement requirements without explicit consideration.

Female piles to secant piled walls are not normally reinforced. However, when designing the wall as a hard/hard wall, the female pile will be constructed from a structural concrete mix (with a specified characteristic strength) and will be suitably detailed to facilitate subsequent male pile construction. The requirement for the male piles to cut into the female pile clearly imposes constraints on the amount of reinforcement that can be accommodated within the female pile. Notwithstanding this limitation, reinforcement of the female pile can provide the additional wall capacity (in terms of bending resistance), which may otherwise require larger-diameter male piles or alternative construction methods to be adopted.

It is possible to vary the pile reinforcement within fabricated cages to the structural requirements at different levels within the pile. Bars can potentially be curtailed or changes to bar sizes made across cage splice zones. It should be noted that it is not generally possible to economise pile cages to the same degree as within diaphragm wall cages; this is partly due to the requirements to consider unfavourable cage orientation within the pile bore and the design of the pile as a column element.

Where cage lengths are to be spliced, the splice detail should be carefully detailed to limit bar congestion. This will assist in maintaining a high-quality finished product. Reinforcement bar congestion is often the primary cause of poor-quality concrete at the exposed face of the pile. As with detailing of reinforcement cages for diaphragm wall panels, the cage splices should be detailed to ensure that operatives are not required to place their hands within the cage where serious injury could be incurred should the cage sections move relative to each other.

It may be possible to introduce couplers and box-outs within pile reinforcement cages. However, it is the authors' experience that a high degree of redundancy (in terms of the number of couplers fabricated into the reinforcement cage) is usually required to ensure that sufficient couplers can be located when the box-out is exposed. Pile reinforcement cages have a tendency to twist within the pile bore. This is particularly the case where pile cages are plunged within wet concrete, but can also occur where cages are hung or suspended within the empty pile bore with concrete subsequently being placed via tremmie pipe. Another consideration of pile box-out design is to ensure that there is sufficient space for concrete to flow between all the reinforcing elements and to ensure that the box-out (typically constructed with polystyrene or Styrofoam to facilitate exposure of the couplers) does not cause buoyancy instability of the pile cage.

14.3.7 Concreting
As described in Section 14.3.5, a variety of piling techniques can be adopted. Where piles are constructed adopting CFA or SFA techniques, concrete will be introduced from the toe of the pile and brought up to piling platform level. Reinforcement cages are installed following the concreting operation.

For open bore piling techniques (e.g. large-diameter rotary bored piling, cased and auger piling, etc.), concreting of the pile (or grouting for small diameter piles) will usually be undertaken following installation of the reinforcement cage. For open bore techniques, sectional tremmie pipes are generally employed which typically have a diameter of between 200 mm and 300 mm. The diameter of tremmie pipe will depend on individual contractors' equipment and the depth of tremmie pipe. Consideration of the diameter of reinforcing cage is also important in order to ensure the tremmie pipe can easily be inserted and removed without causing damage to, or snagging on, the cage.

14.4. Design
14.4.1 Scope
This section on design is not intended to provide full guidance on how to design embedded retaining walls. This subject is covered in detail within the various codes of

practice and best practice guidance listed at the end of this chapter. In particular, the reader is referred to CIRIA Report C580 (2003), BS 8002 (1994) and BS EN 1997-1 (2004).

The intention for this section is to provide commentary on specific design aspects of contiguous and secant piled walls. High-level guidance on the most relevant aspects to the design of embedded retaining wall is provided in Chapter 13, Section 13.4.3.

14.4.2   Temporary support for lateral wall stability

Contiguous and secant walls may be designed as cantilever walls. This will depend upon the depth of excavation, the depth to which the wall piles can be economically installed, the prevailing ground conditions and the magnitude of tolerable wall displacement and associated ground movement.

Where the various factors are unfavourable, some form of temporary support will be required. This may take the form of temporary berms (generally to facilitate installation of another temporary support measure), temporary props or temporary ground anchorages. Each of these measures will require suitable design. Should temporary ground anchorages be adopted, this may require a wayleave if the anchorages are to be installed beyond the site boundary. The wall will also require a design check to be undertaken to ensure that vertical stability is maintained, since the anchorages will impart a downward vertical load onto the embedded retaining wall.

Temporary ground anchorages and temporary props will generally require a waling beam to span along the wall to distribute the load between wall and anchors/props. Often an in situ capping beam will be constructed which can be used in lieu of a waling beam. Waling beams for ground anchors can be more complex, particularly if they are fabricated from steel. A twin parallel flange channel arrangement is often adopted which allows the anchorage to pass between the two channel sections at the required angle of declination (often 30–45° below horizontal). An alternative solution for ground anchorages is to construct an in situ head block detail (see Figure 14.6) which spans adjacent reinforced piles.

14.4.3   Instrumentation

Where wall deflections are a critical element of the design (most particularly where the observation method is being employed), inclinometer reservation tubes can be installed within the reinforced piles. A suitably sized thin-walled steel tube (with a sealed end) is attached to the reinforcement cage (in sections with threaded couplings if spliced cages are required). The reservation tube facilitates subsequent installation (grouting in) of inclinometer tubes, which generally take the form of plastic ducts with orthogonal guides for the inclinometer torpedo. It is usual for the inclinometer duct installation to be undertaken outside the piling contract.

Alternative methods of monitoring wall deflections are available such as cast-in-place inclinometers; these are more limiting by their very nature, however, allowing monitoring of deflections only at the levels the instruments are installed (compared to a full

Figure 14.6 In situ anchor head block
Courtesy of Cementation Skanska Limited

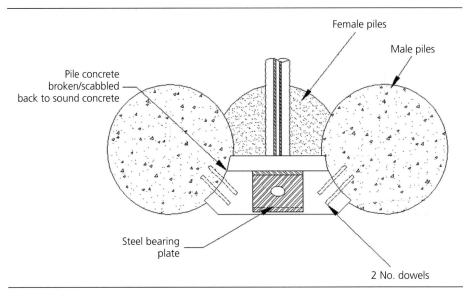

deflection profile for conventional inclinometer instruments). Cast-in-place inclinometers are particularly useful in situations where access is difficult or impossible.

Other forms of instrumentation can be installed within wall piles, generally fixed to reinforcement cages (e.g. vibrating wire strain gauges or fibre-optic strain gauges to monitor the state of stress within wall piles). Again this is most commonly associated with the observational method, for example, when assessing whether additional temporary support measures may be omitted. For full details on the observational method, refer to CIRIA Report 185 (1999).

14.4.4 Reinforcement design
Reinforcement requirements should be determined adopting analysis methods compatible with the stability analysis, for example, EC2 for EC7 geotechnical design.

Care needs to be taken to ensure that the reinforcement design is compatible with the method of pile construction proposed. For example, plunging cages within CFA/SFA piles has practical limitations on the depth attainable for a given cage weight and rigidity. A maximum practical reinforcement cage plunge depth of around 15 m is often adopted. Although it is possible to adequately reinforce these pile types to deeper levels, specific guidance from specialist piling contractors should be sought.

There may be opportunity to refine the reinforcement design according to the distribution of bending moment and shear force magnitude with depth. Bars can potentially be curtailed or bar sizes changed across splice zones to provide the most economic configuration.

When designing reinforcement cages, the recommendations of BS EN 1536 (2010) regarding bar spacing should be applied to avoid cage congestion and the potentially negative effect on construction quality.

The reinforcement cage design should take into account any requirements for handling/ lifting the cages to ensure that they are sufficiently robust. This may require the inclusion of suitable lifting bands, etc. Where cages are required to be spliced, sufficient attention to detail should be given to the method used to form the splice such that operatives are not required to put their hands within the cage during the splicing operation.

14.4.5 Watertightness and wall toe level for groundwater cut-off (secant walls only)

Secant walls must be designed to ensure they maintain interlock to the required level. It should be noted that whatever degree of interlock is designed for, secant walls cannot be guaranteed to provide a watertightness greater than BS 8102 (2009) Grade 1.

While it is usual to maintain male/female pile interlock to below dredge level, there may be opportunity in certain circumstances to found the female piles above dredge level if a suitable low-permeability stratum is present. It is important to clearly communicate any risks that may be present in such an arrangement, and have suitable contractual arrangement in place covering risks associated with watertightness and the costs of any potential remedial works.

Where water-bearing strata are retained by the secant wall, it is often a requirement to take the toe of the retaining wall to a depth where it will provide a vertical cut-off by effectively sealing in to a low-permeability stratum. This relies on the presence of such a suitable stratum within a sensible depth of the toe level which is designed for wall stability. Additionally, a check should be undertaken to ascertain the level to which male/female pile interlock can be maintained.

Where a low-permeability stratum is not present within a depth considered to be economically or practically viable, the required toe level of the secant wall can be assessed from undertaking a flow net analysis in conjunction with an assessment of flow rates into the excavation which are considered to be tolerable. A sensitivity analysis should be undertaken to assess the likely envelope of inflow rates based on potential permeability variations (both vertical and horizontal) which in turn will depend upon the degree of anisotropy of the soil. Guidance on ground water control is given in Chapter 6.

14.4.6 Vertical capacity of walls

Embedded retaining walls can also be required to carry vertical loads. The embedded retaining wall can be constructed to a deeper toe than required for wall stability alone. Any additional depth of wall can be constructed from plain concrete, i.e. constructed unreinforced, subject to the net vertical loading being compressive in nature. Clearly the additional depth would need to be suitably reinforced to carry any tensile loads (e.g. hydrostatic uplift forces). When designing embedded retaining walls to withstand vertical loads, it is usual to consider only that part of the wall below the deepest excavation level (i.e. the fully embedded length of the wall).

Where temporary lateral support to the wall is provided through ground anchorages, the vertical stability of the wall should be checked due to the increased vertical loading on the wall from the anchorages.

14.4.7 Other aspects

CIRIA Report C580 (2003) recommends that embedded retaining wall design makes an allowance for unplanned excavation of 10% of the design retained height up to 0.5 m, although this requirement may be reduced or omitted entirely subject to the agreement of all interested parties and the implementation of sufficient control measures to ensure the design constraints are fully realised.

Where cohesive materials are present at dredge level, consideration should be given to the potential for these materials to degrade and soften, usually just within the top 1 m, thus potentially adversely affecting the passive resistance afforded to the retaining wall.

Design surcharge load (generally a minimum surcharge of $10\,kN/m^2$) should be allowed to act on the active side of the retaining wall.

As well as considering the required wall toe level to maintain lateral and vertical stability, certain ground conditions may require the wall toe to be taken deeper by consideration of more global factors. One such scenario is where an embedded retaining wall is to be constructed within deep soft cohesive deposits. The potential for basal failure of the excavation, whereby the soft cohesive materials affecting flow around the toe of the wall should be assessed in such situation. Piping failure may need to be avoided and potential slip planes may need to be intercepted (see Chapter 10).

REFERENCES

BSI (1994) BS 8002: Code of practice for earth-retaining structures. BSI, London.
BSI (2004) BS EN 1997-1: Eurocode 7: Geotechnical Design. Part 1 General Rules. BSI, London.
BSI (2009) BS 8102: 2009 Code of practice for protection of below ground structures against water from the ground. BSI, London.
BSI (2010) BS EN 1536: Execution of special geotechnical works – Bored piles. BSI, London.
CIRIA (Construction Industry Research & Information Association) (1999) The observational method in ground engineering: principles and applications. CIRIA Report 185. CIRIA, London.
CIRIA (2003) Embedded retaining walls – guidance for economic design. CIRIA Report C580. CIRIA. London.

FURTHER READING

BSI (1986) BS 8004: Code of practice for foundations. BSI, London.

BSI (1997) 8110-1: Structural use of concrete. Part 1: Code of practice for design and construction. BSI, London.

BSI (2004) BS EN 1992-1-1: Eurocode 2: Design of concrete structures. Part 1-1 General rules and rules for buildings. BSI, London.

CIRIA (Construction Industry Research & Information Association) (1999) Temporary propping of deep excavations – guidance on design. CIRIA C517. CIRIA, London.

CIRIA (2000) Prop loads in large braced excavations. Project Report 77. CIRIA, London.

ICE (Institution of Civil Engineers) (2007) *ICE Specification for Piling and Embedded Retaining Walls*, 2nd edition. Thomas Telford, London.

ICE R&D (Institution of Civil Engineers Research & Development Enabling Fund) (2009) *Reducing the Risk of Leaking Substructure: A Clients' Guide*. ICE, London.

Puller MJ (2003) *Deep Excavations: A Practical Manual*, 2nd edition. Thomas Telford Publishing, London.

Useful web addresses

Federation of Piling Specialists: www.fps.org.uk

European Federation of Foundation Contractors: www.effc.org

Deep Foundations Institute: www.dfi.org

Temporary Works: Principles of Design and Construction
ISBN 978-0-7277-4177-6

ICE Publishing: All rights reserved
http://dx.doi.org/10.1680/twpdc.41776.193

Chapter 15
Caissons and shafts

Andrew Smith Contracts Director, Joseph Gallagher Ltd

This chapter deals with the construction of shafts and caissons using pre-cast segmental linings together with the use of sprayed concrete lining (SCL) in shaft sinking operations.

Caissons in the marine environment are not covered in this chapter. Construction methods used including types of shaft linings generally available, other materials and construction plant commonly used together with a brief description of specialist processes that can be used to provide ground stability when required are all discussed. Comments on design considerations for the construction of shafts and caissons using pre-cast segments are also included.

15.1. Introduction

Shaft sinking in the UK is generally carried out using circular pre-cast segmental linings, originally developed after the war as an alternative to the original and more expensive cast-iron linings. They are typically used to provide access for tunnelling operations where they can then be converted to permanent access chambers. More recently, they are increasingly being used to form storage chambers and pumping stations, etc. where they can offer a cost-effective solution to more expensive alternatives such as in situ construction within a piled cofferdam. The advantages are that the permanent works materials are, in effect, used as the temporary works during construction and also that the construction 'footprint' is kept to a minimum (an important consideration in urban areas).

Specification clauses for shaft construction and break-outs from shafts can be found in the British Tunnelling Society (BTS) *Specification for Tunnelling* (2010).

For small-diameter shafts in the range up to 4 m, full-circle segmental rings are available but high unit weights need to be considered when specifying the construction plant required.

As circular structures, segmental shafts normally require no additional bracing during construction since all the ground loads are evenly distributed to produce only compressive loads in the lining. Another advantage is that, properly constructed, the risk of settlement is kept to a minimum; the construction process should ensure that the exposed ground is supported with the minimum of delay and there are no large temporary working spaces to be backfilled on completion.

Pre-cast shaft linings were originally designed to mirror the earlier cast-iron linings so that they had a rib and recessed panel appearance. As such, they had a limited use in the context of depths exceeding around 20 m and are no longer readily available. These linings have now been replaced with solid units, normally 1000 mm wide, in standard diameter ranges from 4 m to 25 m with different manufacturers having their own bolting systems. The individual segments are cast to very exacting tolerances to ensure accurate alignment between components. The design of these units normally incorporates a sealing system utilising hydrophilic strips or rubber gaskets, the latter being factory fitted. Increasingly, these segments are being manufactured using fibre reinforcement which has a beneficial effect in terms of fire resistance and also makes it easier to break-out openings and attach fixings. Although the majority of manufacturers produce a standard range of products to a set design suitable for the vast majority of projects, they will also provide a design service and special manufacture of linings to suit more demanding or specific design conditions. Additionally, as part of their service, manufacturers are able to provide specialist items such as corbel units to accommodate landing slabs and also complete roof slabs designed to the engineer's loading requirements.

A more recent development, often used in conjunction with segmental shaft construction, is the use of sprayed concrete lining (SCL). SCL is used to replace the segmental lining and can be used in conjunction with reinforcement and/or lattice arches or, alternatively (and now more commonly), with fibre reinforcement. Typically, segmental ring construction might be used for the upper levels of the shaft where ground conditions and surface features make this appropriate with a change to SCL in the underlying more stable strata. For permanent works, use of a secondary in situ lining may be required to create a smooth finish. SCL can be used in conjunction with either sprayed-on or sheet-membrane waterproofing. One considerable advantage with SCL is that openings, etc. required in the shaft lining can be formed by the use of additional framing reinforcement but without the need to introduce expensive temporary works support while the portal structures are constructed. On the other hand, openings in shafts built with segmental rings generally require considerable temporary support during construction (particularly at deep levels) as the inherent compressive strength of a shaft ring is lost once an opening is formed in it, until the permanent works are completed.

15.2. Major alternatives

Alternatives to shaft sinking methods not covered in this chapter include

- sheet piled cofferdams (Chapter 11)
- diaphragm walls (Chapter 13)
- contiguous and secant walls (Chapter 14).

15.3. Common methods of construction

Shaft sinking methods are broadly subdivided into two categories: underpinning and caisson sinking. See the BTS (2004) publication, *Tunnel Lining Design Guide*, for more details.

15.3.1 Underpinning

Underpinning involves the excavation and erection of each ring of the segmental lining beneath the previously constructed ring. As each ring is completed cementitious material is injected behind the lining to fill any voids and secure it in the ground, ready to support the next ring which is bolted up from beneath. Different manufacturers have their own bolting systems to do this. This method is normally used in firm self-supporting ground or where ground treatment processes have created stable ground conditions. However, it can also be used to recover a situation where a shaft being sunk as a caisson has become stuck although additional ground stabilisation processes will probably be required in this situation.

The initial segmental ring is placed in a pre-dug excavation and keyed in to a concrete collar cast around it, normally by inserting dowels through the grout holes. It is vital during this process that this initial ring is built within the correct tolerance and fully supported, as any settlement during the casting of the collar could have serious repercussions in keeping the rest of the shaft vertically aligned. Once the first ring of the shaft is fixed in the ground, it is common to fix plumbing brackets around the top of the ring to check verticality as the shaft is sunk.

The grouting process requires the base of each ring to be sealed. There are geotextile hoses available that can be fixed behind the ring before it is built; after building, the hose is inflated with grout to seal the annulus before void grouting begins. It is however more common to push excavated material in under the ring once built to achieve the same result: so-called 'fluffing up'. When using this method, care must be taken not to damage the seals. If an excavator is being used it is possible to fit a purpose-made blade for this purpose. It is also good practice to form small voids in the previously grouted annulus up to the grout holes of the ring above to release any trapped air as grouting takes place.

Excavation of shafts constructed by underpinning is commonly carried out by 360° excavators initially working from the surface and then lowered into the excavation as it becomes deeper. Alternatively, there are a range of pole grabs available (some telescopic) that can be attached to excavators and used from the surface. With the advent of zero tail swing models, it is possible to get machines into all but the smallest shafts. It is very important to accurately trim the excavation to the correct profile; this avoids overbreak and excessive grout use.

Traditionally carried out by hand, adherence to current HAVS (hand arm vibration syndrome) regulations can make this a time-consuming process. One method of overcoming this is to reverse the bucket on the shaft excavator so that it can dig upwards to assist the trimming process (Figure 15.1). Segments are usually placed by crane using specially manufactured underpinning frames, supplied by the segment manufacturers. Grouting normally uses bagged cementitious material supplied shrink-wrapped and on pallets for weather protection and ease of handling by forklift. It can be mixed and pumped in special composite units driven by compressed air. The segment manufacturers generally provide threaded grout sockets in their segments, and it is important to check that the grout gun nozzle is compatible with the fittings supplied.

Figure 15.1 Underpinning showing trimming
Courtesy of Joseph Gallagher Ltd

As well as underpinning using segments, the same basic process can be used with SCL methods (Figure 15.2). Once the shaft has been excavated for the pre-determined length, the SCL is applied using either a hand-held nozzle or a robot sprayer. For most operations, this material is supplied ready-mixed and either discharged directly into the pump or held in a re-mixer on site. As with most operations involving SCL, the material is supplied retarded and an accelerator is added at the nozzle. Reinforcement can be provided in the form of mesh or pre-fabricated arches, but it is becoming increasingly common to use fibre-reinforced concrete which speeds up the process considerably. Openings typically use steel reinforcement locally, and can be formed incrementally as the excavation proceeds without the need for temporary support. If required, sprayed waterproof membranes can be incorporated into the lining, normally by sandwiching them between two separate layers of SCL.

15.3.2 Caisson sinking

Caissons can be round, square or rectangular but must be of a regular cross-section with no protrusions which would cause drag leading to the danger of lock-up. The majority of caissons are circular, however.

Caisson sinking typically involves constructing the first one or two rings of the shaft at ground level within a substantial reinforced concrete collar using a special cutting ring at the leading edge. As with underpinning, it is vital that the initial rings are built accurately

Figure 15.2 Oruga shotcreter and tunnel opening
Courtesy of Meyco-BASF and Joseph Gallagher Ltd

and held in position while the collar is concreted. These rings are surrounded by poly-styrene sheets before concreting the collar to create a sleeve through which the shaft can slide. Sacrificial jacking bases are also positioned before concreting within the collar onto which the shaft jacks are then fixed. For shaft sizes up to around 10 m diameter, most segment suppliers manufacture their own pre-cast cutting edges. Over this size, it is necessary to use a fabricated steel unit which must be designed to suit the sizes and fixing patterns of the rings to be used. For larger diameters and demanding ground conditions, it is essential to have a steel unit which can be welded on site to increase rigidity and prevent shaft distortion during sinking.

The cutting edge (Figure 15.3) must provide an overcut to the rings to be used so that an annulus is formed as the shaft sinks, enabling a lubricant to be introduced. This annulus is typically of the order 50 mm. There are a number of products on the market suitable for this operation. The caisson is sunk by excavating from within and then letting the shaft sink in a controlled manner, almost always by the use of vertical hydraulic jacks positioned around the collar. The size and hence weight of this collar must be sufficient to counteract the anticipated jacking loads required. As the shaft sinks further, rings are added at the surface with specially designed working cages needed for this operation (Figure 15.4).

The annulus created by the cutting edge is kept filled with a thixotropic material such as Bentonite or one of a range of synthetic products currently available to support the

Figure 15.3 Steel cutting edge (during trail erection) ready to receive pre-cast units
Courtesy of PL Manufacturing Ltd

Figure 15.4 Building PC segments from a working cage
Courtesy and copyright NATM Magazine 2009

excavated ground and to minimise friction. On completion of sinking, this material is replaced by the injection of cementitious grout in one operation to lock the caisson into position and to replace the lubricant with solid material to minimise settlement. During sinking, a constant check must be kept on the verticality and square of the shaft and corrections made on the jacks to keep it within tolerance.

Once a caisson becomes badly out of alignment the consequences can be severe, including getting it stuck and/or segment damage. In this regard, careful attention should be paid to the lubrication process, particularly where there is a risk of ground coming onto the caisson. In addition, a careful analysis of the ground conditions should include a determination of the likelihood of large obstructions such as boulders blocking the cutting edge. Caissons have far less danger of becoming stuck in fine-grained homogeneous soils than in, say, gravels or boulder clay, where alternative methods might be more appropriate.

Caisson excavation can be carried out 'dry' or 'wet' depending on ground conditions. If the ground is naturally stable or has been stabilised by, for example, dewatering (see Chapter 6), excavation can be carried out from the surface or from within the shaft using excavation plant described for underpinning above. If the conditions are unstable and/or waterlogged, or where the hydrostatic conditions could cause the base of the excavation to 'blow', excavation must be carried out with the shaft flooded to the prevailing hydrostatic level. In these circumstances the excavation plant normally used is either an excavator-mounted pole grab, where special telescopic models can reach depths of around 20 m (see Figure 15.5), or a rope-operated digging grab mounted on a crawler crane. With the latter, the digging ability is governed by the hardness of the material and the submerged weight of the grab. In hard material it is possible to add weights to the grab; if this is not successful, measures such as pre-auguring or the use of chisels suspended from the shaft crane must be considered.

It is becoming more common to use caisson sinking, even in stable ground, because the method eliminates the need for the trimming process required when underpinning. The method also minimises the need for personnel to be in the shaft, as the ring building takes place at the surface.

The same plant is used for mixing and pumping the lubricant as for the final grouting, and is described in Section 15.3.1 on underpinning.

With wet caissons it is normally necessary to seal the base with the shaft submerged. This is because dewatering, once the shaft has reached its depth, might cause the base to heave or 'blow' under hydrostatic pressure. Even if dewatering is a possibility, sealing the base in wet ground conditions can be extremely difficult. The depth of the so-called concrete 'plug' must be sufficient to provide enough resistance to the hydrostatic uplift in conjunction with the weight of the shaft rings and the weight of the collar. The latter is normally attached to the shaft, once sunk to its final position, by fixing dowel bars through the top rings into the collar designed to provide the shear resistance required. The concrete plug is placed by tremmie methods, almost always using concrete pumps. To provide a key it

Figure 15.5 Jacks pushing PC units down, with clam-shell excavator
Courtesy of Joseph Gallagher Ltd and Specialist Plant Associates Ltd

is usual to install recessed panel rings in the plug location or, alternatively, corbel rings. Segment manufacturers usually supply these as part of their shaft segment range. The plug must be left in place for a minimum of 5 days to cure before dewatering begins. Preparation of the surface can then commence, usually by placing a regulating blinding, to allow construction of the structural base above.

Current practice in the UK in calculating temporary resistance to uplift normally ignores any resistance provided by grouting the annulus or the shear resistance of the ground at the base, and usually assumes a groundwater level at ground level. On top of this, a safety factor of the order of 1.05 is typically applied.

Where the base of the shaft is founded in stable ground or it has been rendered temporarily stable by dewatering/pumping or another ground stabilisation process, as an alternative to a deep plug it is possible to provide uplift resistance by under-reaming. The shaft is first stabilised by normal annulus grouting and the cutting edge is usually removed, which in the case of a steel fabricated unit can be re-used. The base excavation is then under-reamed, using temporary supports if required, to extend it beyond the shaft footprint. Once the reinforced concrete base is cast, this mobilises passive resistance of the undisturbed ground above the toe to counteract uplift.

There are a number of ground stabilisation processes that can be used to aid shaft sinking and to reduce construction risks; these are discussed in detail in Chapters 6, 8 and 9. It is worth bearing in mind that if the shaft construction involves excavating, moving and disposing of large amounts of saturated material, particularly in urban areas, it may be prudent to consider ground stabilisation on environmental grounds to lessen the impact (see Chapter 7). Likewise, if the shaft is to be sunk using sump pumping to control groundwater, the issues of silt separation and discharge facilities should be seriously considered; very exacting standards are normally demanded from licensing authorities before such discharges can be accepted into surface water disposal systems. If deep well dewatering is being considered, there are issues to be addressed with regard to abstraction and discharge licenses.

The use of such processes needs to considered and decided upon at the construction planning stage as installation is more difficult to achieve once construction has started, likely to be less effective and can be very disruptive and costly.

15.3.3   Pre-cast roof slabs

Most shafts require some form of roof slab for the completed structure. As an alternative to costly in situ construction, often requiring expensive temporary formwork support, most shaft segment manufacturers will provide a pre-cast solution as part of the service they offer. This can also have the benefit of time savings as the manufacture takes place off site with the installation itself normally taking 1–2 days. The pre-cast manufacturer will typically design the slab to the engineer's requirements as part of this service. However, the whole process normally takes of the order 8–10 weeks, so early planning for this option is advisable.

15.4.   Principles of design

The design of a shaft, the method of sinking and the selection of the lining depend on many factors. Shaft projects can vary from small, simple schemes to large and complex systems, and the final use will affect the design.

The most important factor which influences shaft design is the type of ground and whether it is unstable or competent and self-standing when excavated. The presence of groundwater exacerbates the unstable ground conditions and imposes hydrostatic pressures which increase linearly with depth in both unstable and competent strata.

Once ground conditions are known from site investigations, the basic parameters for excavation and muck removal, groundwater control, ground stability control and lining installation can be evaluated and the shaft lining type chosen. Calculation of active pressures from the ground on to the walls is covered in Chapter 11. These figures are also used to give upward pressures to check the stability of the base in the temporary as well as the permanent condition. Note that it is the situation before the base is installed that is the critical condition, and that particular dangers are created by the hydrostatic forces.

Structural design of pre-cast units follows standard reinforced concrete or fibre-reinforced design as appropriate, but is a service provided by the supplier.

Design of plan-circular structures in the ground is by using hoop compression, suitably factored to make allowance for non-uniformity of ground loading, and allows a very light efficient structure to be used. Openings in hoop compression attract very large concentrated loads around their edges.

It is always prudent to design out any plan shape with intrusions or a non-uniformcross-section, not only for the high stresses at angles but because of the danger of such shapes becoming stuck when being sunk as a caisson.

REFERENCES

BTS (British Tunnelling Society) (2004) *Tunnel Lining Design Guide*. Thomas Telford Publishing, London.

BTS (2010) *Specification for Tunnelling*, 3rd edition. Thomas Telford Publishing, London.

Useful web addresses

For details of shaft lining types, visit http://www.alanauld.co.uk/index.php

Temporary Works: Principles of Design and Construction
ISBN 978-0-7277-4177-6

ICE Publishing: All rights reserved
http://dx.doi.org/10.1680/twpdc.41776.203

Chapter 16
Bearing piles

John Hislam Director, Applied Geotechnical Engineering Ltd

A review of differing piling methodology and design principles is presented for short-term temporary works bearing piles. Depending upon the nature of the works, it is quite normal to adopt lower load factors compared to permanent works since the duration of use is short and activity adjacent to the installations decreases the risks associated with non-observation of possible problems. It is accepted practice to adopt the observational method as a means of realising economic solutions; an intrinsic requirement of such methodology is to ensure contingency plans are assessed and prepared.

16.1. Introduction

In temporary works, bearing piles are used for a variety of purposes such as: test pile loading reaction systems, jetties, plant working platforms, crane bases, façade retention, supports for site access/accommodation/existing structures, etc. (see Chapters 4, 17 and 26). In extreme cases, they can be utilised for the provision of general site working conditions in very weak or soft ground conditions. As well as environmental considerations, very often the type of pile adopted is an adjunct to main works piling as lead-in times and mobilisation/demobilisation costs and time are saved. Both driven and bored piles are used; driven piling provides the advantage of instant load-carrying capability outweighing the usually more acceptable environmental advantages of bored piles. While timber piles can be included here, it is more usual that steel or concrete piles are adopted (dependent upon material availability).

16.2. Types and installation
16.2.1 Use of bearing piles in temporary works

Temporary piles used for pile-loading test reactions systems are usually of a similar type to the main (or temporary) works piles that are to be evaluated. As a series of steel cross beams are invariably used to carry the pile reaction back to the restraint piles, they are usually installed in a regular grid arrangement relative to the pile being tested. Any possible interference between the reaction piles and the test pile must be taken note of.

Crane base piles are more usually of the bored pile type as environmental considerations associated with urban development tend to rule out noise and vibration issues associated with driven piles. In-service and out-of-service crane loadings have to be considered for any pile layout group in order to determine the worst case design. Pile cap self-weights have to be included within such considerations, although it is quite normal to neglect the pile self-weight.

In many cases temporary piles are required to provide support or access for permanent works. The 'heavy' engineering cases are usually associated with marine works, where either a temporary jetty or pile guidance system is required. In these cases, it is more normal to adopt driven piles, either of H- or circular-section. Modern pile-driving equipment is readily able to pitch and drive a variety of steel sections to reasonably precise tolerances, usually with the ability to predict load-carrying capacity via wave equation analysis.

16.2.2 Installation methods

For speed of installation, driven steel or precast concrete piles are preferred as there is no delay time while concrete attains strength. It is more normal for steel piles to be adopted as they lend themselves to fast on-site connection to other temporary falsework, etc. Current driven piling equipment is fast to erect and sophisticated in operation, allowing the rig to handle the piles without the need for support craneage. There is also the advantage of negligible spoil removal.

Other installation methods such as vibratory are more usually used for sheet piling which, if being used elsewhere on the site, could be also used for bearing loads. Ground-borne vibration, from either driven or vibratory methods, is generally less of a problem than it is conceived to be. Relatively light hand-held equipment including adapted breakers and impact moles are used to install scaffold pole-size steel piles in difficult access conditions, particularly useful for the provision of access/working platforms and safety fences on embankments and cuttings. Screw piles, installed by rotation, are very useful for lighter loads for similar duties as above, together with falsework support. As driven piles, their other advantages are negligible spoil removal and the ability to be instantly loaded.

In many cases, temporary works for façade restraint or the support of existing structures while manifest changes are made require relatively small equipment as either working area and/or headroom can be restricted. This has possibly been one of the largest growth areas in piling technology over recent years, only matched by similar strides in continuous flight auger piling. There is now a wide variety of specialist piling equipment suitable for pile diameters ranging from around 150 mm to over 500 mm that can work in such restricted areas. The health and safety requirements associated with such equipment must be observed, as these require the use of guarded rotary machinery.

In all cases, any piling methods which are specified for permanent works should be considered and the benefits of avoiding duplicating establishment charges, etc. compared against the greater efficiency of using the technically best method for the temporary works. An example of this could be on a project where diaphragm walling has been specified, where a choice might be made to use barrettes for load-bearing (a method not normally considered unless large numbers could justify the high set-up costs; see Chapter 13).

16.3. Design principles
16.3.1 Ground parameters
As with permanent works, adequate site investigation information is a necessary requirement for efficient (and therefore economic) pile design. It is highly desirable that the pile designer has input to the scope of such investigatory work in order to be provided with pertinent information on the ground conditions and thus derive design parameters. In simplistic terms, it is more usual to adopt driven piling in granular or weak soils and bored or drilled piles in cohesive soils or weak rocks, although this does not imply such exclusivity of choice.

The design of driven piles is usually based upon the use of the empirical formulae (e.g. the Hiley formula), but there are many alternatives and derivatives. It is suggested that the reader reviews explanations of this type of predictive methodology (see *Further reading* list at the end of the chapter); note however that the technology is based upon large-diameter piling and could therefore be misleading for smaller-diameter piles. It is best to seek advice from specific practitioners who maintain databases of case histories upon which they can judge more accurate predictions. As a fundamental point, it is not unreasonable to require statically installed pile design theory to be used as a basis for driven piles.

The design of bored piles follows fairly well-understood principles that rely on the calculation, or estimation, of the combination of shaft friction and end bearing. In clays the shaft friction can be derived from the product of undrained shear strength and pile shaft surface area, the undrained shear strength being empirically factored to realise a match with many years of practical feedback from pile testing. The base resistance is derived from the product of a bearing capacity factor (for isolated piles, usually 9), the pile base area and the undrained shear strength at the pile toe.

In granular materials the shaft friction is derived from a factored product of the average effective overburden pressure over the shaft length and the material's characteristic or average angle of friction between the pile shaft and soil. The factors that are used are essentially based upon the method of pile installation; driven piles have larger values than bored piles. In rocks (particularly weak rocks), much empirical work has been carried out as reviewed, for example, by Tomlinson and Woodward (2008) and specialists should be consulted in order to assist with such design. Chalk is somewhat of a special case in that pile design has become accepted as being dependent upon the factored effective overburden pressure rather than standard penetration test empirical data (CIRIA, 2002 and 2003).

Where end-bearing can be located on rock, the Arcelor *Piling Handbook* (2010; Chapter 10) provides some useful capacities.

16.3.2 Load factors
It is quite normal for lower factors of safety or load factors to be adopted for these types of pile installations, as the longevity and risk is usually of lower order than permanent works. In many cases, such piles are required to carry lateral loading and the simplest

Figure 16.1 Cross-bracing of piles for lateral loading and effective length

expedient is to adopt interconnected raking piles to form a foundation A-frame that relies on axially compression and tension loads. It is also quite normal to design vertical piles to resist lateral loading, for which various specialist computer-aided design (CAD) packages are available. Wherever possible, the designer should endeavour to cross-brace the structure in order to limit pile lateral loading (see Figure 16.1).

The adoption of lower design load factors of less than 2 can lead to the requirement for verification of such designs, especially in cases where such piling works may not be in areas where adequate ground condition information is fully available. Static and dynamic load testing can be used, although it is preferable to have correlation data available for site conditions in order to add confidence to the dynamic results.

16.3.3 Loadings

Lateral loading conditions can arise from impact loading from either berthing vessels or operational impacts in the case of marine works or land-based construction plant. In addition, wind and/or water flow (possibly with floating debris impact or damming loadings) must be included in possible load cases. These loadings are described in greater detail for jetties and load platforms in Chapter 17 and for crane bases in Chapter 4. Guidance can also be found in BS 5975 (2011), pertinent to all temporary works.

Where vertical loading from deck beams or walers on piling frames are taken on to the sides of the piles (e.g. by corbels), eccentric loading will be induced. The eccentric effect should be treated as another form of horizontal loading for its effect on the pile.

16.3.4 Analytical process

Analysis philosophy is also covered in detail in sources such as SCI *Steel Bearing Piles* (1989) and Tomlinson and Woodward (2008).

REFERENCES

ArcelorMittal (2008) *Piling Handbook*, 8th edition reprint. ArcelorMittal, London.

BSI (2011) BS 5975: 2008 + A1: 2011 Code of practice for temporary works procedures and the permissible stress design of falsework. BSI, London.

CIRIA (Construction Industry Research & Information Association) (2002) Engineering in chalk. Report C574. CIRIA, London.

CIRIA (2003) Shaft friction of CFA piles in chalk. Project Report 86. CIRIA, London.

SCI (Steel Construction Institute) (1989) Steel Bearing Piles. P156. SCI, Ascot.

Tomlinson MJ and Woodward J (2008) *Pile Design and Construction Practice*, 5th Edition. Spon, London.

FURTHER READING

AGS (Association of Geotechnical and Geoenvironmental Engineers) (2006) *Guidelines for Good Practice in Site Investigation*. AGS, Kent.

BSI (2000) BS EN206-1: Part 1 Specification, performance, production and conformity. BSI, London.

BSI (2000) BS EN 1536: Execution of special geotechnical work. Bored piling. BSI, London.

BSI (2001) BS EN 12699: Execution of special geotechnical work – Displacement piles. BSI, London.

BSI (2004) BS EN1992-1-1: Eurocode 2: Design of concrete structures. Part1-1: General rules and rules for buildings. BSI, London.

BSI (2007) BS EN 12794: Precast concrete products – Foundation piles. BSI, London.

BSI (2007) EN1993-5: Eurocode 3 Design of steel structures. Part 5: Piling. BSI, London.

BSI (2009) BS5228-1: Code of practice for noise and vibration control on construction and open sites. Part 1: Noise. BSI, London.

BSI (2009) BS5228-2: Code of practice for noise and vibration control on construction and open sites. Part 2: Vibration. BSI, London.

Fleming WGK, Randolph M, Weltman A and Elson K (2009) *Piling Engineering*, 3rd edition. Taylor & Francis, London.

FPS (Federation of Piling Specialists) (2006) Handbook on Pile Testing. FPS, Kent.

Healy PR and Weltman AJ (1980) Survey of problems associated with the installation of displacement piles. Report PG8 1980. CIRIA, London.

ICE (Institute of Civil Engineers) (2007) *Specification for Piling and Embedded Retaining Walls*. Thomas Telford Publishing, London.

Turner MJ (1997) *Integrity Testing in Piling Practice*. Report 144. CIRIA, London.

Useful web addresses

Federation of Piling Specialists: http://www.fps.org.uk

Geosolve Ltd, a provider of CAD packages: http://www.geosolve.co.uk

Steel Construction Institute, bearing pile guide and other steel guides: http://www.steel-sci.org

Temporary Works: Principles of Design and Construction
ISBN 978-0-7277-4177-6

ICE Publishing: All rights reserved
http://dx.doi.org/10.1680/twpdc.41776.209

Chapter 17
Jetties and plant platforms

Paul Boddy Head of Temporary Works, Interserve Construction Limited

This chapter explores the options available to a site and designer when a jetty or platform is required. It highlights the materials and design approaches possible and the importance of obtaining good information about the expected loadings. The chapter also highlights the importance of good communication between the site team and the designer.

17.1. Introduction

In marine and river temporary works terms, a plant platform is a structure constructed at the edge of a watercourse to allow the loading and off-loading of materials, plant and personnel from a vessel. A plant platform would be necessary where the existing bank is not considered strong enough to withstand the plant loadings.

If the river bed profile is such that a barge cannot approach the bank, then the plant platform may need to extend out further to where the river depths are greater. If this is the case, the structure becomes a jetty (see Figure 17.1).

Plant platforms are also used to gain high-level access in dry sites, for example, at street level for craneage and trucks to stand above a building basement under construction. In structural terms, these can equate to jetties but without being subjected to the mooring and environmental loadings as described in Sections 17.5.2.3 and 17.5.3.

Three types of structure could be considered when specifying a plant platform or jetty: solid structure, open jetty structure and floating jetties, as described in the following sections.

17.2. Solid structure

This is a totally enclosed structure which will not allow water flow through it. This might be the most straightforward to design and install, but its size may however be governed by restrictions imposed by controlling bodies such as the Environment Agency in the UK due to the possibility of it impeding river flow.

17.2.1 Mass fill gravity platform or jetty structure

This is the simplest method and generally consists of mass fill rock (rip rap). This can however result in large structures being constructed, as the sides will need to be battered. Compaction is difficult and the side angles can therefore be relatively

Figure 17.1 Situations for jetty and plant platform: (a) barge can approach the bank, but the bank is weak; (b) plant platform installed; (c) barge cannot approach river bank; and (d) jetty installed

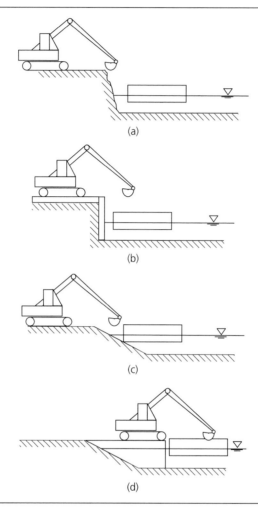

(a)

(b)

(c)

(d)

shallow. Ensuring that the entire structure is removed when the works are completed can also be difficult.

The stone could be installed by floating plant such as a pontoon and excavator working with a hopper. To ensure the stone structure meshes together, the machine driver would need to choose the stone sizes to ensure they interlocked as far as practically possible. Issues for access would have to be considered, as described in Chapter 18.

The alternative is to progressively build the structure outwards by tipping stone at the riverbank; lorries would then back onto the completed section to place stone for successive sections.

Figure 17.2 Sheet-pile (a) platform and (b) jetty

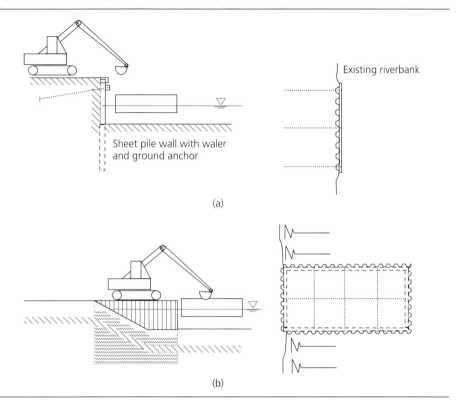

Existing riverbank

Sheet pile wall with waler
and ground anchor

(a)

(b)

17.2.2   Sheet-piled platform or jetty structure

This would be constructed in a similar way to a cofferdam with either a line of piles installed at the riverside to form a plant platform or a three-sided box being installed for a jetty structure (Figures 17.2a and b). Refer to Chapter 11 for details of sheet piling. To complete the jetty, it would be filled with stone to provide the running surface.

In both cases, ties and walers should be provided to prevent lateral movement. For long sheet-piled jetties, it is prudent to form compartments with regular sheet-pile cross-walls.

17.3.   Open jetty structure

For longer structures an open structure may be more appropriate, as this means that river flow underneath is not impeded. This would consist of a series of piers bearing on the river bed or driven into the bed (see Figure 17.3).

The decking design will depend on the use of the jetty and therefore what loading it will need to resist. Steel plate is a durable option but can become slippery when wet; a timber decking (timber sleepers or ekki mats) may be more appropriate. As the structure is temporary, the main structure will almost certainly be in steel as concrete will require time to cure and be difficult to remove afterwards. Proprietary systems such as steel

Figure 17.3 Open jetty general arrangement

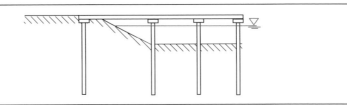

Figure 17.4 Typical span arrangements

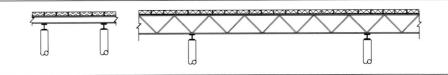

soldiers may also be considered, as they can be hired and returned when the job is completed.

The span sections will almost certainly be steel and can either be a beam/column section or a truss section. Beam/column sections are more economical for short spans, but when they increase then a truss section may be more feasible (Figure 17.4).

As spans increase then the beam/column-section size will increase considerably to resist not only static moments but also deflections due to dynamic loading. Deflections under loading need to be controlled to ensure that the platform does not become unstable.

Lateral stability also becomes an issue at long spans and bracing will therefore be necessary. For shorter spans, column sections provide better resistance against torsion and impact (although structurally less efficient than beam sections).

The pier sections will be chosen for simplicity of installation and so will be circular H or circular sections which can be installed by plant and removed afterwards. To resist lateral forces, raking piles should also be considered as they require smaller sections than if the vertical piles have to resist all lateral loads (Figure 17.5). For information on installation and design of temporary bearing piles, refer to Chapter 16.

17.4. Floating jetties

Floating jetties (Figure 17.6) can be constructed from a variety of materials such as Unifloat pontoons, plastic modular pontoons such as jet float and proprietary systems such as floating walkways (more frequently found in marinas). To ensure the jetty is kept at the same location, guide piles can be driven and fastened to the pontoon. Clearly, the fixing should ensure the pontoon can freely rise and fall with the water levels. To assist with access to the bank, the first section can articulate. Refer to Chapter 18 for further details of floating plant.

Figure 17.5 Typical cross-section with raking piles

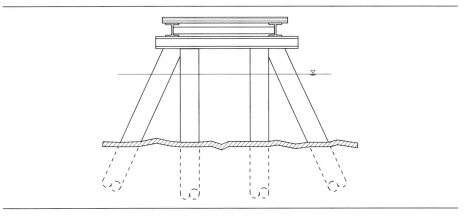

Figure 17.6 Floating with guide piles

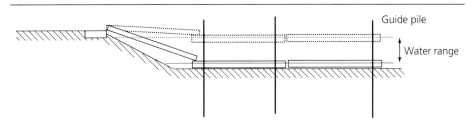

17.4.1 Mooring points

The jetty will be required to hold the vessel in place while it is being loaded/unloaded. Bollards therefore need to be installed on the top to tether the boat or barge. The spacing of these should ensure the barge can be held in place without a pendulum effect occurring (Figure 17.7).

The bollard and connection should be designed to prevent it breaking off under the force from a moving boat. The designer may also wish to consider the design case where the vessel has set sail, forgetting to untether.

17.4.2 Connections

All sections for a working platform or jetty will typically be large, heavy and generally difficult to connect, particularly if being installed by a crane on a pontoon. All

Figure 17.7 Mooring points arrangement to prevent pendulum effect

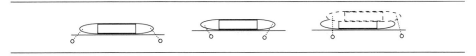

Figure 17.8 Guide lug details

connections should therefore be large, simple and with plenty of redundancy should it be found that not all the designed connections can be installed. If welding is to be considered, then ensure that the specified weld is larger in length and size to that required to allow for difficulties in maintaining weld consistency. This is particularly the case if welding is required underwater by divers, who will be relying on touch and feel to undertake their works (assume a throat strength of $110 \, \text{N/mm}^2$). It may also be prudent to provide lugs to hold two sections together while the connection is being undertaken (Figure 17.8).

17.4.3 Consents
Any works being undertaken in or around a watercourse in the UK require Temporary Works Consent from the Environment Agency (EA), who may issue conditions on the use and design of a loading platform or jetty. Such conditions will be issued to ensure that any pollution risk is kept to a minimum and that the structure does not impede river flows, particularly in flood conditions.

17.4.4 Interface with site team
As with temporary works, the initial concept may actually begin with the site team who will have a good idea of what is required and (just as important) what materials are available in terms of steel sections.

A prudent temporary works designer will therefore ask for a sketch from the site team with initial sizes based on what is available and where connections are required. The designer can then back-calculate to confirm with the site team about whether the sections work and, if not, enquire as to what else is available.

17.4.5 Installation of piles
As with all piling, the critical issue is the initial setting-out to ensure that the pile is located where it is required and within the specified tolerance. This is particularly challenging with raking piles, where the setting-out relates the pile to where it will be on the river bed. A piling gate should be used to fix the location and angle of the pile at deck-connection level, which can be hung over the side of a barge or pontoon. Piling gates are discussed in Chapter 11 and the process in Chapter 16. When piling is to be from floating plant, refer to Chapter 18.

17.5. Loadings
When designing a loading platform or jetty, the loads to be imposed on it must be considered. At the beginning of the design process the designer and the site supervisor

should agree what plant and materials are to be transported over the structure in order to determine the possible loadings.

The loadings that the structure will be subjected to include

- self weight
- imposed load from plant
- environmental loads (wind and water)

as described in the following sections.

17.5.1 Self weight
The self weight should be considered in the design of the member as for any other structure, but will generally not be the significant part of the loading.

17.5.2 Plant
17.5.2.1 Tracked plant
Tracked plant typically includes excavators, crawler cranes or piling rigs. The loading will be from the tracks. The loading from excavators and crawler cranes clearly varies depending on working radius and load being lifted. This will typically induce a trapezoidal load distribution under the tracks. The designer may then wish to convert this load using a rectangular or Meyerhof distribution (Figure 17.9).

For a crawler crane, the pressure diagrams should be available from the crane supplier and will be based on crane type and counterweight, boom length and maximum load at working radius.

For the excavator this information may not be as readily available; some judgement therefore may be necessary to determine the track loads. The designer should consider the three load cases of working over front, over side and diagonally. Plant may need to be controlled in its operation to ensure that it does not overload the platform or jetty.

Figure 17.9 Trapezoidal and Meyerhof rectangular distributions

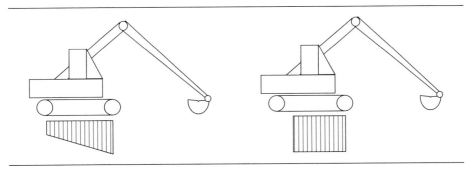

A piling rig will also induce track loads onto the jetty. A Federation of Piling Specialists (FPS) contractor will provide a pressure diagram similar to that of a crawler crane (e.g. Chapter 5). The designer must review the criteria on which the pressure diagram is based to ensure it is as required, in particular that dynamic load is factored up.

17.5.2.2 Wheeled plant
Axle weights should be confirmed with the supplier or, in the absence of this, then a credible reference should be sought. For a solid cofferdam structure, the recommendations of CIRIA Report C580 (Gaba et al., 2003) which gives recommendations on road going vehicle loadings may be applicable. In addition, Highways Agency document BD21/01 (HA, 2001) provides axle loadings for critical vehicles expected on UK bridges. Note that dynamic loadings from wheeled plant will comprise a larger percentage of dead load than for tracked machines.

17.5.2.3 Craft
The jetty should be designed for a nominal impact loading from craft coming alongside the structure and should allow for some accidental loadings; refer to BS 6349-1 (BSI, 2000) for assistance. Fendering may need to be fitted to the structure or, if the loadings are too high, it will need to be free-standing.

17.5.3   Environmental loadings
17.5.3.1 Wind loadings
These can be derived from current wind codes such as BS 6399 (BSI, 1997) or BS EN 1991-04 (BSI, 2010). The designer may also consider using BS 5975 temporary works code (BSI, 2011), which provides further relaxations on loadings due to the time of year. In all wind calculations, the most challenging part is to decide on the Cpe value to use for the shape of the jetty where engineering judgement can play a critical role.

17.5.3.2 River flows and wave actions
Generally, these are far more significant than wind loading; river flows can be calculated using basic Bernoulli formulae. The pressure q (N/m^2) for a given flow velocity v is defined:

$$q = 500 \, v^2.$$

An allowance should be made for the shape of the structure and a cw value given accordingly to derive the force on the structure. Further reference can be sought from BS 6349-1 (BSI, 2000), which also provides guidelines on wave actions.

Where flood conditions are possible, consideration should be given to the loading from the damming effect of trapped debris against the structure. If flow is restricted, then this loading will be considerable.

17.6.   Analysis
The analysis of platforms and jetties can be conducted using traditional methods of analysis; only specific aspects are covered here. Once the forces are known and the

materials chosen, then the design is generally straightforward. The designer must however consider the factors of safety being applied to the loadings and be satisfied that an allowance for dynamic loading has been taken into account, particularly with excavators or wheel plant that may need to brake when on the structure.

REFERENCES

BSI (1997) BS 6399: Loadings for buildings. Part 2: Code of practice for wind loads (incorporating Amendment No. 1 and Corrigendum No. 1 2002). BSI, London.

BSI (2000) BS 6349: Code of practice for general criteria (including amendment 1 2005). Part 1-Maritime structures. BSI, London.

BSI (2010) BS EN 1991-1-4: Eurocode 1. Actions on structures. Part 1–4: General Actions Wind Actions (incorporating corrigendum A1, January 2010). BSI, London.

BSI (2011) BS 5975: 2008 + A1: 2011 Code of practice for temporary works procedures and the permissible stress design of falsework (incorporating corrigendum No. 1). BSI, London.

Gaba AR, Simpson B, Powrie W and Beadman DR (2003) Embedded retaining walls – guidance for economic design. CIRIA Guide C580. CIRIA, London.

HA (Highways Agency) (2001) The Assessment of highway bridges and structures (includes correction dated August 2001). Report BD21/01. HMSO, London.

FURTHER READING

Blake LS (2004) *Civil Engineers Reference Book*, 4th edition. Elsevier Butterworth-Heinemann, Oxford.

Ehrlich LA (1982) *Breakwaters, Jetties and Groynes: A Design Guide* (Coastal structures handbook series). Sea Grant Institute, New York.

Elson WK (1984) *Design of Laterally Loaded Piles*. CIRIA Report 103. CIRIA, London.

Williams BP and Waite D (1993) *The Design and Construction of Sheet-piled Cofferdams*. CIRIA Special Publication 95. CIRIA, London.

Useful web addresses

Temporary Works Forum: http://www.twforum.org.uk/

Pontoon Works: http://www.pontoonworks.co.uk/

Temporary Works: Principles of Design and Construction
ISBN 978-0-7277-4177-6

ICE Publishing: All rights reserved
http://dx.doi.org/10.1680/twpdc.41776.219

Chapter 18
Floating plant

Paul Boddy Head of Temporary Works, Interserve Construction Limited

This chapter explores the range of equipment types available when it is necessary to go afloat. It highlights the importance of good planning, both in terms of using the plant and also ensuring the vessel can actually be used at the location. This chapter gives advice on the necessary calculations and checks that need to be undertaken for a given scenario, and stresses the importance of these checks being carried out by an engineer or naval architect who has both technical competence and practical experience.

18.1. Introduction

There are many situations in the field of construction where conventional plant cannot be used, and to undertake works, the contractor may need to go afloat. This would typically be for works being undertaken either at the edge of a water course or actually in it.

The need to go afloat occurs for two main reasons as follows.

■ The works involved are too remote from the edge of a watercourse for plant to physically reach. Examples of this may be the driving of piles for bridge piers in a wide river or undertaking works to an inlet structure in a reservoir.
■ The works are located at the edge of a watercourse, for example, sheet piling but there is no easy access for conventional plant, for example, a piling rig. This situation may arise if the topography is too steep to allow plant to approach the bank, or the ground simply cannot support the weight of the proposed plant. The distance travelled to reach the site may also be great, making it cheaper to procure floating plant rather than to provide a haul road.

Other non-engineering reasons why access cannot be gained to a river bank include where there are issues with third parties not permitting access across their land. This can be common place with Inland Waterways, where there is history of conflict between landowners and the waterway. There may also be environmental factors which may prohibit the use of plant in sensitive areas (e.g. Sites of Special Scientific Interest).

As with all engineering projects, and in particular marine engineering projects, the access to the site is key and the planning engineer should ensure that all options are considered both in terms of practicality and cost before the decision is made. In many circumstances, gaining access to a site can be more expensive than actually carrying out the works themselves.

Once the decision has been made to go afloat, further logistical issues may arise as marine plant is generally heavy and will have to be lifted into the water course at a convenient location. This may itself require further temporary works, such as constructing jetties or strengthening river banks to accommodate a heavy crane. Alternatively, it may need to be floated from a remote location. If the latter is viable, then the planner should consider the time required for the plant to be moved from the ingress location to the work site.

In either situation, the planning engineer must also consider possible obstructions such as locks or bridges which would impede the movement of plant and also whether there is adequate water depth for the plant being considered. Tidal and river flows should also be considered and what contingencies are necessary should be river be in spate. The time of year should also be considered.

If the plant needs to be supported from a canal/river bed then other environmental considerations need to be taken into account, such as whether disturbing the riverbed will damage habitats. Canal beds are historically lined with puddle clay to prevent water loss, which could be punctured by plant.

The use of marine plant provides challenges for both the operator and design engineer alike to ensure it is used effectively and safely. The planning engineer should not underestimate the amount of work required in not just the use of floating plant itself, but also in its transportation to and from and set-up at the work site.

18.2. Types and uses
18.2.1 Pontoons and barges

These are normally rectangular 'tanks' with flat tops which allow plant such as excavators and crawler cranes to be safely used and carry out their duties as if they were on dry land (see Figure 18.1).

A barge is generally a single structure which is large in dimensions, meaning it will remain in the water and be towed from location to location by a tug boat or similar. In most circumstances, the plant on the barge will remain permanently on board.

A pontoon is typically modular and is designed to be dismantled and moved from one location to another, typically by road, and then craned into the water along with the necessary plant.

Clearly the primary concern for the use of barges or pontoons with plant is to ensure the vessel is large enough to be stable while the given plant is undertaking its specified duties. Each load case should be considered by an appropriately trained design engineer or naval architect to ensure the barge or pontoon remains stable.

It is also essential that the site team understand the limitations of the plant use on the barge or pontoon, and do not stray outside of the boundaries set. Any required changes to site operations should be referred back to the designer to confirm it is safe to proceed.

Figure 18.1 Typical barge with crane and ancillary plant

As well as cranes, excavators can also be used on barges for such activities as dredging or grading of river banks or for positioning of bank protection such as rip rap (large stonework). An excavator working is more dynamic than a crane and the pontoon can experience more roll, which can make working difficult. In these circumstances, the barge may be fitted with 'spud legs' which are generally circular tubes running through the deck of the pontoon. These can be lowered so they embed themselves into the riverbed to provide extra stability (see Figure 18.2).

Care does need to be taken when using spud legs purely for stability if the watercourse is subject to wave action or the pontoon is operating during an ebb tide. The reason for this is that in either scenario an air gap could appear below the pontoon, meaning its weight is transferred onto the spud legs rather than being supported by the water. If the pontoon has not been designed for this scenario, then the pontoon could either become unstable or individual elements could fail due to the change in load path.

If any of the above scenarios could occur, then a jack-up barge may be more appropriate (described in Section 18.2.3).

Where access is required but a barge cannot reach the location (e.g. the river is not wide enough or there is an obstruction such as a canal or river lock, which can be as narrow as 7 feet) then a modular pontoon may be a more appropriate solution. The Uniflote is the classic example (Hathrell, 1968). It is a steel box approximately 5 m long by 2.5 m wide

Figure 18.2 Modular pontoon with spud stabilisers

by 1.2 m or 1.8 m deep, and can be connected to others to provide a range of different-sized working platforms depending on the requirements. It was developed for the army and had three requirements

- able to work with a Bailey Bridge (another example of Army Engineering)
- can be connected together in the water
- can be transported by a 3 tonne truck.

There are now numerous copies of the original concept; an example is depicted in Figure 18.2. These are used very frequently on inland waters either for dredging works, lifting operations and other typical construction activities. Whatever the activity, the ensemble still needs to be checked for stability and pontoon size adapted if necessary. In addition, the connection details should be considered to ensure load can be safely transferred from one unit to another.

The decision of whether to use a barge or a pontoon will depend greatly on the plant size being proposed and the access restrictions at the location where the floating craft is required. The barge shown in Figure 18.1 could only be transported by water because of its size and would also be restricted by any constrictions along the route; it could be used anywhere on the River Thames within London and could be transported to other estuarial locations in the UK and abroad. However, it could not be used upstream of Teddington Lock as the barge width is considerably wider than that of the locks at that location. On the other hand, a modular pontoon could be transported via road to an ingress point and constructed on the water.

Barges tend to be more robust in construction, therefore able to accommodate larger payloads and undertake larger marine projects.

Clearly, if considering a pontoon, the planning engineer must ensure that a suitable location is available to launch the pontoon, which may require vehicular and crane access. As already stated, this will require additional considerable temporary works (Chapter 17). Pontoon sections can allow flexibility in the shape of the working platform allowing for non-standard shapes to be developed, thus optimising the size of the pontoon for the required works. This is particularly useful in activities such as inland dredging where the width of the watercourse can be limited.

18.2.2 Lightweight modular systems

For locations where only lightweight access is required and/or there is limited crane access, there are further options that can be considered. One example is 'Jetfloat', which is a system of modular plastic boxes nominally 500×500 mm in plan and fitted together with lugs and plastic fixings. Originally designed as temporary floating platforms for marinas, they are now being used in far more innovative applications as access platforms for bridge and lock inspections, and have even been used as floating bridges to transport cars and tanks. Other similar systems are available, all with the advantage that they can be constructed on land and pushed into the water with a lightweight machine (see Figure 18.3).

The perceived weak spot of these pontoons units is the connection lugs. Various independent studies have been undertaken to check the long-term durability of the connections and Finite Element analysis has been performed on the stability of the pontoons due to the inherent flexibility of the product.

18.2.3 Jack-up barges

In certain circumstances, the need to provide a fully stable platform in order to carry out works may arise. In this scenario, the use of the 'jack-up' barge may be the most appropriate.

A jack-up barge is in effect a barge or pontoon which can be lifted clear of the water. Typically, it will have four spud legs (one in each corner) which embed themselves in the watercourse bed, allowing the pontoon to be raised using jacks (see Figure 18.4).

Jack-up barges have been used extensively in offshore works such as wind farms and in the petrochemical industry, but are now also used in tidal rivers and estuaries. They can either consist of a single section or be built up of individual units connected by lugs. This gives the user some flexibility in transporting the barge and the shape.

Examples of the use of a jack-up barge include the following.

Figure 18.3 Modular pontoon used as access platform

- Undertaking ground investigations in tidal conditions where it is necessary for the platform to remain at a constant level. A special unit can be provided for this with a hole (or Moon Pool) in the centre to allow an investigation rig to be positioned over it.
- To hold the pile gate (or guide) in place during single-pile (circular or H-section) driving, giving more confidence that the pile is being driven in the correct location. This is particularly useful with raking piles.

Figure 18.4 Typical elements of a jack-up barge

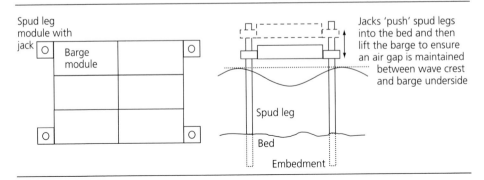

18.2.4   Other

18.2.4.1 Crane barges
These are bespoke vessels designed with an integral crane unit. These vary from the small boats working on inland waterways to the large vessels constructing oilrig platforms.

18.2.4.2 Hopper barges
These are open barges allowing materials such as dredging arisings or aggregates to be transported from one location to another, sometimes with opening or tipping arrangements for self-unloading.

18.3.   Design principals
18.3.1   General stability principals
To prove the stability of a barge or pontoon, various calculations should be undertaken by the design engineer or naval architect. Various texts are available, varying from the straightforward such as Major J.A.E. Hathrell's *The Bailey and Uniflote Handbook* (1968) to the more complex such as *Introduction to Naval Architecture* (Tupper, 2004).

In basic terms, the stability of any floating plant is a function of its combined centre of gravity and a theoretical height known as its 'metacentric' height. It is easiest to relate distances from the keel, K. Figure 18.5 depicts the basic principals; see also Webber (1990).

For the pontoon and its plant to be stable, the theoretical distance KM should be greater than KG, i.e. the metacentric height is higher than the centre of gravity. If not, the craft will rotate until the above is true, which may mean that it capsizes. KB is computed by calculating the centre of buoyancy, which is a function of the water displaced by the

Figure 18.5 Key principles for a stability study

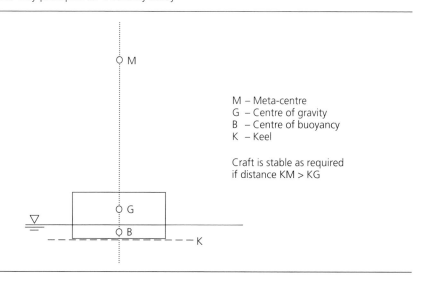

M – Meta-centre
G – Centre of gravity
B – Centre of buoyancy
K – Keel

Craft is stable as required
if distance KM > KG

Figure 18.6 Determining BM for a flat pontoon

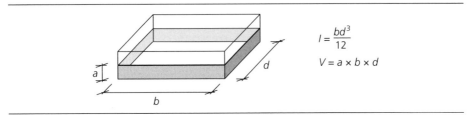

$$I = \frac{bd^3}{12}$$

$$V = a \times b \times d$$

weight of the pontoon and the plant thereon. KG is computed by determining the combined centre of gravity for the pontoon and the plant.

The distance BM is defined as I/V where I is the second moment of area for the plan of the pontoon and V is the volume displaced by the pontoon. We therefore have

$$KM = KB + BM$$

For a simple pontoon, see Figure 18.6.

Increasing the size of the pontoon or reducing the volume of water displaced will clearly increase the metacentre height. However, increasing the volume of water displaced will increase KB.

The weight of the pontoon, crane, load and ancillary items depicted in Figure 18.1 are all known as well as their centres of gravity about the pontoon keel; the stability of pontoon can therefore be confirmed. The crane would have been given particular examination and split up into its tracks, body and jib, and the weight and centre of gravity of each item considered separately.

The location of the plant on the deck will also tend to make the pontoon rotate, reducing freeboard on one side and increasing it on the other (Figure 18.7). This should be checked because if the roll experienced exceeds 7°, the pontoon can be difficult to work on. In addition, if the freeboard is reduced excessively, there is the possibility water could flood onto the deck.

The crane would have also been closely examined because when it slews around, the amount of roll of the pontoon will vary. It may be necessary to down-rate the capacity of the crane while working on the barge. The reason for this is that as the crane lowers its jib to reach out further, the pontoon will roll accordingly. This rolling effect will increase the working radius of the crane and could mean it is working outside of its load envelope.

To assist with stability, the barge may have been constructed with a series of internal or baffle walls. These compartments can be individually filled with water to assist with stability by rebalancing the barge should a heavy item of plant be required at one end. The barge itself would need to be designed or checked to ensure it is structurally adequate to support the weight of the plant on the pontoon.

Figure 18.7 Effect of eccentric loading on a pontoon or barge

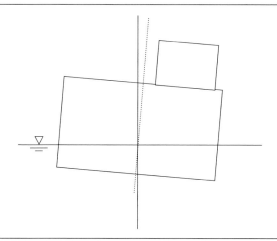

Environmental effects such as wind, water current and tides also need to be considered in the stability of a barge and the plant thereon. The wind load on a lattice jib can be considerable.

The actual types of plant may also give rise to different load patterns. A crawler crane generally operates slowly, both when lifting and slewing, and the loads that are being dealt with are generally fully understood. On the other hand, an excavator undertaking dredging duties will be operating faster as it first excavates the river bed and then drops the arisings into a hopper. It will therefore exert a larger dynamic load onto the barge, and this must be taken into account by the engineer checking the pontoon and barge.

A situation where the machine needs to dig into a stiff ground, so that the machine is pulling harder than expected, may occur. The engineer needs to consider the likely conditions the driver will be operating within and that additional loading criteria are checked. This can increase the expected loads on the pontoon between 25% and 100% of those calculated in theory. Good judgement and experience is just as important as being able to 'crunch' numbers.

18.3.2 Design of jack-up barges

The analysis of a jack-up barge can be quite involved, as many different criteria need to satisfied. The engineer needs to be proficient in stability, structural engineering, dynamics and geotechnical engineering. These disciplines are covered in depth elsewhere in the book.

The barge will generally be towed to the works location and may for some of its duties act as a floating platform. It therefore needs to be checked for stability in the same manner as a floating pontoon or barge.

When it is in its elevated position, the barge must also be analysed to ensure that it is not overloaded due to the loaded plant. A structural analysis is therefore needed to ensure that the structure can transfer the plant loads onto the spud legs. In a barge, this will ensure the structure is adequate in bending and in shear. In a modular system, the connecting lugs between units will also need to be reviewed for shear and tensile capacity. The lugs are a critical item and should be visually inspected on a routine basis; there have been several examples of lugs failing under load.

The loads in the spud-leg jacks should be compared against the jack capacity. The capacity of the leg itself will depend on the length of leg below the barge. The analysis in its simplest term can consider the leg as a pinned column and the capacity determined by the leg's radius of gyration and the effective length.

However, the critical item with a jack-up barge is the foundation for the spud legs. The legs would typically need to embed into the river bed far enough so that when the barge is lifted, no further settlement occurs. When planning a jack-up barge operation, topographic and geotechnical investigations should ideally be undertaken. This is not always possible, however, particularly if the jack-up barge is being used to obtain the geotechnical information in question. A successful jack-up relies as much on the skill of the barge master as it does on design and analysis. The barge master will monitor for settlement during its deployment and will undertake load-tests to be satisfied the set-up is stable. Topography is important to ensure the barge is not being deployed on a slope.

Once jacked-up, the spud legs will be subjected to forces from the current and wave action. Care has to be taken to ensure the barge is positioned higher than the top of the waves, so it is not lifted and dropped by the resonating wave action. The designer needs to identify the water flows in the location and the expected high-water level. In an estuary or further out at sea, the barge legs will be further subjected to wave action. In this situation, the designer must indentify the critical wave height about the maximum high-water level.

These heights should be related to chart datum, allowing the designer to specify the height of the barge above the bed level so that, in normal working conditions, the water level does not approach the underside of the barge. In an extreme weather event, the barge will be jacked-up as high as possible so that it is clear of high wave action.

The other main concern for a jack-up barge is when lifting the spud legs so the barge can be moved. Considerable suction may need to be overcome by the embedded length of tube, and the skill of the barge master is critical for the safe extraction of the spud legs.

The use of the jack-up barge has considerable risk involved and the International Jack-up Barge Owners Association has been formed to share best practice. There are also many HSE documents on the subject. A best-practice guide, *Guidelines for Site-specific Assessment of Mobile Jack-up Units* has also been drafted by the Society of Naval Architects and Marine Engineers (SNAME) (Bennett *et al.*, 1994).

This section on design has only covered aspects pertinent to stability. Structural adequacy checks follow standard design procedure.

REFERENCES

Bennett WT, Hoyle MJR and Jones DE (1994) Guidelines for Site Specific Assessment of Mobile Jack-Up Units. SNAME, New Jersey.

Hathrell JAE (1968) *The Bailey and Uniflote Handbook*, 3rd edition. Acrow Press, London.

Tupper EC (2004) *Introduction to Naval Architecture*, 4th edition. Elsevier Butterworth-Heinemann, Oxford.

Webber NB (1990) *Fluid Mechanics for Civil Engineers*, SI edition. Chapman and Hall, London.

FURTHER READING

Blake LS (1994) Civil Engineering Reference Book, 4th edition. Elsevier Butterworth-Heinemann, Oxford.

Useful web addresses

Jetfloat: http://www.pontoonworks.co.uk

Society of Naval Architects & Marine Engineers: http://www.sname.org

International Jack-up Barge Owners Association: http://ijuboa.com

Temporary Works: Principles of Design and Construction
ISBN 978-0-7277-4177-6

ICE Publishing: All rights reserved
http://dx.doi.org/10.1680/twpdc.41776.231

Chapter 19
Temporary bridging

Bernard Ingham Engineering Manager, Mabey Hire Services Ltd

Temporary bridges combine the performance of a permanent structure with the ability to re-use most or all of the constituent parts. This has set a challenge for military and bridging suppliers to develop solutions which are easily transported, installed and removed, but which offer features associated with permanent structures for relatively short periods. A great deal of knowledge has been built up in bridging systems and working methods over many years. The key to success with any temporary bridge scheme is to find the specialist skilled and experienced personnel who are able to make the best use of knowledge developed over many years.

19.1.   Introduction

Temporary bridges may be required to carry pedestrians, services, public highways, site access roads, site haul roads, special loads, railways or military vehicles. The obstacles to be crossed can include rivers, canals, footpaths, public roads, railways, site roads, services and construction areas. Bridge spans may also be required to form link spans to jetties or ramps, thus eliminating the use of temporary fill. They can also be used to provide a low-level removable canal crossing, for example, to move construction plant.

The bridge may be required for just a few hours, for example, to carry a special load over a weak bridge or canal, or for several years. Lead times from initial concept to installation can also vary greatly from several months for larger schemes to just 1–2 days for emergency applications such as following flood damage.

Whatever bridge is required, its foundations will also be temporary works and require design. The interface responsibilities between the procurer, temporary bridge supplier and the constructor of the foundations need establishing at an early stage; see Chapter 2 on management. The Temporary Works Coordinator (TWC) has an important role in temporary bridging.

Many different temporary bridge systems and installation solutions are available from launching from one side to using heavy craneage to lift into position. The military solutions have led the development of many of the modern bridge systems.

Detailed design of temporary bridging systems and individual scheme designs can be influenced by the following factors

231

- the need for easy and rapid transportation to site, installation and removal
- the availability and versatility of components to maximise utilisation
- the need to take economic advantage of the relatively short-term design life
- the use of suppliers' technical knowledge due to lack of EuroCode or UK design codes or standards specifically written for the design of temporary bridges
- the ground conditions for the construction of temporary foundations
- the suppliers' data available from testing of full-scale bridges and their components.

Although the following sections include information about procedures adopted in the UK, many of the principles apply to other sites throughout the world. Information on the temporary works involved in the installation of permanent bridges, for example, 'push-launch' structures, is given in Chapter 27 on bridge installation techniques.

19.2. Temporary bridge types

19.2.1 Historical: the Bailey Bridge

Temporary crossings have been used in different forms for hundreds of years. However, the most significant development was that of the Bailey Bridge, developed during the Second World War and assembled from distinctive individual panels. The construction industry generic term 'Bailey Bridge' is often used to describe all types of temporary bridge.

Named after the civil servant Donald Bailey who designed the radical new steel bridge system, the Bailey Bridge was adopted as the standard Military Bridge in 1941. It was revolutionary in that its light but strong and versatile system could be manually erected without craneage, and proved to be one of the greatest inventions of the war. It played a significant part in the allied victory; by 1947 it had been used to build more than 1500 bridges in northwest Europe.

Other temporary bridge systems have subsequently been developed for both military and civilian use. Figure 19.1 illustrates a modern military bridge, which incorporates many of the principles of Donald Bailey's 1940s design.

19.2.2 Proprietary bridging systems

The many different bridging systems available today range from derivatives of the Bailey Bridge to modern all welded deck and beam systems. The advice and user guidance from specialist suppliers should always be sought. The most common systems are described in the following subsections.

19.2.2.1 Panel bridges

Modern systems copy the original structural benefits of the double diamond truss Bailey panel layout that provides the combination of strength and lightness, yet retains the ability to resist high local roller forces during launching. The manual handling limitations in construction mean that most bridges in UK use will require craneage for assembly. This has led to the use of larger panels.

Figure 19.1 Modern day military logistical support bridge
Courtesy of Mabey Hire Services

A feature of the panel bridge is the use of high-strength pins to connect panels together. The pins are in shear, and design of the pin housing has always been a critical area for stress concentrations/welding.

Major improvements have, however, been made in the following areas

- use of higher grades of steel and increases in sizes of truss panels
- improvements in welding and detailing for fatigue
- development of numerous deck systems ranging from footbridge decks to heavy systems designed for up to three lanes of public highway and for heavy construction plant
- parapet and anti-skid surfacing systems.

Current panel bridges such as the Mabey and Leada Acrow products remain the most widely used (Figure 19.2 depicts a typical example). They have the advantages of

- the large span range, typically 6–80 m
- high efficiency due to the truss proportions and versatility
- being easily transported on standard vehicles on the road and/or in standard containers
- the option available to launch, eliminating the need for large cranes, although craneage is generally required for assembly.

19.2.2.2 Other truss bridges

Development of other truss bridge systems has taken place for longer spans and semi-permanent situations where the panel bridge trusses become less efficient. Examples

Figure 19.2 Panel bridge with reinforced concrete pads on temporary reinforced fill abutments
Courtesy of Mabey Hire Services

Figure 19.2 Panel bridge with reinforced concrete pads on temporary reinforced fill abutments
Courtesy of Mabey Hire Services

are the Mabey Delta and Unit Construction Bridges that are designed for spans in the range 50–130 m. Certain types use bolted connections in line with the trusses. This can allow pre-cambering of the structure to cater for deflections during use, a significant benefit when temporary bridge equipment is used as falsework (see Chapter 22 on falsework). Other lightweight truss bridge systems exist for footbridge applications.

19.2.2.3 Plate girder bolted bridges
Advances in girder manufacturing techniques and increases in the sizes of mobile cranes have encouraged the use of plate girders for temporary bridges. Such systems are less versatile than the truss systems and are generally used for relatively long-term use. They are generally site-specifically designed, thus allowing the inclusion of features such as special deck widths and skewed supports.

19.2.2.4 Prefabricated deck sections
The demand for rapid installation has led to the development of all welded deck systems that can be installed simply and rapidly, such as the Mabey Quickbridge. Multiple units are used side by side to form the deck with parapet pre-fitted to the outer units prior to delivery. The main longitudinal members are incorporated beneath the deck plate. Span capability (typically 6–20 m) is considerably less than that of the panel bridge systems, but installation speeds and costs are generally more favourable. Figure 19.3 depicts a typical application.

19.2.3 Special designs
There are a few occasions when a special-purpose design may be the best solution. Examples include

Figure 19.3 Deck-type bridge with trestle piers and 3 m high concrete lower piers for impact resistance
Courtesy of Mabey Hire Services

- railway bridges (although temporary systems have been adapted for rail use)
- sites where dimensional constraints eliminate the use of any standard system
- simple short-span footbridges where the use of scaffold systems, unit beams, etc., is acceptable.

19.2.4 Foundations types and intermediate supports

The foundations for temporary bridging are loaded differently to those of other temporary works, such as falsework or scaffolding. There will be substantial lateral loads from vehicle or plant braking loads, in addition to axle loading. Designs of these foundations are specialised, and guidance should be sought from the suppliers of temporary bridges. Guidance on temporary foundation types is given in other chapters in this book. Many different types of foundation are adopted for supporting temporary bridges, ranging from simple timber mats placed on granular fill to concrete spread footings and various piled solutions. BS 5975 (BSI, 2011) Clause 18.9 states allowable bearing pressures on compacted fill for use in temporary works. Figure 19.2 depicts reinforced bank seat with end walls supported on temporary fill with gabion walls. Figure 19.4 depicts a typical example of a bank seat arrangement for a temporary site haul road bridge.

Key factors in the choice of type of foundations are economy, speed of installation and method of removal or making good following dismantling of the bridge. Cost and time savings can be made by not adopting specifications of permanent structures

Figure 19.4 Typical bank seat detail for temporary panel bridge
Courtesy of Mabey Hire Services

- minimising concrete reinforcement (e.g. anti-crack steel for durability may not be required)
- allowing greater settlement than for a permanent design
- considering reductions in vertical and horizontal specified loading to the bridge deck (e.g. some load values such as highway longitudinal loads that may be deemed inappropriate for temporary site construction applications)
- the use of pre-cast concrete and timber foundation elements
- the bridge supplier can provide intermediate piers using a proprietary braced trestle system.

19.3. The design process

Considerations of management, safety and other legislation in relation to the provision of temporary works are dealt with in Chapters 1 and 2. BS 5975 (BSI, 2011) sets out the main items of legislation and procedures that are to be followed. Some key design and checking aspects specific to temporary bridge design are outlined below.

19.3.1 Programme

Establishing an outline programme from the outset is a vital part of the design process. The requirement for bridging will have been identified in the temporary works (TW) register. The likely start date and period of use of the bridge will influence the choice of system due to considerations of economy, performance and availability. Sufficient time should be given to checking the design.

19.3.2 Loading
19.3.2.1 Public use
For public highways and footpaths, the relevant highway authority will specify the imposed loading, including any guardrail and/or barrier loading. They are most likely to adopt a load rating from a standard specification such as the Highways Agency HA, HB and pedestrian loading. Traffic loads on bridges is provided in BS EN 1991-2 (BSI, 2003). Where side protection is specified, the solidity of any such barriers can impart significant wind forces onto the bridge.

19.3.2.2 Site bridges
Loading for site access routes will be specified to the bridge procurer in a design brief, usually prepared by the principal contractor after TW consultations. The brief can be carried out in a number of ways, and the following aspects should be considered.

- Single vehicle loading: adopting one vehicle per span is accepted practice as long as measures are established to control vehicle movements and allow for vehicle breakdown (e.g. towing off by second vehicle). Emergency vehicles should be considered where lighter vehicles are specified.
- Bridge Assessment Standards: Highways Agency's bridge assessment standard BD21/01 (HA, 2001) is a useful document for specifying loading for multiple vehicles where the maximum gross vehicle weight is under 44 tonnes.
- Vehicle numbers for fatigue: the approximate total number of vehicle passes should be established.
- Edge protection requirements depending on use of the bridge, guardrails and/or vehicle edge protection barriers may be required; these can impart high lateral forces.
- Pedestrian loading for non-public applications can be specified in a number of ways providing measures are established to control the loading on site. It is recommended that Service Class 1 ($0.75 \, kN/m^2$) be the minimum, although each member of any platform should be designed for a minimum Service Class 2 loading ($1.50 \, kN/m^2$).

19.3.3 Cross-section and span considerations
Finding the optimum width is important both for economy and safety as excessive width can encourage higher vehicle speeds, possible passing traffic with risks of collision and incur unnecessary cost.

With regard to spans, the minimum clearance envelopes for vehicles, pedestrians, railways, water-borne traffic, flooding and any other obstacles should be established with the relevant authorities and included in the TW design brief. Consider areas that may be required for construction, as this can affect the choice of span arrangement. Establishing the dismantling method is important, as the site layout will often change significantly while the bridge is in use and the method of dismantling may not be the reverse of the assembly procedure.

The TWC should ensure that the deck and foundation design are compatible to find the optimum arrangement. Choice of articulation will be a part of this process. An

example of severe constraints in the design of foundation and bridge is depicted in Figure 19.5.

19.3.4 Detailed design and checking
Having established the construction type and layout, design output is generally as follows.

■ Confirmation of the design brief and submission of any client technical approval documentation (e.g. Form C on railway works).
■ General arrangement drawings, including foundations.
■ Calculations from (a) suppliers and (b) foundation designers.
■ Drawings and calculations for any special scheme-specific components.
■ Design risk assessments. Particular considerations for temporary bridges are: control of loading on the deck; clearances below for vehicle impact or flooding, etc.; temporary loads and stability during installation and dismantling; ground conditions for installation and dismantling; site security (bridges are often outside scope of regular site control measures).
■ Design check certificates.

Note that although the bridge supplier may issue a design check certificate to its own check category, there should be a separate design check certificate for the temporary works as a whole, including the foundations (see Chapter 2 on management).

19.3.5   Design standards and strength data

The specific requirements for temporary bridging are not the same as those required for permanent bridges. Established bridging manufacturers have the advantages of knowledge gained from experience in developing, testing and using their systems, however. This is incorporated into published strength tables with specified factors of safety for temporary bridging.

19.3.6   Client technical approval

The Client could be Network Rail, the Highways Agency, a local authority or British Nuclear Fuels Ltd, and so procedures to obtain technical approval from clients for temporary bridges can vary greatly. Successfully navigating the more complex client procedures can be confusing, especially as many were developed for permanent works. The key to success is to (1) identify the procedure to be followed at an early stage, and allocate engineers with suitable specialist experience and qualifications from each organisation involved and (2) plan the approval process including identification of key stages and dates.

19.3.7   Other design considerations

Details that the designer may need to consider include the following.

- Deck surface: the use of anti-skid surfacing with high levels of skid resistance and durability. These can be factory applied to temporary bridge steel deck.
- Deck drainage: most temporary bridge decks are formed of a series of relatively lightweight deck units which flex independently under load. Such units are designed for water to pass through the joints, and sealing is not a practical option.
- Parapet: various proprietary parapet systems are available from the bridge suppliers.
- Impact protection: consideration must be given to the risk of vehicle, train or vessel impact to temporary bridge soffits and supports. Common solutions include increasing clearances outside the zone of risk, barrier systems, earth bunds, sacrificial goal posts or beams and concrete piers (see Figures 19.2 and 19.3).

19.4.   Transportation and construction

19.4.1   Transportation

Bridging systems have generally been developed with transportation in mind. Panel bridges and other truss systems can all be transported on standard road vehicles. The main factor in the development of all welded deck systems is to minimise components and improve the speed of installation; they are therefore manufactured and delivered to the site in fixed span lengths of 20 m or more. The longer spans will often require specialised transportation, but cost of transportation is offset by the significantly faster erection rates.

19.4.2   Range of installation methods available

The constraints of space, time, foundations, access, safety, environment and cost result in a broad range of installation techniques being adopted. The most common methods are described below.

■ Assembly in place: this simply involves assembling the span(s) in place, for example, where the bridge is being built on top of an existing bridge or on the ground where excavation beneath will follow installation. Site craneage would be required.

■ Lift into place: the development and availability of large mobile cranes has permitted the lifting of ever larger and heavier spans. Safety and speed are the main beneficiaries of lifting. Particular attention is required for the design and installation of the temporary works of the crane pad foundations to cater for the outrigger loads.

■ Traditional advancing launch: this is often the only practical method for medium- and long-span applications. Standard bridging is used to form a temporary lightweight cantilevered nose connected to the front of the structure. The completed deck is then easily moved forward and controlled using site plant, winches or tirfors. As the bridge is advanced on ground-mounted rollers, the position of the centre of gravity of the bridge must be carefully monitored (particularly where the bridge is advanced and sections of completed bridge added to the rear end). As the launching nose advances, the tip will deflect and suitable allowances made. The physical act of rolling a bridge will cause top and bottom booms to change from tension to compression and vice versa; in such cases it is even more important that the bridge supplier's instructions are followed.

■ Other launch methods such as the tail launch, which uses additional bridging at the rear of the structure, can be used. Other installation methods include floating on pontoons and cantilever build, as illustrated in Figure 19.6.

Figure 19.6 Side spans of a panel bridge being installed using the cantilever method
Courtesy of Mabey Hire Services

19.4.3 Site planning and execution

19.4.3.1 Site constraints

It is important to establish access and site constraints at the start of the design process, as the choice of bridge system and span arrangement is very often determined by these details. These should be included in the design brief. Timely site visits and making good use of the bridge supplier's specialist knowledge is the key to success.

19.4.3.2 Construction programme

Time constraints such as for rail and road closures will often be the main factor for determining the installation and removal methods. Lifting in a pre-assembled deck is favoured if it means that road or rail closure times will be short.

19.4.3.3 Site safety and planning

Careful planning must be carried out and documented. The responsibilities should be established at an early part of the design process. The CDM coordinator and the site TWC have important roles in controlling the process (see Chapter 2 on management). The overall design must be reviewed to ensure that structural stability of the temporary bridge is maintained at all phases of construction and use and, often forgotten, during dismantling.

The documentation should include the following

- a schedule of site facilities, plant and equipment together with clarification of individual responsibilities
- construction sequence and drawings including sufficient detail to ensure health and safety, highlighting any identified design risks
- a risk assessment specific to the scheme together with measures as required to reduce the risks to acceptable levels, such as minimising working at height
- a detailed and approved method statement and operating manuals for the equipment.

19.4.3.4 Site operations

Although bridging systems are designed for ease and speed of installation, there are still many risks involved. Experienced and skilled supervisors and (where appropriate) steel erectors familiar with bridging systems should be used. Good communications between all parties is vital. The use of suppliers' training DVDs and possible site-based workshops are important to familiarise operatives in the specialist equipment in use.

19.4.3.5 Inspections

Inspection requirements should be established before construction commences, and will include short- and long-term inspection regimes. Many factors will influence the frequency and extent of inspections such as the bridge type and intensity of loading. Conventional means of access methods are usually employed, such as the use of mobile elevated working platforms (MEWP). Although temporary bridging would be inspected on a construction site as part of the statutory inspection, the specialised nature of the equipment often requires specific regular checks to be carried out by persons familiar with the equipment who also have the training to know which part of the structure can be susceptible to fatigue or wear. The advice of the specialist supplier should be sought.

19.5. Other applications of temporary bridging parts

The versatility of many standard bridge parts allows alternative uses in temporary works applications, including the following.

- Panel bridge truss elements used for spanning falsework girders. As the elements are joined by pins in shear, there is no control over the deflection of the assembly and allowance has to be made either by tapered firring pieces and/or a falsework skeletal system seated on the girders with facilities for height adjustment (see BS 5975; clauses 19.5 and 19.7.1).
- Truss elements in the vertical plane to form supports for bridges and other structures.
- Bridge decking elements used with panel or trestle systems to form site working platforms.
- Deck elements placed on compacted fill and used to spread the applied load and reduce the applied bearing capacity required on the compacted fill.

REFERENCES

BSI (2003) BS EN 1991-2: EuroCode 1: Actions on structures. Part 2: Traffic loads on bridges. BSI, London.

BSI (2011) BS 5975: 2008 + A1: 2011 Code of practice for temporary works procedures and the permissible stress design of falsework. BSI, London.

HA (Highways Agency) (2001) BD21/01: The assessment of highway bridges and structures. HMSO, London.

FURTHER READING

HA (2005) BD2/05: Technical Approval of Highway Structures. HMSO, London.

Harpur J (1991) A Bridge to Victory. HMSO, London.

Joiner JH (2001) One more River to Cross. Leo Cooper (imprint of Pen and Sword, Barnsley).

Network Rail (2004) Technical Approval of Design, Construction and Maintenance of Civil Engineering Infrastructure. Network Rail, London.

Useful web addresses

http://www.dft.gov.uk/pgr/roadsafety/drs/drivingforwork/largeorheavyloads

http://www.hse.gov.uk

Temporary Works: Principles of Design and Construction
ISBN 978-0-7277-4177-6

ICE Publishing: All rights reserved
http://dx.doi.org/10.1680/twpdc.41776.243

Chapter 20
Heavy moves

Martin Haynes Sales & Marketing Director, Fagioli Ltd
Andrea Massera Engineering Director, Fagioli SpA

This chapter deals with the horizontal and vertical movement of heavy loads. It outlines the reasons for choosing this method of construction and discusses the various methods that are available and used within the industry. Although conventional cranes are mentioned, priority is given to alternative techniques including trailers, hydraulic jacks and various skidding systems.

20.1. Introduction

Firstly, what constitutes a 'heavy move'? For the purposes of this chapter, a heavy move is something that cannot be installed using conventional site plant. This could be as low as five tonnes (e.g. retrofitting a vault into an existing bank basement) or as heavy as 30 000 tonnes (lifting of a complete oil platform). The idea of constructing a component somewhere other than its final location must offer a significant advantage over in situ construction for it to be considered. These are usually seen as one or more of the following.

20.1.1 Programme savings

The heavy moving technique allows construction activities to take place concurrently. For example, during the construction of Kylesku Bridge in Scotland, in situ construction of the approach spans together with offsite casting of the centre span with installation using a combination of heavy move techniques allowed lost programme time to be regained (see Figure 20.1).

Occasionally, the programme will dictate that a heavy move technique is necessary. This is commonly seen during replacement of rail and motorway bridges. The new bridge is constructed close to the existing bridge, and the old bridge is moved out (by skidding or trailers) and the new bridge installed in a similar manner. The on-site programme and therefore disruption to the public is kept to a minimum (refer to Chapter 27 on bridge installation techniques). In addition, off-site prefabrication permits the erection of industrial plants, for example, in locations where climatic conditions are adverse and the available site construction period restricted to a few months a year.

20.1.2 Improved safety

The main improvements to safety are associated with minimising work at height; construction at ground level is inherently safer than working at height. This not only applies to falling personnel but to the potential injury due to dropped objects.

Figure 20.1 Kylesku Bridge
Courtesy of PGS Films

20.1.3 Improved quality

As with improved safety, the improved quality aspect is largely associated with work at height. Workers at ground level are more likely to take care over their work. Likewise, inspections are easier to perform and likely to be more thorough.

20.1.4 Cost savings

Construction work is generally won by competitive tender. For the heavy move technique to be considered, it must normally offer a significant overall cost saving to in situ construction. The fact that so many techniques and companies offering these services are available is a good indication that the technique works.

20.2. Techniques
20.2.1 Cranes

Two types of crane are widely available for heavy lifts: these are truck-mounted telescopic boom cranes and crawler-mounted lattice boom cranes. Many other types of crane are available (e.g. tower cranes) but are not considered because of lack of capacity and/or availability.

20.2.1.1 Truck-mounted telescopic boom cranes

Truck-mounted telescopic boom cranes are available in capacities up to 1200 tonnes. These cranes are quick to mobilise and set up. They normally arrive at site with their

boom attached; they are ready to lift after placing their outriggers and extending their boom. They can lift, slew (rotate) and boom up or down, but cannot travel under load. Note that this type of crane can only lift its quoted capacity with the boom at minimum extension and radius; capacities reduce quickly as the boom length and/or radius is increased.

20.2.1.2 Crawler-mounted lattice boom cranes
Crawler-mounted lattice boom cranes (Figure 20.2) are available in capacities up to 3000 tonnes. Typically they will arrive in several truckloads and require site assembly. They have higher capacities, however, and, unlike truck cranes, can travel with the load.

20.2.1.3 Crane selection
In general, if a truck-mounted telescopic crane can perform the lift then the choice is simple; such a crane will be quicker and cheaper than a crawler crane.

The selection of which crane to use will take into account

- the weight and centre of gravity location of the lifted item (the hook of the crane must be over the centre of gravity or the load will tip)

- the dimensions of the lifted item
- the delivery and final locations of the lifted item
- the space available for the crane including that required for assembly/dismantling
- the allowable ground bearing including the point loads if using a crane with outriggers
- any client/contractor/project/site-specific regulations regarding the use of cranes.

Once these points have been established, the best practice is to consult the crane hire companies who will select the most suitable crane and prepare the necessary rigging studies. This will allow the selection of the most suitable crane that is available.

An alternative is to carry out the rigging studies oneself. Starting with the information above, the crane location should be set on plan together with the build/delivery and final locations of the lifted item. The distance between the centre point of the crane slew ring and the centre of gravity of the load is the lift radius. The length of the boom is decided next and will depend upon the lift height required. Once these physical dimensions have been established, crane duties (a series of charts/tables showing lift capacities with various combinations of boom length and lift radii) must be consulted to see which crane and configuration is most suitable. Cross-referencing the lift radius with boom length will give the safe lifting capacity of the crane.

Operationally, crane lifts are relatively quick when compared to alternative methods with most lifts being completed within one hour. When in operation, however, all cranes have a limiting wind speed; in general the longer the boom, the lower the operational wind speed. The crane duties will specify the limiting wind speed for the crane which can be as low as 9 m/s.

20.2.2 Trailers

Self-propelled modular transporters (SPMTs) have the ability to move huge loads over long distances with minimal ground preparation (see Figure 20.3). The item to be moved will generally be built on temporary supports leaving a clear space 1500 mm high underneath to allow the SPMTs to be inserted. The SPMTs have an integral jacking system to lift the item from the temporary supports. Once the load is on the trailer bed it can be moved to location and, if required, the trailer hydraulics can be used to transfer the load into the permanent supports.

SPMTs come in two basic module sizes of four axles and six axles with capacities around 32 tonnes per axle line, which is in excess of even major road capacities. These modules can be connected together to provide the correct capacity and physical configuration necessary for a particular move. Once inter-connected, they act as a single unit and are operated from a single point. Linking SPMTs together allows massive structures to be moved; loads in excess of 10 000 tonnes are not unusual.

If considering the use of SPMTs, then consult the specialist transport companies offering such equipment. They will need to know the following information

- the item weight and the centre of gravity location
- the construction location and support details
- the final location and details of the permanent supports (if the SPMTs will be used for load transfer)
- details of the route including allowable ground loading, potential obstructions and gradients.

Operationally, SPMTs are quicker than alternative systems (e.g. skidding) with operational speeds of up to 5 km/h; speeds in excess of 500 m/h will however result in a reduced load-carrying capacity. There is no wind speed rating for using SPMTs as there is with cranes; however, the wind load on the item needs to be considered and may result in a limiting wind speed for any particular operation.

20.2.3   Jacking systems
20.2.3.1 Cylinder jacks
Due to limited stroke, cylinder jacks (and flat jacks, air bags, etc.) are normally used for load transfer only rather than lifting. However, they are normally required in conjunction with skidding systems (see Section 20.2.4) to transfer load.

In cases where a relatively short lift (e.g. less than 2 m) is required, then cylinder jacks can be used to jack and pack the load (see Figure 20.4). This technique can be used in

Figure 20.4 Jack and pack (12 × 200 tonne)
Courtesy of Fagioli Group

conjunction with trailers or hydraulic skid shoes to allow the item to be built closer to ground level.

Most cylinder jacks will operate with a full load at around 700 bars of pressure, so expect bearing loads around 70 N/mm^2 above and below the jack. Flat jacks operate at 150 bars and air bags even less, so there are generally no bearing pressure problems.

20.2.3.2 Strand jacks

Unlike cylinder jacks, strand jacks are not constrained by limitations of jack stroke (see Figure 20.5). They operate by pulling on a strand cable in repeated cycles and are therefore effective lifting, lowering and pulling devices. The strand cables comprise multiple pre-stressing strands: the more strands in a cable the greater the lifting capacity. Strand jacks are available in sizes from 15 tonnes capacity to over 1000 tonnes for a single unit. They can be used individually or in multiples to give the required lifting capacity. Over 150 strand jacks have been used in single-lift operations and lift weights of over 20 000 tonnes have been achieved.

Strand jacks are only one part of the overall lifting system; in addition, they will require pumping systems and control systems. It is important that the systems are correctly matched to ensure a properly controlled and synchronised operation. The control systems available are very precise, which is useful when setting weld gaps or fitting bolts.

Figure 20.5 Strand jacks mounted on a purpose-built structure (2000 tonne lift)
Courtesy of Fagioli Group

Strand jacking arrangements are very flexible and can easily fit with the shape of the item being lifted. They can be used in situations where cranes would be impractical or even impossible (e.g. an aircraft hanger roof where there are multiple lift points with differing loads).

Strand jacks need a support structure (see Figure 20.6). Wherever possible, the supports should utilise the permanent works with only minor modifications. There are no specific design requirements for the strand jack supports; most are steel which is designed in accordance with normal codes. The speed of operation of strand jacks (m/h rather than m/min) means that dynamic loads are not really applicable.

If it is not possible to utilise the permanent works then it may be necessary to consider a complete temporary support system. This can be purpose-built or configured from a modular support system available to hire. Such support systems are available with very high capacities (500 tonnes on a 100 m unguyed tower and much more for guyed towers) and the combination of a modular support system and strand jacks can be a viable alternative to heavy cranes.

When specifying a strand jack system, the following should be considered

■ number of lift points
■ load at each lift point

- jack support detail
- anchor connection detail
- lift speed required.

Limiting wind speeds will depend on the support structure and the wind area of the lifted item. The typical limiting wind speed for strand jack operations is 16 m/s.

20.2.4 Skidding systems

Skidding systems can be fully self-contained units incorporating skid tracks, low-friction skidding interfaces, load-transfer mechanisms and horizontal movement units (typically the hydraulic skid shoes described in Section 20.2.4.2). However, most systems are a combination of items brought together for a particular move. For example, rollers will need skid tracks, a vertical jacking system and a pulling or pushing system.

20.2.4.1 Rollers

Mechanical rollers have been in use for many years. They work by using an endless chain around a central bearing plate to provide a low-friction interface. Typical friction values are quoted at around 5% but could go as low as 2% so beware, especially if moving downhill. Rollers do not normally require a breakout force (i.e. a greater force to start the movement) and are smooth in operation.

Rollers are available in capacities from very low values up to 1000 tonnes per unit, but this size would be unusual. Multiple units are typically used to give the desired load capacity. The rollers should be suitably sized to suit the load at every support point, and should also have sufficient additional capacity to cope with possible unknown affects (e.g. differential settlement). For loads over 1000 tonnes, the recommendation is that rollers should be used at 50% of capacity.

Some of the rollers will need to be provided with guides to ensure that the item to be moved follows the correct path. Note, however, that providing too many guides can lead to binding during the move. Care is also required at joints in skid tracks to ensure continuity of line and level.

The main drawback with rollers is that they have high localised bearing loads which need to be spread through the skid tracks, possibly using mats or cribbing as an additional layer. This will affect the build height and may also require extensive jacking down on completion of the operation.

20.2.4.2 Hydraulic skid shoes

Hydraulic skid shoes are self-contained movement systems in that they contain load transfer jacks, a low friction interface and horizontal movement jacks (see Figure 20.7). The item will need to be built on temporary supports leaving a clear

Figure 20.7 Skid shoe (600 tonne capacity)
Courtesy of Fagioli Group

space of at least 1500 mm underneath to allow the shoes to be inserted. The 1500 mm height may need to be increased to allow for the depth of the skid tracks and any load spreading. The low-friction interface is normally stainless steel–PTFE (polytetra-fluoroethylene) which needs to be lubricated.

The control systems available with skid shoes allow a high degree of control over the loads and displacements; high tolerances of accuracy can be achieved both during the movement and final placement.

The limitation of skid shoes is that they work in one direction only. Changes of direction will require a set down of the load onto temporary supports followed by re-alignment of the track and shoes.

20.2.4.3 Low-friction interfaces
An alternative to mechanical rollers is to use a low-friction skid interface under the moved item. This can be included at the build stage so that a load transfer system is not required. Also, this can be as large as required on plan so that bearing loads are minimised. The skid interface has a static base layer (the skid track) and a moving upper layer (fixed to the item). The combinations of layers in normal use have the coefficients of friction as listed in Table 20.1.

All sources for coefficients of friction advise the use of care in using the values. For the purposes of a heavy move, this means that the movement system should consider a worst-case scenario and be conservative in specifying the forces required. For example, it would be normal to specify a pulling force of 10% if using PTFE on steel.

With low-friction interfaces there may be a requirement for breakout (a higher pulling force to start movement), particularly if the item has been static for an extended period of time.

20.3. Design
20.3.1 General
The heavy move technique requires accurate preparation. Engineering design is the key element for the success of the operation from the point of view of safety, technical, budget and schedule. Engineering targets are to identify the most safe, robust, economic method and equipment and to produce complete and clear technical documentation for

Table 20.1 Slide friction coefficients
Data taken from http://www.engineersedge.com/coeffients_of_friction.htm

Layer 1	Layer 2	Dry	Lubricated
Steel	PTFE	0.04	0.04
Steel	Steel	0.80	0.16
Steel	Wood	0.20–0.60	0.20

the safe execution of the operations, avoiding any miscommunication from engineering to site.

Input for the engineering activities, which is carefully reviewed and assessed by a competent and experienced engineer, includes the following

- lay-out, dimensions, drawings of the item
- weight (including inaccuracy factor) and centre of gravity location (CoG envelope is recommended to allow for position inaccuracy)
- identification of the handling points of the item (main structures, lifting lugs, trunnions, etc.)
- information about the transport route (site survey) and existing infrastructures (bridges, etc.)
- information about the installation yard (available space, underground services, ground capacity, etc.)
- applicable client documents, national/international codes
- previous experience and lessons learned.

The main output for the engineering activities include

- transport and lifting drawings as well as installation phases drawings for the item
- installation procedures, operation manuals
- calculation reports for installation hardware
- design, shop drawings for structures as well as fabrication/inspection plans
- 3D simulations where appropriate.

Engineering documents are the base for analysis of all safety aspects of the operations. HAZID (hazard identification study), HAZOP (hazard and operability study) and Safety Job Analysis are structured review techniques for identification and assessment of operation hazards, techniques which need sound and detailed engineering documents.

20.3.2 Crane lifting design

Crane lifting engineering consists of

- selection and design of adequate lifting points for the item
- analysis of the structure to be lifted
- selection of crane(s) of adequate capacity
- selection of appropriate lifting hardware (rigging)
- definition of operational criteria.

The load distribution in a lift is normally calculated as a static load case by applying the dynamic hook load (DHL) at the hook position and distributing weight and any special load to each element. The DHL is the product of lifted load (including rigging) and the dynamic amplification factor (DAF). The skew load factor (SKL) allows for the extra loading on slings caused by the effect of sling-length and lift-point manufacturing tolerances as well as rigging arrangements, which will affect a statically indeterminate lift. For statically indeterminate lifts, such as 4 slings in a pyramid arrangement, the SKL could vary over a wide range of 1.0–2.0, dependent upon sling-length tolerance and load shape. A figure of 1.25 is often taken, where sling length tolerance is within ±0.25% of its nominal length.

The maximum dynamic forces calculated as explained above are the design forces for lifted item structure and its pad-eyes for slings, grommets and lifting hardware (e.g. lifting beams).

Shackles are selected on the base of the static hook load (SHL) since their safety factor also covers the dynamic effect. Cranes are selected on the basis of SHL applied at the hook position and by determining the reactions for each crane involved in the lifting operation, considering the CoG envelope as appropriate.

Recommended DAFs for onshore lifting, according to DNV (2000; Part 2, Chapter 5) Rules, are as shown in Table 20.2. As a general rule, lift operation shall be studied in such a manner that the maximum tilt of the lifted item is less than 2%, unless there is a different requirement of the client. The maximum operational wind speed shall be defined according to the crane manufacturer instructions, taking into consideration the weight and shape (drag factor) of the lifted item. A normal value for the maximum operational wind speed is $v = 9.0 \, m/s$ (taken at top of crane boom). The maximum ratio of exposed surface/weight for the lifted item is $1 \, m^2/tonne$ (otherwise the operational wind speed shall be reduced).

Lifting a load with two or more cranes requires greater planning since many factors affect the operation: accuracy of weight/CoG, capacities of lifting accessories, synchronisation of crane motions, crane instrumentation, site conditions and supervision. When such factors cannot be accurately evaluated, good engineering and industry practice dictates that an appropriate down-rating should be applied to all cranes involved (BSI, 2006) as follows.

- Single lift: crane de-rated to 90% of the allowable capacity.
- Multiple lift: all cranes de-rated to 80% of the allowable capacity.
- Crane used as tailing crane during lifting with tower system: crane de-rated to 90% of the allowable capacity.

Higher values for the de-rating factor can be used, but should be based on individual cases. The load transferred by the crane to the ground should be carefully evaluated. The pressure under a crawler crane varies over the range 40–60 tonne/m^2 (crane working at more than 70% of its capacity). Adequate spreader mats should be placed

Table 20.2 Dynamic amplification factors
Data taken from DNV (2000)

Static hook load: tonnes	50–100	100–1000
DAF onshore	1.10	1.05

under the crawler to reduce the soil bearing pressure to less than 20 tonne/m². Good practice is to require a ground bearing capacity for crane operational area of 25 tonne/m² (refer to Chapter 5 on site roads and working platforms).

The crane lifting area should be adequately prepared and tested for the maximum ground pressure to ensure that (1) the maximum inclination of the ground is within ±0.3° (±0.5%) in any direction and (2) the maximum ground settlement under pressure of 25 tonne/m² for crane lifting is within 30 mm (this will vary with crane model).

Where required, adequate installation guides should be provided for placing the lifted items to ensure that the load lands at the correct location. Design load for the guides is a horizontal force of not less than 5% of the weight of the lifted item.

As a general rule, the lifting operation should be studied in such a manner that load does not get any closer than 1 m to the crane boom or any other structure. This limit can be changed depending on the operational conditions (height, visibility, wind, etc.).

Clearance from energised power lines should be as described in the American Society of Mechanical Engineers document B 30.5-2000 (ASME, 2000), see Table 20.3. Typical output documents of lifting engineer include

- the lifting plan showing crane operating radius
- crane configuration
- position with respect to site and crane usage factor with capacity of each component
- the rigging drawing
- the operational procedure.

20.3.3 Heavy transport using SPMTs

Heavy transport engineering documents include the following

- analysis of the item structure to be transported (inputs for this analysis are the transport drawings and the SPMTs reactions against the item structure, issued by the Heavy Transport Contractor)

Table 20.3 Required clearance for normal voltage in operation near high-voltage power lines
Data taken from ASME (2000)

Normal voltage: kV	Minimum required clearance: ft (m)
<50	10 (3.05)
>50–200	15 (4.60)
>200–350	20 (6.10)
>350–500	25 (7.62)

- design of the transport beams/stools and of the lashing/stopper system
- selection of appropriate transport arrangement for the SPMTs
- stability and structural check of the convoy (tipping angle for structural stability and for structural overload within safe limits)
- definition of the operational requirements for the transport and issue of operational procedure.

For the design transport weight (DTW), the vertical DAF is 1.0. The transported item is subject to horizontal inertia loads in the longitudinal direction (direction of motion) and in the transverse direction due to acceleration/deceleration. It is also subjected to horizontal loads due to the road slope, SPMT type, number of driven axles, convoy arrangement and operational criteria.

For SPMTs (maximum design speed 5 km/h), normal ranges for horizontal accelerations are as follows

- longitudinal acceleration $a1 = (0.10 - 0.30) \times g$
- transverse acceleration $a2 = (0.05 - 0.15) \times g$
- slope effect (due to transport path slope longitudinal or transverse) $a3 = slope(\%) \times g$.

When on slope, the acceleration a3 is added to a1 or a2. Between the underside of the transported item and top steel of SPMTs frame/stools, plywood is used for a higher friction coefficient. An adequate lashing/stopper system should be provided, designed to withstand (with the contribution of the friction, when appropriate) the total horizontal load.

The loads/reactions distribution in the transport system is calculated as a static load case by distributing the DTW to each temporary transport element and to SPMTs. As a general rule, the SPMT hydraulic circuits are arranged in such a way that a 3-point system is achieved. With this system (isostatic), the reactions on the trailers are practically constant and there is no overstress in the transported item or in the SPMT structure/hydraulic system. If tall items are transported with only one SPMT line, then the 4-point system is considered to have more stability. SPMTs are also suitable equipment for the execution of load-in/load-out operations, since they can spread heavy loads within the capacity limits of a barge or ship deck.

The design operation conditions which are generally considered are as follows

- DTW of the item and CoG location
- out of verticality due to operator tolerance $\pm 2°$
- maximum transport path slope longitudinal and transverse
- design wind speed of 16 m/s (3 s gust at 10 m height) for site transport operations
- design wind speed of 12 m/s for load-in/load-out operations
- maximum barge/ship vertical motion due to swell of ± 100 mm, minimum period 10 s (for load-in load-out operation)

- ship maximum trim 1%, maximum heel 1% (for load-in load-out operations)
- ship in level with the quay: ±100 mm (for load-in load-out operations).

In the operational condition, considering the most unfavourable loads combination, the SPMTs axle loads should not exceed the allowable loads stated by the manufacturer (which depend on the travelling speed). When several axles are overhanging, the trailer spine beam bending capacity should not be exceeded.

The SPMTs tractive power (as per the Manufacturer's data sheet) should be at least 20% greater than the theoretical power required to overcome rolling friction and slope.

As general rule, the transport path should be checked in order to verify there is a minimum lateral and top clearance of 1 m from existing structures. Less clearance can be accepted after checking on a case-by-case basis.

When SPMTs are loaded to full capacity (36 tonnes per axle), the maximum ground gross pressure is 10 tonne/m^2 (with reference to the SPMT frame projected area). The local contact pressure under the wheels is c. 9.5 kg/cm^2 (tyre inflation pressure of 10 bar). Maximum ground pressure for each specific transport shall be transmitted to the client to check the existing bridges, culverts, underground services, retaining walls, quays, etc.

Typical output documents include transport drawings (showing trailers arrangement under the item, hydraulic circuits, maximum operation axle loads, axle capacity and lashing details) and the transport operational procedure (with definition of responsibilities of the key persons, operation criteria to be respected and contingency plan).

REFERENCES

ASME (American Society of Mechanical Engineers) (2000) B 30.5-2000: Mobile and locomotive cranes. ASME, New York.
BSI (2006) BS 7121: Safe use of cranes. BSI, London.
DNV (Det Norske Veritas) (2000) Rules for planning and execution of marine operations. DNV, Høvik.

FURTHER READING

Bates GE (1998) Exxon Crane Guide: Lifting Safety Management System. Specialized Carriers and Rigging Association.
GL Noble Denton (2010) Guidelines for Marine Lifting Operations. 0027/ND. Noble Denton.
MacDonald JA, Rossnagel WA and Higgins LA (2009) *Handbook of Rigging*, 5th edition. McGraw-Hill Professional, New York.
Shapiro H, Shapiro JP and Shapiro LK (1999) *Cranes and Derricks*, 3rd edition. McGraw-Hill Professional, New York.

Useful web addresses

Rollers: http://www.hilmanrollers.com

Strand jacks: http://www.fagioli.com
Cylinder jacks: http://www.enerpac.com
Flat jacks: http://www.flatjack.co.uk
Trailers: http://www.fagioli.com
Telescopic cranes: http://www.ainscough.co.uk
Crawler cranes: http://www.weldex.co.uk

Temporary Works: Principles of Design and Construction
ISBN 978-0-7277-4177-6

ICE Publishing: All rights reserved
http://dx.doi.org/10.1680/twpdc.41776.259

Chapter 21
Access and proprietary scaffolds

Peter F. Pallett Pallett Temporary*Works* Ltd
Ian Nicoll Chief Engineer, Interserve Industrial Ltd

The provision of temporary safe working platforms for the erection, maintenance, construction, repair, access or inspection, etc. of structures is known as scaffolding. It can be formed from individual tubes with fittings or proprietary components. The design philosophy for stability of scaffolds and loading limits, together with the information necessary to source the safe height of most UK scaffolds without the need for further calculations, is discussed. The designation and simple rules for inspection are included.

21.1. Introduction

Wherever it is required to provide a safe place of work for the erection, maintenance, repair or demolition of buildings and other structures and to provide the necessary access, a temporary structure known as a scaffold is erected.

In the middle ages, a 'skaffaut' was a mobile tower equipped with battering rams used for assaulting castles. Shakespeare referred to the gallery structure at the Globe Theatre in London as the 'scaffoldage'. The first tubular steel scaffolding was seen in the UK around 1920, using standard 2 inch diameter water pipes that were available in 21 feet lengths. This type of scaffolding with 2 inch tubes connected together remains a common method, but more recent scaffolding equipment comprises proprietary components connected together. By its nature, such structures are usually temporary and, unlike permanent structures, require to be dismantled after use. This introduces a re-use aspect to scaffold structures which are almost always erected using material previously used. This generates an industry of supply (generally on hire), erection, use, inspection and maintenance, followed by dismantling, removal and inspection prior to reuse. Managing the scaffold is important in terms of maintaining its capability to provide adequate access.

Falls from height account for over 50% of fatal accidents in construction (see Chapter 1 on safety) and scaffolders are particularly at risk. The recommended procedures for controlling scaffolds and all temporary works are given in BS 5975: 2008 + A1: 2011 *Code of practice for temporary works procedures and the permissible stress design of falsework* (BSI, 2011). Industry guidance on scaffolding recognised by the Health and Safety Executive (HSE) is provided by the National Access and Scaffolding Con-federation (NASC). TG20 *Guide to good practice for scaffolding with tube and fittings* (NASC, 2008a) is the technical guidance on the European Standard BS EN 12811-1

259

(BSI, 2003a). NASC has also published a very useful 'toolbox talk' booklet on TG20. Guidance on proprietary scaffolding should be sought from the supplier/importer of the particular scaffold. Training courses are run through Construction Skills and NASC, and there is also a National Certification scheme for all scaffolders.

All users of scaffolding on site should be aware of the statutory requirements under the Work at Height Regulations and the Construction (Design and Management) Regulations (CDM). They should also be aware that it is their duty to provide a 'safe place of work'. The authoritative guidance is given in SG4:10 *Preventing Falls in Scaffolding* (NASC, 2010a) and its useful site booklet SG4:You (NASC, 2010b).

21.2. Selection and designation
21.2.1. Selection
Do I actually need a scaffold? When carrying out the initial design risk assessment to perform a task, the activity should be carefully considered. Ideally, the operation could be carried out at ground level, in which case no access might be required; conversely, painting the outside of a building would require access to the working area. The procurer would need to consider the risk alternatives; these might include rope access, mobile elevated working platforms (MEWPs), mast climbing scaffolds or provision of accessible working platforms. Often in modern multi-storey new build construction, the design has removed the need for external access platforms and scaffolding can be avoided. There will however be many applications where provision of regular access platforms will be required. In fact, they may often need to be considered by Permanent Works Designers under the CDM Regulations for future access requirements, such as planned long-term maintenance.

The two main types of scaffold are

- freestanding scaffolds (e.g. independent towers)
- independent tied scaffolds (where the scaffold itself is freestanding, but relies on the adjacent structure for its stability).

A typical arrangement of an independent tied scaffold using tube and fittings is shown in Figure 21.1, which also includes the terms regularly used in scaffolding.

Other types of scaffolds include

- birdcage scaffolds, generally on a 2.1 × 2.1 m grid with a single platform
- mast climbing scaffolds, which comprise a rigid tower with a bridging unit connected that elevates vertically up and down (proprietary items of equipment)
- putlog scaffolds: where there is an outside vertical standard and the inside of the platform is supported by the structure (commonly used on small housing projects with brickwork such that the inside support is a flattened tube end built into the bedding planes of the brickwork)
- slung/suspended scaffolds: where the platform is hung from above on either vertical tubes or wire ropes.

Figure 21.1 A typical independent tied scaffold in tube and fittings
Courtesy of Pallett Temporary*Works* Ltd

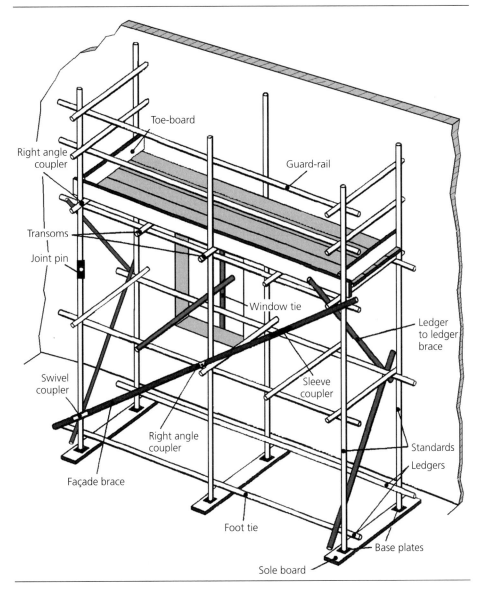

With the exception of mast climbing scaffolds, each type of scaffold discussed above is available either as traditional tube and fitting scaffolds or as proprietary prefabricated system scaffolds. The big advantage of traditional scaffolding is its adaptability on complex-shaped structures. Adaptability is often hard to achieve within the dimensional constraints of a proprietary system. Further decisions would include whether the scaffold is required to be left unclad, fitted with debris-netting or fully sheeted. Obviously there are significant design implications when sheeting or debris netting is considered on a scaffold, due to the increase in the applied wind loading.

Once the type of scaffold has been selected, the procurer needs to consider the activity for which the scaffold is required, the number of platforms, its width, any projections and, most importantly, the imposed loading per platform which will change depending on the activity to be performed. BS EN 12811-1 (BSI, 2003a) has introduced six designated imposed load categories for scaffolds, discussed later in this chapter.

21.2.2 Designation
NASC introduced a three-number designation for scaffolds which describes the type of scaffold used and assists procurers in selection of the majority of scaffolds, namely N1–N2–N3 where

- N1 is the BS EN 12811-1 (BSI, 2003a) load class (1–6)
- N2 is the number of boards between the vertical standards
- N3 is the number of inside boards (limited to 0, 1 or 2 maximum).

A typical designation would be 3–5–2, meaning load class 3 with 5 scaffold boards between the uprights and with 2 scaffold boards fitted on the inside adjacent to the structure being scaffolded. The cantilevered inside board is assumed lightly loaded. Where the inside boards are required to have the same load as the platform, a suffix F is added. Certain scaffolds are limited to only 1.8 m bay lengths, and these are designated with the suffix S.

The importance of the designation is that it defines the size and loading of the scaffold platforms, and is used by the designer to establish the safe height. The safe height of basic tube and fitting scaffolds for a range of wind conditions in the UK and Ireland, as a function of the scaffold designation, is listed in the tables in TG20 (NASC, 2008a).

21.3. Materials and components
21.3.1 Scaffold tube
21.3.1.1 Steel scaffold tube
The most common material in scaffolding is the scaffold tube, specified in BS EN 39 (BSI, 2001) with two wall thicknesses of scaffold tube, namely 3.2 mm and 4 mm for the same outside diameter. The tubes are known as Type 3 and Type 4, respectively. The general UK practice is to use Type 4 tube which means a thicker walled tube of 4 mm. Users should be aware that certain scaffold companies are using a thinner walled tube, but to a higher steel specification. Information on its use should be referred to the supplier. In the UK, an allowance for corroded tubes whose wall thickness is reduced by not more than 10% is considered and known as 'used' tube. The majority of scaffold tube used in the UK is galvanised, so use of the 'as new' values is recommended in TG20 (NASC, 2008a).

The safe load of any strut (member in compression) is limited by its buckling, so its effective length L_E and slenderness ratio L_E/r should be considered. For scaffold tubes

Table 21.1 Allowable axial load (kN) in scaffold tube struts

Effective length of scaffold tube: mm	BS EN39 Type 4		BS 1139: 1982 tube		BS EN39 Type 3		
	As new	Used	As new	Used	As new	Used	
500	73.5	65.6	66.5	59.2	60.2	53.7	
1000	58.6	52.0	53.9	47.9	48.1	42.8	
1500	42.1	37.1	39.9	35.2	34.9	30.9	
2000	29.1	25.6	28.2	**24.8**	24.2	21.4	
2500	20.6	18.1	20.1	17.7	17.2	15.2	
2700	**18.2**	15.9	17.9	15.7	15.4	13.6	
3000	15.1	13.3	14.9	13.1	12.7	11.2	
3200	**13.6**	11.9	13.4	11.7	11.7	10.1	
3500	11.6	10.1	11.4	10.0	9.7	8.5	
4000	9.1	8.0	9.0	7.9	7.6	6.7	
4250	8.1	7.1	8.1	7.1	6.8	6.0	
4500	7.3	6.4	7.3	6.4	6.1	5.4	≪limit as brace or strut
5000	6.0	5.3	6.0	5.2	5.1	4.5	
5500	5.0	4.4	5.0	4.4	4.2	3.7	
6000	4.3	3.8	4.3	3.7	3.6	3.2	
7000	3.2	2.8	3.2	2.8	2.7	2.4	≪limit as tie
8000	2.4	2.1	2.4	2.1	2.0	1.8	

Notes: Axial loads derived using a quasi-permissible stress approach according to BS EN 1993-1-1 (BSI, 2005b) with partial safety factors of $\gamma_f = 1.5$ and $\gamma_m = 1.1$.
The shaded values are for comparison purposes, and should *not* generally be used in scaffolds unless the scaffold has been designed

in compression, the slenderness ratio should meet the condition $L_E/r < 271$ for struts and braces intended to carry wind and lateral loads, i.e. the lacing and diagonal bracing should be less than 4.25 m long. Safe working loads of scaffold tubes related to the effective length L_E are listed in Table 21.1. Scaffold tube struts which have a free cantilever at the end, such as at the bottom of a freestanding scaffold, are regarded as having an effective length of the adjacent strut length plus twice the length of the free cantilever; see TG20 (NASC, 2008a; appendix D).

The safe axial tensile load for Type 4 scaffold tube is 79.1 kN but is usually limited by the safe slip load capacity of one coupler, i.e. 6.1 kN.

21.3.1.2 Aluminium scaffold tube
In certain cases, for example, to reduce weight, aluminium scaffold tube can be used. Some guidance is given in TG20 (NASC, 2008a). However, because of the different elastic properties, steel and aluminium scaffold tube should never be used together within a structure.

Table 21.2 Safe working loads for individual couplers and fittings

Type of fitting	Class	Type of load	Safe load: kN
Right angle coupler	BS EN 74-1 Class A	Slip along tube	6.1
	BS EN 74-1 Class B	Slip along tube	9.1
Swivel coupler	BS EN 74-1 Class A	Slip along tube	6.1
	BS EN 74-1 Class B	Slip along tube	9.1
Sleeve coupler	Class A	Tension	3.6
	Class B	Tension	5.5
Putlog coupler	BS EN 74-2	Force to pull tube axially out of coupler	0.63
Internal joint pin	–	Tension	nil
		Shear strength	21.0

21.3.2 Scaffold fittings

Also known as couplers, there are a great variety of different types manufactured, for example, right-angled (doubles), swivels, putlogs, band and plates, sleeves, etc. and each can be made as pressed steel, spring steel or drop forged. BS EN 74 (BSI, 2005a) covers the specification and testing of many couplers for use with steel tubes. The safe working loads summarised in Table 21.2 are from TG20 (NASC, 2008a). All couplers should be tightened correctly using the correct spanner.

21.3.3 Proprietary scaffolds

System scaffolds are relatively simple arrangements of scaffold using patented connections to reduce and sometimes eliminate the need for scaffold couplers (Figure 21.2). They essentially comprise separate standards, ledgers and transoms in modular lengths and are designed for fast assembly and dismantling. Although the standards are generally the same outside diameter as the scaffold tube, some have a thinner-walled tube which reduces the weight and therefore makes transporting and handling easier. The decking members are rarely interchangeable, often in steel, and fit into special transoms.

Figure 21.2 Some system scaffold connections
Courtesy of RMD Kwikform (UK) Ltd

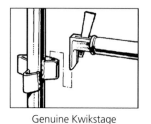 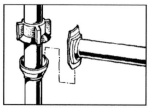 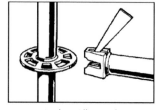

Genuine Kwikstage	Harsco Cuplok	Layher All-round

21.4.   Scaffold design
21.4.1   General
A very simple view is generally taken in the design, and imponderables such as stiffness of couplers is generally ignored. (The use of a complex computer program to analyse scaffolding allowed NASC to take account of some cruciform stiffness in preparing the safe height tables in TG20; NASC, 2008a, 2011.) The design methods cater for the safety factors for the materials and components. Provided that the scaffold is erected within certain workmanship limits for verticality, joint connections, etc., the couplers are rarely considered as giving any stiffness and merely act as connections. In tube and fitting scaffolds, the couplers will eccentrically load the standards as the tubes are separated by about 60 mm so, in theory, they apply torsion. This is ignored provided the diagonals are connected within 300 mm of the standards and the arrangement of bracing to counter the torsion is considered.

When considering the design of all scaffolds, the fact it can buckle or fall over in any direction should be taken into consideration. The accepted rule is: 'Think vertical, think horizontal, then think horizontal again'. The procurer will have previously decided whether the scaffold will be unclad, sheeted or debris-netted.

21.4.2   Permissible stress or limit state design
The design method traditionally used for scaffolding was 'permissible stress design' where the failure load was divided by a factor of safety (usually 2) to derive a safe working load. BS EN 12811-1 (BSI, 2003a) considers 'limit state analysis' where the structure is designed for the ultimate condition at failure and also at the time of loading (serviceability). Limit state analysis requires knowledge of the partial safety factors and the characteristic strength of the members to be considered before being able to establish its ability to resist load. This is a very difficult concept for site personnel who understand the 'safe working load' concepts. To enable scaffolding to be understood by the regular users, TG20 (NASC, 2008a) has accordingly adopted a quasi-permissible stress approach to scaffold design. This is why the loads for axial load in tubes and the capacities for couplers have been stated as 'safe loads' in Tables 21.1 and 21.2.

21.4.3   Loading on scaffolds
In addition to the self weight of the scaffold, its boards, guardrails, toeboards, etc., the scaffold has to withstand the imposed allowable load on the working platform(s) and environmental loads such as the wind.

21.4.3.1 Imposed loads
The imposed load depends on the nature of the work and all loads are assumed to be distributed.

- Service class 1: 0.75 kN/m^2; inspection and very light duty access.
- Service class 2: 1.50 kN/m^2; light duty such as painting and cleaning.
- Service class 3: 2.00 kN/m^2; general building work, brickwork, etc.
- Service class 4: 3.00 kN/m^2; heavy duty such as masonry work and heavy cladding.

BS EN 12811-1 (BSI, 2003a) states that a scaffold in use shall be loaded with one platform (generally the top) with the full service class load and an adjacent platform with 50% of that service class load. If more platforms are in use or the scaffold is taller than permitted, then the scaffold needs to be designed. TG20 Volume 2 (NASC, 2008a) provides a method for calculating the safe height of an unclad independent tied scaffold which has more than the two platforms loaded, by considering individual loads in the standards.

BS EN 12811-1 (BSI, 2003a) also requires a notional horizontal load of 2.5% of the vertical imposed load (minimum of 0.3 kN per bay) applied to each bay of the scaffold, and also states specific concentrated and partial area loads on the platforms.

21.4.3.2 Loading towers
When material has to be moved into a building, a specific loading tower may have to be considered. They require a separate design as the nature of the loading, its type and the safety aspects of loading towers are important considerations. The recommendation from TG20 (NASC, 2008a) states that where storage of material in palletised form is envisaged, the platform should be designed for a minimum distributed load of $10\,kN/m^2$ or the actual weight of material to be stored. Proprietary system scaffolds designed as loading towers will generally support the actual weight of material to be stored on more than one lift. The procurer of the scaffold should specify which use the platform is to be put to and the location and levels of such platforms.

21.4.3.3 Wind loading on scaffolds and the wind factor S_{wind}
The wind is a variable force and gets stronger the higher the position above the ground. It also blows stronger in exposed locations, and is dependent upon location. The wind force acts on the tubes, bracing, couplers, rakers and on any debris netting or sheeting attached to the scaffold. The magnitude of the wind forces will alter the required capacity of the ties and may affect the tie frequency.

To cater for the wind on all temporary works a simplified method of calculating the wind forces was developed for BS 5975: 2008 + A1: 2011 (BSI, 2011) and TG20 Supplement 1 (NASC, 2011) by introducing a wind factor S_{wind} for any particular site (see also Chapter 22 on falsework). It should be noted that the determination of the wind factor S_{wind} is only required once for each site.

To check the safe height of a scaffold at a site location using TG20 Supplement 1 (NASC, 2011), the wind factor S_{wind} needs to be evaluated. This is defined:

$$S_{wind} = T_{wind} \times v_{b,map}\left(1 + \frac{A}{1000}\right)$$

where $v_{b,map}$ is the fundamental wind velocity at the location (m/s), T_{wind} is the topography factor considering the ground conditions and A is the altitude of the site (m). Values for $v_{b,map}$ and T_{wind} are listed in both BS 5975: 2008 + A1: 2011 (BSI, 2011) and TG20 Supplement 1 (NASC, 2011).

When using debris netting or sheeting, it is recommended to place it on the outside of the outside standards. This will reduce the wind forces on the scaffold, especially those associated with drag when wind blows parallel to the façade.

21.4.4 Design of tube and fitting scaffolds

21.4.4.1 General

The use, loading class, number of platforms in use, maximum bay length and number of boards, etc. are determined using table 1 in TG20 (NASC, 2008a). This is the starting point of all design work.

The Work at Height Regulations requires calculations to be completed for all scaffolds unless there is either a pre-existing design, i.e. already completed in the office for a similar job, or the scaffold is erected in accordance with a recognised standard configuration. The latter refer to the use of basic scaffolds detailed in TG20 (NASC, 2008a), erected correctly and conforming to the bracing, loading and tying patterns established. Additionally, the latter also refers to technical data contained in the user guide for each system scaffold.

As with all structures when carrying out a full design, the three design requirements to consider having established the loads are the strength and stability of the members, followed by the lateral stability of the structure and finally the overall stability of the structure.

21.4.4.2 Element strength and element stability

Lift heights in scaffolding are generally 2.0 m although, in certain conditions, a pavement lift of 2.7 m may be considered. For a pavement lift, the first tie should be at the 2.7 m level. The bay length will vary depending on the load class, for example, a general purpose class 3 scaffold will have a maximum bay length of 2.1 m. The transoms will be spaced to suit the permissible span of the chosen boards; generally 225 mm wide × 38 mm thick scaffold boards will safely span 1.2 m, but a better quality of board is required to safely span 1.5 m.

Designers will be aware of the effect of effective lengths on the load capacity of the scaffold members. Buckling of struts is prevented by adequate sideways restraint in two directions at right angles, known as 'creating effective node points'. The value of the restraint force is usually only 2.5% of the load in the strut. The amount of fixity of the coupler to the tube is generally neglected; Table 21.1 lists the safe load for various effective lengths.

The effective length of the vertical standards in an independent tied scaffold is not always obvious. Lift heights were previously considered relevant, but engineering analysis supported by full-scale testing of scaffolds by NASC (2008a) has shown conclusively that two parameters control the effective lengths in a tube and fitting scaffold: the vertical spacing between the levels of the tie positions and the bay length. A fuller treatise is given in TG20 (NASC, 2008a; volume 2). The effective lengths of Type 4 scaffold tube related to the vertical tie arrangement and the bay length for normal 2.0 m lift scaffolds are listed in Table 21.3.

Table 21.3 Effective lengths (LE) for fully ledger-braced independent tied scaffolds with 2.0 m lifts
Data taken from TG20 (2008)

Vertical interval between lines of ties	Bay length: m						
	1.2	1.5	1.8	2.0	2.1	2.4	2.7
2 m (every lift)	2.7	2.7	2.7	2.7	2.7	2.9	3.2
4 m (alternate lifts)	3.2	3.2	3.2	3.2	3.2	3.2	3.2
6 m (every third lift)	4.0	4.0	4.0	4.0	4.0	4.0	4.0

A scaffold tied at alternative lifts (4 m) with any bay length therefore has an effective length of 3.2 m, giving a safe axial load of 13.6 kN using Type 4 'as new' tube; see Table 21.1.

21.4.4.3 Tying scaffolds to structures

Independent tied scaffolds are restrained by tying the scaffold to the building and using the permanent structure work for stability. The ties will prevent the scaffold from moving into the building, away from the building and from longitudinal movement parallel to the building (left and right). The two arrangements of tie layout for basic scaffolds in the safe height tables in TG20 (NASC, 2008a) are: (1) lines of ties fitted to every lift and (2) lines of ties fitted to alternate lifts.

This spacing applies to unclad, debris netted and sheeted scaffolds. TG20 (NASC, 2008a) classifies three capacities of tie: light duty (capacity in tension 3.5 kN), standard duty (capacity in tension 6.1 kN) and heavy duty (capacity in tension 12.2 kN).

Four main types of tie are used, namely the through tie, box tie, reveal tie and anchor tie. Ties should preferably be fitted to the standard or at least within 300 mm of the standard on the ledger.

The selection of tie positions, whether the tie fixing into the building should be tested before use and even the suitability of the fabric of the building to carry ties are all part of the discussions at the early stage of procurement of scaffolds. Structures with minimal provisions for ties will obviously require more detailed design.

21.4.4.4 Lateral bracing to scaffolds

Bracing is required in tube and fitting scaffolds to stiffen the scaffold in two directions

- façade bracing: parallel to the building
- ledger bracing: away from the building.

Although BS EN12811-1 (BSI, 2003a) states that ledger bracing should be omitted at working lifts to give 'a completely unimpeded area', the best-practice opinion of the HSE and the NASC is that, for the majority of scaffolds in the UK, all scaffolds

Figure 21.3 Typical part boarded independent tied scaffold
Courtesy of Pallett Temporary*Works* Ltd

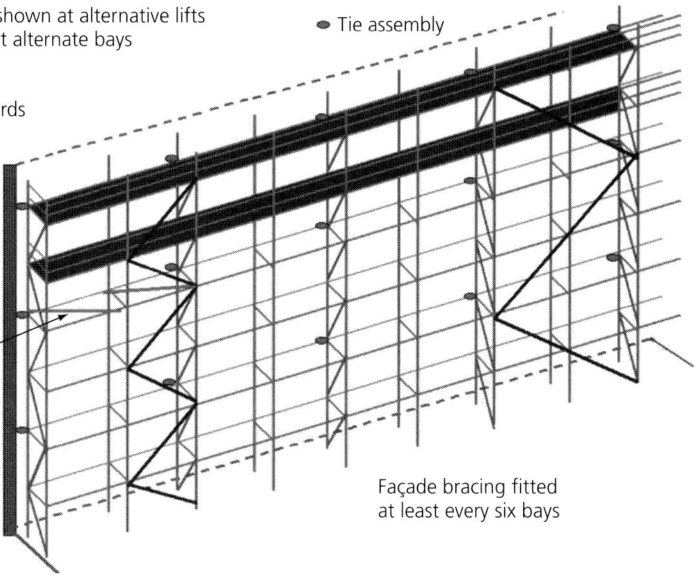

Ties to the diagram are shown at alternative lifts (i.e. 4 m vertically) and at alternate bays

Ledger bracing fitted to alternate rows of standards

Scaffold is part boarded with two lifts of boards

Plan bracing is required to be fitted if façade braces are NOT between the ledger braced standards, e.g. over one bay. It is fitted between ties every four lifts, and every twelve bays along the scaffold

Tie assembly

Façade bracing fitted at least every six bays

should have full-height ledger bracing on alternate bays. Where a client requests the omission of up to two lifts of ledger bracing to a scaffold, referred to as a 'part ledger braced scaffold', information on the significantly reduced safe height is given in TG20 (NASC, 2008a; volume 2).

The bracing is fitted as diagonals at an angle between 35° and 50°, creating stiff triangles. Loads are transmitted down through the scaffold to ties and/or the ground, etc. and the brace direction is unimportant (see Figure 21.3). If the bays are less than 1.5 m, then ledger bracing is fitted onto every third pair of standards. Façade bracing is fitted to the outside standards at least every 6 bays, either across 2 bays as shown on the right side of Figure 21.3 or continuously from bottom to top. Where façade bracing is across a single bay or not fitted between ledger braced frames, plan bracing is required.

21.4.4.5 Basic scaffolds

Provided the scaffold is braced correctly, is within the loading limits and correctly tied to the building, it can be regarded as a 'basic scaffold'. The safe height in metres for either an unclad, debris-netted or fully sheeted scaffold can then be obtained from tables in TG20 Supplement 1 (NASC, 2011). This is considered a standard configuration of scaffold and further calculations are not required. It should be pointed out that the summary tables in TG20 give conservative results for most scaffolds. An improvement in the safe height of independent tied scaffolds, taking more advanced wind conditions and loadings into account, is possible by fuller calculations using current European Standards.

As soon as any of the parameters alter, such as the decision to have the full imposed load on more than one platform at a time, the structure is invalidated as a basic scaffold and calculations are required. A method of evaluating the safe heights for such scaffolds with more levels loaded, for unclad scaffolds only, is also given in TG20 (NASC, 2008a; volume 2).

21.4.5 Design of proprietary system scaffolds

21.4.5.1 General

There are many types of proprietary system scaffolds available, and some of the components were discussed in Section 21.3.3. Typical examples are shown in Figures 21.4 and 21.5. Under the Health and Safety at Work Act, the supplier or importer of articles for use at work has a duty to ensure that the items are suitable, have relevant safety information and are fit for purpose. BS EN 12810-1 and 2 (BSI, 2003b and 2003c, respectively) provide specifications and design information for scaffolds made of prefabricated components.

Figure 21.4 Typical proprietary unclad system scaffold
Courtesy of Harsco Infrastructure

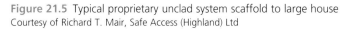
Figure 21.5 Typical proprietary unclad system scaffold to large house
Courtesy of Richard T. Mair, Safe Access (Highland) Ltd

Suppliers/importers have duties under the Sale of Goods Act to ensure the items are supplied as described. This imposes duties on the users of such scaffolds to ensure that they are supplied, used and subsequently dismantled following the instructions of the suppliers or importers. This is usually in the form of a user guide which provides the loading capability and safe heights of scaffolds, including tying patterns. Proprietary equipment suppliers will often provide erection manuals, safety DVDs and, in certain cases, run training courses and/or workshops to familiarise users with the system. It is important that such scaffolds are used as intended.

The use of fixed-length transom units with patented fittings to each end are regarded as proprietary scaffold and not tube and fittings. Information on their use should be sought from the supplier of the system.

21.4.5.2 Design considerations
Although the vertical standards are generally the same outside diameter as scaffold tube, some have a thinner-walled tube reducing the weight and make transportation and handling easier. The individual member connections have different strengths in each plane and often provide enough stiffness to eliminate ledger bracing in the direction away from the building. Façade bracing is generally still required, but there are alternatives on some proprietary systems.

One significant design consideration is the lack of continuity along the length of the scaffold. The ledgers are not continuous and stop at each standard; each pair of standards generally requires to be tied to the building and this can increase the amount of tying needed. It is always recommended to refer to the latest supplier's technical data.

The imposed load on proprietary systems is often higher than the equivalent tube and fitting scaffolds. This can have advantages due to the speed of erection, particularly on large and straightforward façades. The platforms have to fit at the modular connection points of the scaffold, so platforms cannot always be fitted to suit the ideal work location. This is in contrast to tube and fitting scaffolds, where they can be fitted to suit the work required.

21.5. Workmanship and inspections

Scaffolds will be erected and dismantled by competent people under supervision and following industry standards. The recognised trade association for tube and fitting scaffolds is the National Access and Scaffolding Confederation, which provides up-to-date guidance and codes of good practice. A useful pocket book is the TG20 *Overview toolbox talk* (NASC, 2008b). The document SG4 *Preventing Falls in Scaffolding* (NASC, 2010a) provides recommendations for safe systems of work and best practice. All scaffolds will require means of access/egress and the document SG25:10 (NASC, 2010c) provides detailed guidance on access to scaffolds. For recommendations on working and safety issues with proprietary equipment, refer to the supplier or importer.

Work at Height Regulation 12 requires that all working platforms be inspected prior to use after exposure to conditions likely to have caused deterioration (i.e. after high winds or local flooding) and at suitable intervals. The latter refers to scaffolds erected for some considerable time, say more than 3 months, where the fittings may become loose. It should also be considered that the lifespan of a scaffold should not be greater than 2 years. After this time, more permanent loads (especially wind loading) should be considered and the scaffold may require additional design.

In addition, for all platforms used in construction where a person could fall 2.0 m, the Work at Height Regulations state that they should be inspected every 7 days. All contractors and subcontractors should be aware of this and be maintaining a register of such inspections.

REFERENCES

BSI (1982) BS 1139: Part 1 Metal scaffolding. Specification for tubes for use in scaffolding. (Withdrawn October 1990 and replaced by BS EN 39.) BSI, London.

BSI (2001) BS EN 39: Loose steel tubes for tube and coupler scaffolds. Technical delivery conditions. BSI, London.

BSI (2003a) BS EN 12811-1: Temporary works equipment. Part 1: Scaffolds – Performance requirements and general design. BSI, London.

BSI (2003b) BS EN 12810-1: Façade scaffolds made of prefabricated components. Part 1: Products specifications. BSI, London.

BSI (2003c) BS EN 12810-2: Façade scaffolds made of prefabricated components. Part 2: Particular methods of structural design. BSI, London.

BSI (2005a) BS EN 74-1: Couplers, spigot pins and baseplates for use in falsework and scaffolds. Couplers for tubes. Requirements and test procedures. BSI, London.

BSI (2005b) BS EN 1993-1-1: EuroCode 3. Design of steel structures. General rules and rules for buildings. BSI, London.

BSI (2011) BS 5975: 2008 + A1: 2011 Code of practice for temporary works procedures and the permissible stress design of falsework. BSI, London.

NASC (National Access and Scaffolding Confederation) (2008a) TG20 Guide to good practice for scaffolding with tube and fittings. NASC, London.

NASC (2008b) TG20: Overview Toolbox Talk. NASC, London.

NASC (2010a) SG4:10 Preventing Falls in Scaffolding. NASC, London.

NASC (2010b) SG4: You. User Guide to SG4:10 Preventing Falls in Scaffoldings. NASC, London.

NASC (2010c) SG25: Access and Egress from Scaffolds. NASC, London.

NASC (2011) TG20 Supplement 1, The effect of the introduction of the European Wind Code BS EN 1991-1-4: 2005 on Basic Scaffolds and TG20; Appendix H. NASC, London.

Useful web addresses

http://www.nasc.org.uk
http://www.construct.org.uk
http://www.temporaryworks.info
http://www.twforum.org.uk

Temporary Works: Principles of Design and Construction
ISBN 978-0-7277-4177-6

ICE Publishing: All rights reserved
http://dx.doi.org/10.1680/twpdc.41776.275

Chapter 22
Falsework

Peter F. Pallett Pallett Temporary*Works* Ltd
Godfrey Bowring Consultant

Falsework comprises the temporary structure used to support other structures, usually permanent, until they can support themselves. Falsework is loaded for a short term, often highly stressed, and after loading has to be destressed under load. Constructed generally of pre-used equipment, the skeletal nature of such structures makes their stability during erection, use and dismantling a crucial design consideration. In certain cases they may rely on parts of the completed permanent works for stability. The design philosophy of falsework differs to that for permanent works, and good procedures and workmanship can contribute significantly to its safety.

22.1. Introduction

Any temporary structure used to support a permanent structure while it is not self-supporting is known as falsework. Although usually considered as the support of in situ concrete for slabs, bridges, etc., it is also used to support precast units/segments, structural steelwork and timber structures and as backpropping. Falsework has a different design philosophy to that used in the permanent works: it is loaded for a short time; rarely is it an item in a Bill of Quantities; it often uses reusable components; it has the unique structural requirement to be de-stressed under load (so that it can be removed); it is rarely tied down and therefore relies on its own weight for stability; and it is usually stressed to 90% of its safe capacity. Often assembled from proprietary components, the falsework is then re-used. The design process has to make allowances for erection tolerances and take into account that the components are re-used many times.

The first document in the world of falsework TR4 (CS/ISE, 1971) was a Concrete Society Report. It is interesting to note that it proposed a number of classes of falsework. A BSI code committee on falsework was formed shortly afterwards in 1972. Coincidentally, this was only two weeks before the collapse of heavy falsework over the River Loddon near Reading, which in turn generated a Government Advisory Report known as the Bragg Report (Bragg, 1975). BS 5975 was eventually published in 1982, taking account of the recommendations in that report. It contained procedures as well as sufficient technical content to enable a permissible stress design of falsework to be completed without reference to other sources of information. The current version of BS 5975: 2008 + A1: 2011 (BSI, 2011) has made clear that the procedures apply to all temporary works, including falsework (see Chapter 2).

275

A limit state code on falsework, BS EN 12812 (BSI, 2008) was first published in December 2004 and classifies falsework design into three classes as A, B1 and B2, but makes no provision for the safe management of either falsework or temporary works. Note that the existing code BS 5975 exists in parallel with BS EN 12812.

This chapter provides information on the design and use of falsework in the UK.

22.1.1 Permissible stress versus limit state

BS EN 12812 (BSI, 2008) is a limit state code, where the structure is designed for the ultimate condition at failure and also at the time of loading (serviceability). Limit state analysis requires knowledge of the partial safety factors to be adopted and the characteristic strength of the members before being able to establish its ability to resist load. This will always be a difficult concept for site personnel who work with and understand the 'safe working load' concept. For example, a crane on site is known to be able to lift, say, 10 tonnes. Its rating says so, and although its original design will have been to limit state, the end user information is defined in 'safe working load' terms. It is therefore important that authoritative guidance remains for site personnel, which has been prepared by engineers, communicating in known site terms. This is also discussed in Chapter 21 on access scaffolding. The design method using 'permissible stress design' is given in BS 5975 (BSI, 2011).

The different philosophy of the two design codes means that you cannot combine them. Permissible stress uses the elastic properties of the material, whereas limit state uses the plastic properties.

Permissible stress (BS 5975 (BSI, 2011)) assumes that the applied load is less than the safe working load of the material, defined

$$\text{safe working load} = \frac{\text{failure load}}{\text{factor of safety}}$$

The usual recommendation for the factor of safety for temporary works is 2.0.

Limit state (BS EN 12812; BSI, 2008) assumes that the design value of the loads is less than the design resistance at ultimate load. Allowing for the partial safety factors, we have

$$(\text{actual loads}) \times (\text{partial safety factor}) \leqslant \frac{\text{characteristic strength}}{(\text{partial material factor}) \times (\text{class factor})}$$

where the partial safety factor is 1.35 for self weight and 1.50 for all other loads and the partial material factor for both steel and aluminium falsework is 1.1. BS EN 12812 introduces different class factors for Class B1 (1.0) and B2 (1.15).

Note that the partial safety factors used in falsework are not the same as those used in permanent design, and that the class factor for B2 is a 15% penalty for designing using that class. The characteristic strength, or characteristic value of a member or component, is its ultimate load (usually stated with a 95% confidence limit, i.e. 5% will fail below the value stated). Characteristic strength is therefore *not* the safe working load.

Note that using a factor of safety of 2.0 against failure in permissible stress is not directly comparable with using a combined $1.50 \times 1.1 = 1.65$ factor in limit state design, as the former is based on the elastic properties of the material and limit state uses the plastic properties.

22.1.2   Choice of class/standard

The existence of two parallel codes, one in permissible stress and the other in limit state terms, implies that an early decision must be made during procurement of falsework. The choice of design method will affect many factors to be used in the design. For example, if specified to limit state but it is a small structure, then it would be BS EN 12812 Class A. This is defined as a slab less than 300 mm thick, with support to the underside of the permanent works less than 3.5 m and a span less than 6 m. In other words, about 95% of all building construction within Europe is Class A. While BS EN 12812 (BSI, 2008) gives no structural guidance on designing Class A falsework its national foreword recommends that, in the UK, Class A falsework be designed using the philosophy of BS 5975 (BSI, 2011).

What happens if the checking organisation uses BS 5975, but the falsework has been designed to BS EN 12812? The philosophies and factors discussed in Section 22.1.1 are different; you cannot 'pick and choose'. The design method and the falsework class to be considered therefore needs to be established at a very early stage of procurement (see Chapter 2 on management).

22.2.   Materials and components
22.2.1   Proprietary falsework equipment

There are many different types of falsework system on the market; many are available for hire as well as for purchase (see Figure 22.1). Always refer to the recommendations of the supplier for load capacity, etc. The load capacity is not always obvious, for example, a steel modular system using vertical standards of 48.3 mm outer diameter (OD) (generally to suit the scaffold couplers) may have a different wall thickness and/or be of different grades of steel. The thinner/lighter materials are less expensive, reduce transportation weight and make erection/dismantling easier.

Proprietary aluminium support systems and bearers from suppliers, which are being increasingly used, have high strength to weight ratios. Since aluminium is more ductile than steel, it results in greater elastic deflection and the stiffness is more critical in designs. To utilise the higher load capacities, the vertical legs are often spaced further apart. This may not always be economic when you consider other factors such as providing access for operatives to strike out the soffit forms and the permanent work deflection limits as set in the specification. Figure 22.2 depicts a typical example of an aluminium support system.

Figure 22.1 Typical fully braced proprietary steel falsework to a bridge
Courtesy of Harsco Infrastructure

Figure 22.2 Typical partially braced proprietary aluminium falsework with ledger frames
Courtesy of Jim Murray, PERI (UK) Ltd

The majority of aluminium systems rely upon the soffit formwork being restrained by elements of the permanent works to provide lateral restraint for the falsework. This is known as 'top restrained' falsework and is discussed later in this chapter. Refer to BS EN 12813 (BSI, 2004) and BS 5975 (BSI, 2011) for the methods of structural design for load on bearing towers when using prefabricated components.

22.2.2 Scaffold tube and fittings

The use of scaffold tube and fittings, described in more detail in Chapter 21 on access scaffolding, is usually limited in falsework to providing additional components. Some examples include as diagonal bracing, providing extra working platforms within the falsework, to connect sections of falsework together and to assist alignment of members.

22.2.3 Adjustable telescopic props

The adjustable steel telescopic prop, generically referred to as an Acrow, was the traditional method of support for many years. BS EN 1065 (BSI, 1999) introduces 32 types of adjustable steel props in 5 strength classes, and states load capacity in terms of characteristic strength. BS 5975: 2008 + A1: 2011 (BSI, 2011) states the capacity of these props in terms of safe working load.

Adjustable aluminium props are now used extensively in falsework, mostly for building construction. Their low weight and high capacity make them easily transportable and economic to use on site as falsework and as individual back props. Many of the systems have 'gates' or 'ledger frames' to connect the legs together. BS 5975 refers to these as 'bracing frames'. The structural capacity of such systems should be obtained from the suppliers. 'Ledger frames are often fitted as aids to erection and, while not designed as such, may contribute to the stability of the falsework. Designers and users should be clear as to their purpose. When joined together, the systems often make tables of soffit formwork. This is discussed in more detail in Chapter 24 on soffit formwork.

As already inferred, components of steel and aluminium should *never* be mixed because of their different elastic properties. The steel will not compress elastically or shorten sufficiently under load (being elastically stiffer than the aluminium) to allow the aluminium to carry its 'share', implying that the majority of the load would be carried by the steel.

22.3. Loads on falsework
22.3.1 General

Loads on structures, referred to as Actions in EuroCode 1, are given in BS EN 1991-1 (BSI, 2002). Densities, self-weight and imposed loads are given in Part 1.1, snow load in Part 1.3 (BSI, 2003) and wind loads in Part 1.4 (BSI, 2010).

Loads on falsework described in BS 5975 (BSI, 2011) are compatible with BS EN 12812 (BSI, 2008). Loads can either be permanent actions, i.e. self weight, or variable actions, for example, the supported structure and weight of operatives.

22.3.2 Permanent loads

The self weight of the soffit formwork is usually taken as $0.5\,\text{kN/m}^2$. The falsework weight itself is very critical to the design. Falsework is rarely tied to the ground and its self weight is often the only load preventing it overturning under the worst wind loads. Falsework self weight is often related to the volume; typical values are $0.10–0.15\,\text{kN/m}^3$.

22.3.3 Imposed loads

The weight of the structure being built, i.e. the permanent works is an imposed vertical load. It can be just vertical (static and impact) or it can have some non-vertical components, such as lateral load imposed by concrete pressure. Discontinuities in the soffit cause lateral forces; see Chapter 24 on soffit formwork. Wherever there are voids are in the concrete, their flotation can be significant. Remember that the uplift forces are balanced by downward pressure and, depending on the method of restraint, there is generally no upwards force in the supporting falsework.

For design purposes, BS EN 12812 (BSI, 2008) recommends the density of concrete to be taken as $2500\,\text{kg/m}^3$ (i.e. assume $25\,\text{kN/m}^3$). Where smaller building slabs are under construction, the flat slab guide (CS140; CSG, 2003) recommends that the concrete density for backpropping be $24\,\text{kN/m}^3$ but that the falsework supports be designed for $25\,\text{kN/m}^3$.

22.3.4 Loading from construction operations

- Working area load: To allow for the imposed load from construction operations, a distributed load is applied over the whole working area of $0.75\,\text{kN/m}^2$ (i.e. service class 1).
- Variable transient in situ loading allowance: applied over an area $3\,\text{m} \times 3\,\text{m}$ between $0.75\,\text{kN/m}^2$ for slabs up to 300 mm, increasing to a maximum of $1.75\,\text{kN/m}^2$ for solid slabs greater than 700 mm, when placing in situ concrete. Intermediate thicknesses are designed on 10% of the slab self weight (BSI, 2011; clause 17.4.3.1). See Figure 22.3 for a depiction of working area and transient in situ concrete loading. The implication of this transient load when using permanent

Figure 22.3 Working area and transient in situ concrete loading

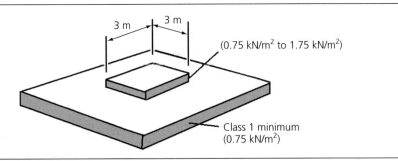

metal decking formwork, often used on up to 3 m spans, is that all such metal decking should be designed for a minimum imposed load of 1.5 kN/m².

■ Striking formwork load: to assist striking and handling of individual items from under a soffit, BS 5975 (BSI, 2011; clause 19.1.1) recommends a working platform fitted about 2 m underneath the soffit forms, designed for an imposed service class 1 load of 0.75 kN/m².

22.3.5 Environmental loads

Unless shielded, falsework will be exposed and requires to be designed to withstand the maximum wind force. The UK wind code BS EN 1991-1-4: 2005 + A1: 2010 (BSI, 2010) is based on a 10 min wind speed likely to occur once in 50 years. BS 5975: 2008 + A1: 2011 (BSI, 2011) introduces the option of using a simplified method to calculate the likely maximum and working wind force on a falsework structure. Because wind codes are written for permanent structures, factors specific to the wind on the soffit and parapet forms are included to give an upper limit to the maximum wind force on the falsework.

The basic equation for the peak wind velocity pressure q_p at a location for a falsework is established from the following relationship:

$$q_p = 0.613 \times c_{prob}^2 \times c_e(z)c_{e,T} \times S_{wind}^2$$

where q_p is the peak velocity pressure (N/m²); c_{prob} is the probability factor (a minimum value of 0.83 is recommended); $c_e(z)$ $c_{e,T}$ is the combined exposure factor (BSI, 2011; clause 17.5.16) and S_{wind} is the wind factor at the location (m/s) (see Section 21.4.3.3 in Chapter 21). The wind factor S_{wind} incorporates the fundamental wind velocity ($V_{b,map}$) for the site, a topographical factor to allow for the terrain and the altitude (m) of the site (BSI, 2011; clause 17.5.1.33).

Generally, placing concrete on falsework will not occur when the wind speed exceeds the operating limits set for the construction plant. This is usually at Beaufort Scale Force 6 and corresponds to a wind speed of 18 m/s. This is known as the working wind, which generates a working wind pressure of 0.20 kN/m².

The procurer will have previously decided whether the falsework will be unclad, sheeted or debris-netted. This will have a significant effect on the magnitude of the wind forces which have to be considered.

22.3.6 Indirect loads: Settlement and elastic shortening

As loads are applied, the supported structure will move because of the actual falsework members shortening elastically and by settlement of the foundations under the load. In certain cases there could be differential settlement between the various members. According to BS 5975 (BSI, 2011; clause 19.3.1), typical values of elastic shortening of falsework are

■ for steel falsework, c. 0.5 mm/metre of height (+0.5 mm per joint + 1.0 mm per timber joint)
■ for aluminium falsework, c. 0.9 mm/metre of height.

22.3.7 Variable persistent horizontal imposed load

BS EN 12812 (BSI, 2008; clause 8.2.2.2) introduces a horizontal load of 1% of the vertical load, in addition to any sway imperfections, as an externally applied load to allow for minor forces not otherwise identified.

22.3.8 Erection tolerance

Whenever falsework structures are erected, the design should take account of any inaccuracy of the erection. It is hard to erect structures which are exactly vertical, etc. This gives rise to 'sway imperfections'. A full design to BS EN 12812 Class B1 would take this into account. BS 5975 (BSI, 2011; clause 19.2.9.1(b)) allows for a nominal horizontal reaction of 1% of the applied vertical forces to take account of erection tolerances. Where there is both eccentricity and sway, a more rigorous analysis taking into account second-order effects known as P-Δ may need to be considered (BSI, 2011; clause 19.3.3.3).

BS EN 12812 (BSI, 2008; clause 9.3.4.2) for Class B2 falsework considers the sway imperfection φ for structures taller than $h = 10$ m is calculated using

$$\tan \varphi = 0.01 \sqrt{\frac{10}{h}}$$

where h is the height (m) and φ is the angular deviation from the theoretical line. Where the structure is <10 m, a lower limit of $\tan \varphi = 0.01$ is considered (i.e. use 1% of applied loads for falsework up to 10 m in height).

22.3.9 Minimum horizontal disturbing force

Investigations during the 1970s and in 2005 (Burrows et al., 2005) identified that one of the principle causes of falsework collapse was the absence of stability in members and the structure as a whole; this is also discussed in Chapter 2 on management. For this reason, BS 5975 (BSI, 2011; clause 19.2.9.1) recommends that all falsework be designed for a minimum horizontal disturbing force F_H applied at the top of the falsework. This is defined as the greater of either a specified 2.5% of the vertically applied loads W or all known horizontal loads plus 1% of the vertical load W, as an erection tolerance load to cater for workmanship during erection.

Note that the foreword to BS EN 12812 (BSI, 2008) states (referring to BS 5975) that 'the application of this force has made a significant contribution to the safe use of falsework since its introduction'.

22.4. Falsework design
22.4.1 General

When designing falsework, consideration must be given to the fact that it could either buckle or fall over in any direction. A general rule to follow is: 'Think vertical, think horizontal, then think horizontal again'. In practice, this means completing four checks, namely:

1   the structural strength of the members and connections, i.e. are the node points restrained and are web stiffeners fitted to beams?
2   the lateral stability of the falsework structure
3   the overall stability
4   the positional stability, i.e. will it slide.

The method adopted for the design, whether limit state or permissible stress, will consider these four checks which are written into BS 5975 (BSI, 2011; clause 19.4.1.1) and are recommended as the starting point of any falsework design. The importance of an accurate and relevant Falsework Design Brief, prepared usually by the TWC (see Chapter 2 on management) for use by both the Temporary Works Designer and the design checker cannot be overstressed. A good brief will provide safe, economic and effective falsework structures.

22.4.2 Check 1: Structural strength

The designer will check for axial load, bending, shear, deflection, occasionally torsion and the stability of individual members and connections, such as welded or bolted joints. When detailing individual elements, account should be taken for the maximum tolerances for workmanship (unless provisions are taken to minimise the eccentricities, etc.).

Many of the proprietary falsework systems have patented joints which provide some moment capacity. These can reduce the effective length factor below unity, thus increasing their safe load capacity. Follow the recommendations of the suppliers; in particular, look out for unrestrained cantilever extensions on falsework at the head and bases. The effective length of such members in cantilever depends on whether or not the structure can sway relative to the cantilever tip; see BS 5975 (BSI, 2011; clause 19.4.2.4.4).

For structural steel beams carrying concentrated loads, web stiffeners should be provided at all loading transfer points including supports, unless calculations are provided to show that such stiffeners are not required (BSI, 2011; annex J). The omission of web stiffeners has been the cause of fatal accidents, so their importance must not be underestimated.

22.4.3 Check 2: Lateral stability

The stability of the falsework needs to be considered at several phases of construction; Figure 22.4 illustrates several of the most likely combinations. BS EN 12812 (BSI, 2008; clause 8.4; Table 1) recommends that normally four combinations of Load Cases are taken into account. Each will require to be considered separately, but there are likely to be two critical phases: (1) that of erected with only self weight but maximum wind (see Figure 22.4a; Load Case 1) i.e. prior to concreting and (2) on the day of concreting with the full vertical load but with the working wind (Figure 22.4b; Load Case 2). In addition, the minimum horizontal disturbing force (Section 22.3.9; Figure 22.4c) is taken into account.

Figure 22.4 Typical load combinations for lateral stability
Courtesy of Pallett Temporary Works Ltd

VERTICAL forces are: self weight of formwork and falsework

**Typical load combinations
to check lateral stability**

LATERAL force
= 1% {self weight}
+ maximum wind force

(B2) = 2% (self weight)
+ maximum wind

Load case 1

Erected but:
not concreted with
maximum wind force
(no working on site!)

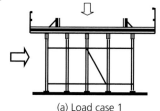

(a) Load case 1

VERTICAL forces from self weight of formwork and falsework,
the construction operations load, and the permanent works (e.g. concrete)

LATERAL force
= 1% {vertical loads listed}
+ working wind force

(B2) = 2% (vertical loads)
+ working wind

Load case 2

During placing of
permanent works with
full vertical load and
reduced wind force

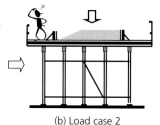

(b) Load case 2

VERTICAL forces from self weight of formwork and falsework,
the construction operations load, and the permanent works (e.g. concrete)

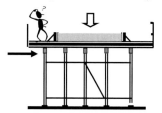

LATERAL force

= 2½% {vertical loads}

UK BS 5975 load case

Lower bound lateral
force for all
freestanding falsework

(c) Minimum horizontal disturbing force (BS 5975)

Note to (c). The lower bound minimum specified load is considered to act at the point of contact
between the vertical load and the falsework. If though the falsework is restrained at
it's head then a different load case needs to be considered, as outlined in (d) below.

RESTRAINT force
= 2½% {vertical loads}

(B2) = 2% (self weight)
+ maximum wind

OR = 2% (vertical loads)
+ working wind

Top restrained load case

Where the structure is
restrained by the permanent
works, the formwork will
have to transmit the lateral
force to suitable restraints

(d) Top restrained falsework

The three load cases depicted in Figure 22.4a–c all illustrate free-standing falsework structures with diagonal bracing providing the restraint. There are falsework systems or arrangements that rely on the top soffit formwork to provide the lateral stability. These are known as top-restrained falsework, depicted in Figures 22.2 and 22.4d. The assumption made by the designer in this case is that the head of the falsework is restrained from movement in both lateral directions. This requires that the permanent works are able to resist these notional stability forces, which is why Table 2.2 in Chapter 2 excludes top-restrained falsework from design check Category 1 (simple design); top-restrained falsework requires the approval of other parties, generally including the designer of the permanent works. More information on top-restrained falsework is given in BS 5975 (BSI, 2011).

All parties should be absolutely clear as to whether falsework has been designed on the assumption that it is top restrained and, if so, whether the permanent works has been designed (i.e. it is stiff enough in the temporary condition?) to provide the required restraint. If not, the falsework should be designed as free standing.

Lateral stability also applies to the webs of steel beams at reaction points and at positions of concentrated loads. Web stiffeners are required at all loading transfer points, including supports, unless calculations are provided to show that such stiffeners are not required (BSI, 2011; annex J). Note that the default condition for steel beams with concentrated loads is to fit them with web stiffeners unless proven otherwise. The comment at the end of Section 22.4.2 applies equally here.

The compression flanges of all beams should also be considered for lateral torsional buckling. Permanent Works Designers (PWD) are aware of the potential instability of steel beams on composite bridge designs (where relatively small top flanges are designed for shear connection to the concrete), but not necessarily for the compression loads during erection which can require additional lateral bracing. See BS 5975 (BSI, 2011; annex K) for the effective length of steel members in axial compression.

22.4.4 Check 3: Overall stability

Tall slender structures and those exposed to high winds will have a tendency to be blown over. As falsework is generally a gravity structure (relying on its own weight for stability), the most onerous condition is often just after the soffit formwork is erected and before reinforcement is fixed, i.e. with minimal restoring self weight. If the falsework is unstable, then holding-down bolts or kentledge may have to be used. Remember that whenever using kentledge (weights) there is no leeway; you know the point at which it will turn over! BS 5975 (BSI, 2011; clause 19.4.3.1) requires a minimum factor of safety of 1.2 against overturning. BS EN 12812 (BSI, 2008; clause 9.2.2.3) refers to overturning as 'static body equilibrium' with different partial load factors for destabilising loads compared to those stabilising the falsework.

When using systems that have cantilever working platforms, there is always a risk of overturning. This is particularly the case when narrow aluminium tables are used, where it may be necessary to tie these down to the slab.

Figure 22.5 Friction forces on slopes

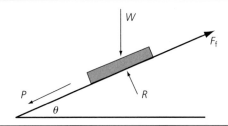

F_f, frictional restraint force (kN)
W, vertically applied force (kN)
R, reaction normal to the surface (kN)
θ, minimum angle (degrees) from the horizontal at which *sliding will commence*
P, the force applied to overcome the static friction (kN)

22.4.5 Check 4: Positional stability

The lateral disturbing forces in the falsework may be transmitted by static friction or mechanical connection into the foundations, but not combined. This interface is usually through base plates and supporting timber sole plates (see Figure 22.5 and BSI, 2011; clause 19.4.5). The recommended values for the coefficient of static friction μ are listed in BS 5975: 2008 + A1: 2011 (BSI, 2011; Table 24), where

$$\mu = \frac{\text{limiting frictional force}}{\text{reaction normal to the surface}} = \frac{F_f}{R} = \frac{W \sin \theta}{W \cos \theta} = \tan \theta$$

where F_f is the frictional restraint force (kN), W is the vertically applied force (kN), R is the reaction normal to the surface, θ is the minimum angle (degrees) to the horizontal at which sliding will commence and P (kN) is the force applied to overcome the static friction (Figure 22.5). The friction restraint does not depend on area of contact. The applied load multiplied by the coefficient of static friction μ gives the value of frictional restraint (the value at which it slides) with no factor of safety.

BS 5975 (BSI, 2011) recommends that minimum factor of safety against sliding is 2.0, whereas BS EN 12812 (BSI, 2008; Table 2) gives different partial safety factors for stabilising ($\gamma_i = 0.9$) compared to destabilising loads ($\gamma_i = 1.35$–1.5).

22.5. Providing a stable structure

The analysis of falsework is increasingly being carried out by computers. The theory is often complicated but, at the end of the day, engineers on site need simple design rules and experience in order to assess and inspect falsework. The '10% continuity rule' for random bearers is an example (BSI, 2011; clause 19.3.3.2). Although booklets like the Falsework Checklist (CS, 1999) are useful, they are poor substitutes for experience when checking and designing falsework structures.

In summary, the four criteria for a stable structure are as follows

■ to ensure stability during erection and dismantling (minimum lateral force 0.5% of W)
■ to improve the load-carrying capacity of the elements by stabilising node points and controlling their effective lengths (normally a notional force of 2.5% of W)

- to provide lateral stability to the temporary structure (a minimum horizontal disturbing force of 2.5% of W is recommended at head level)
- to resist overturning of the whole structure.

The important aspect to remember when designing falsework is that the above four criteria are not cumulative; checking for one criterion may actually be sufficient for all four! For example, bracing a free-standing falsework sheltered from the wind for the minimum horizontal disturbing force of 2.5% of W would also satisfy the structural requirement for creating node points (also 2.5% of W).

22.6. Workmanship and inspections

Since falsework by its very nature comprises re-usable items (often second-hand), and is generally erected, destressed and then dismantled and removed, the procedures and controls are often more rigorous than for permanent works. Constant emphasis is needed on the attention to detail. The reasons for experience and checks are highlighted in the following five examples which all occurred recently.

1   The incorrect lapping of single primary bearers in forkheads, by forgetting to 'cross-lap, led to a major collapse.
2   Installing cross-bracing every 4th bay in a large falsework was interpreted on site as every 4 bays sideways (not in its length). Only 1 in 4 rows of falsework was therefore braced, again leading to a major collapse.
3   While installing soffit formwork on a 10 m high falsework, the operatives removed the bracing as it got in their way. It was not put back, and not noticed during inspection. The 10 m high falsework collapsed during concreting with 7 men on top!
4   A proprietary aluminium system using ledger gates for bracing was used on a bridge falsework; each leg carried over 100 kN. One eye bolt in one place was not tightened up, and the falsework leg buckled sideways under the load.
5   Very large props were used at each end of a pre-cast concrete beam for stability while the top in situ deck was concreted. Unfortunately, one piece of softwood plywood had been fitted to pack one of the 300 kN leg load props. The plywood crushed from 20 mm to 5 mm, causing the entire bridge to drop at one end and skew on its bearings.

All of the above failures of falsework could have been avoided had correct procedures for checking/inspection by competent persons and trained TWCs been adopted. The use of more proprietary items with patented connections means that the integrity of the whole structure may be impaired by the omission of a bolt or wedge, or even just failing to tighten them up correctly. The supplier's advice should always be sought.

Care must be taken when erecting and dismantling the falsework. The NASC booklet SG4:10 (NASC, 2010) is a useful guide on preventing falls in both scaffolding and false-work. The size of falsework structures means that there should be some clearly defined stages in the construction. For example, formal checks might need to be established after completing the foundations, when it reaches its support level and, obviously, prior to loading. In addition to the provision of safe working areas for erecting, striking, etc., are the conditions of use as envisaged in the design brief?

A common error on falsework is failing to take account of the elastic settlement under load (Section 22.3.6). For this reason, experienced erectors will set the top level of the falsework higher than the final required level to allow for shortening under load. For example, a reservoir roof slab support 5.4 m high would be expected to elastically shorten by c. 5–6 mm if steel falsework was used, increasing to nearer 10 mm if aluminium falsework was used.

Safe falsework requires competent experienced people, with an eye for detail. Failures usually occur because small items are missed or forgotten or through lack of proper process and control.

REFERENCES

Bragg SL (1975) Final report of the Advisory Committee on Falsework. HMSO, London.

BSI (1999) BS EN 1065: Adjustable Telescopic steel props: Product specifications, design and assessment by calculation and test. BSI, London.

BSI (2002) BS EN 1991-1-1: EuroCode 1. Actions on structures. General actions. Densities, self-weight, imposed loads for buildings. BSI, London.

BSI (2003) BS EN 1991-1-3: EuroCode 1. Actions on structures. General actions. Snow loads. BSI, London.

BSI (2004) BS EN 12813: Temporary works equipment. Load bearing towers of prefabricated components. Particular methods of structural design. BSI, London.

BSI (2008) BS EN 12812: Falsework: Performance requirements and general design. BSI, London.

BSI (2010) BS EN 1991-1-4: 2005 + A1: 2010 EuroCode 1. Actions on structures. General actions. Wind actions. BSI, London.

BSI (2011) BS 5975: 2008 + A1: 2011 Code of practice for temporary works procedures and the permissible stress design of falsework. BSI, London.

Burrows M, Clark L, Pallett P, Ward R and Thomas D (2005) Falsework verticality: leaning towards danger? Proceedings of ICE, Civil Engineering, Feb 2005: 41–48, Paper 13624.

CS (Concrete Society) (1999) Checklist for Erecting and Dismantling Falsework. Concrete Society Construction Group Leaflet CS123. Concrete Society, Camberley.

CS/ISE (Concrete Society and the Institution of Structural Engineers) (1971) Falsework: Report of the joint committee. Technical Report TRCS 4. The Concrete Society, London.

CSG (Concrete Structures Group) (2003) Guide to Flat Slab Formwork and Falsework. Concrete Society Ref No. CS 140. Concrete Society, Camberley.

NASC (National Access and Scaffolding Confederation) (2010) SG4:10 Preventing Falls in Scaffolding. NASC, London.

Useful web addresses

http://www.nasc.org.uk
http://www.construct.org.uk
http://www.temporaryworks.info
http://www.twforum.org.uk

Temporary Works: Principles of Design and Construction
ISBN 978-0-7277-4177-6

ICE Publishing: All rights reserved
http://dx.doi.org/10.1680/twpdc.41776.289

Institution of Civil Engineers

publishing

Chapter 23
Formwork

Laurie York Consultant
Peter F. Pallett Pallett Temporary*Works* Ltd

'Formwork' is the term used to describe the fabrications and constructions used to form the shape of concrete structures, acting as the mould. It is normally removed once the concrete has achieved sufficient strength, although it is sometimes left in place as permanent formwork which may or may not contribute to the structural capacity of the formed concrete. Formwork is either vertical for walls, columns, beam sides, etc. or horizontal for supporting slabs, cantilevers, underside of beams, etc. Horizontal formwork is described in Chapter 24 on soffit formwork.

23.1. Introduction
Traditional formwork is fabricated using timber-based materials but steel, glass-fibre-reinforced plastics (GRP), glass-fibre-reinforced cement (GRC) and other materials are also used. Proprietary formwork includes the walings, bearers, soldiers, supports and various panel systems available from specialist formwork supply companies. Choice of material is often based on the required number of uses of the formwork and the finish specified for the concrete by the Permanent Works Designer, with more expensive materials often justified by more onerous surface finish and durability requirements for the concrete.

Designing formwork and ensuring its subsequent control on site requires a thorough understanding of the pressures generated during the placing, compacting and setting of concrete. Knowledge of formwork materials and practical experience are both essential to ensure that formwork is economic, easy to fabricate and use. The procedures for and management of formwork are described in Chapter 2.

23.2. Vertical formwork
Formwork is defined as the structure, usually temporary but in some cases wholly or partly permanent, used to contain poured concrete, to mould it to the required dimensions and to support it until it is able to support itself. It consists primarily of the face contact material and the bearers that directly support the face contact material. The authoritative industry guidance for formwork is the Concrete Society book *Formwork: A Guide to Good Practice* (CS, 2011). To resist the large pressure of the concrete on the form face, metal rods in tension known as tie rods are used to connect opposing faces of formwork. This is known as double-faced formwork and a typical example is shown in Figure 23.1 comprising a face material, horizontal members known as

Figure 23.1 A Typical arrangement of double-faced wall formwork with soldiers
Courtesy of Pallett Temporary*Works* Ltd

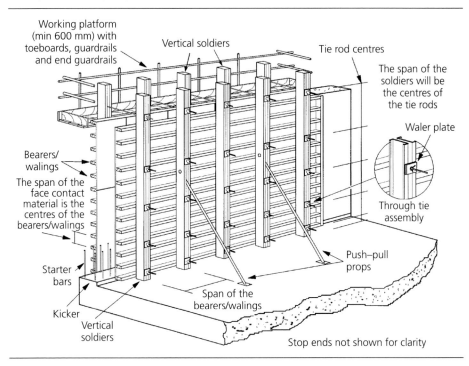

walings and vertical stiff steel soldiers. The tie rods balance the forces and the inclined props provide stability and allow alignment of the forms.

Where there is only one face of the form, such as against an existing wall or the ground, then the formwork is known as single-faced formwork. The forces can be significant and are discussed in Section 23.8.3.

23.3. Economy

Many people in the process can affect the economy of the construction. These include the Permanent Works Designer, the contractor, the subcontractor and specialist suppliers, as well as the site operatives. The cost of formwork will vary depending on the contract specification and also on the number of uses required of the formwork. On a concrete frame building, the cost of formwork and falsework can be 39% of the cost of the structure, increasing on a 'civils' contract to as much as 55% of the cost of the concrete structure. A better-quality face contact material may be more expensive but may be necessary either to produce the required finish on the concrete or to enable re-use of the formwork without costly refurbishment. Similarly, a more robust form may be more expensive but allow more re-use. A considerable percentage of the costs is associated with the labour involved; formwork design that reduces the labour requirement will generally be more economic. Examples include the reduction in the number of tie rods, the use of proprietary panels to reduce initial make-up costs and use of aluminium bearers to reduce the weight of the formwork panels (permitting larger form areas for the same size of crane).

23.4. Specifications and finishes

The surface finish required for the concrete will generally be described by means of a specified performance, where the standards and tolerances required are stated but the contractor is left to decide how to achieve the finish. The concrete surface, together with the surface zone of the concrete, will be affected by the choice of material used to create the face.

British Standard BS EN 13670 Execution of concrete structures (BSI, 2009) defines the generic surface finishes. The two main UK specifications are: National Structural Concrete Specification for Building Construction (NSCS) (ConStruct, 2010; Section 8.6) and the Highways Agency specification (HA, 2004; volume 1, clause 1708). Table 23.1 compares the two specifications. Other specifications used include the UK Water Industry Research Civil Engineering Specification for the Water Industry (CESWI, 2011; clause 4.28) and the National Building Specification (NBS) Formwork for in situ concrete (Section E20) which is published annually online.

The NSCS (ConStruct, 2010) refers to full-size reference panels at seven locations in the UK which may be viewed by visiting the various locations. Other sources of information include the Concrete Society Technical Report 52, *Plain Formed Concrete Finishes* (CS, 1999). As well as generic surface finishes, special finishes required under the contract may be defined.

Table 23.1 Comparison of surface finishes

Highways Agency	NSCS (2010)	Examples
Class F1	Basic	For pile caps, etc.
Class F2	Ordinary	Rear, unseen faces of retaining walls (panel systems give F2)
Class F4	Plain	Quality surfaces to walls
Class F3	Plain	Class F4 but no ties; visible parapets (hardest to achieve)
Class F5	Plain	Class F4 embedment of metal parts allowed (intended pre-cast)
–	Special/fair worked	High-class finish, e.g. potable water tanks, etc.

23.5.   Tolerances/deviations

Tolerances specified for the formwork are not necessarily the same as those specified for the permanent works. The three sources of deviations in the surface of the finished structure are: (1) inherent deviations, such as the elastic movement of the formwork under load; (2) induced deviations, such as the lipping between two sheets of plywood (possibly within plywood manufacturing tolerances); and (3) errors, such as inaccurate setting-out. Inherent deviations include deflection.

It is generally accepted that appearance and function are satisfied if deflection of individual formwork members is limited to 1/270th of the span. In certain cases (such as where decoration is to be applied directly on to concrete walls in housing) reduced limits may need to be specified, but it should be noted that it is the deflection of the individual formwork members that is limited and not the overall final concrete shape.

The acceptable magnitude of the deviations will depend on the specified quality of the work and also the distance from which the concrete surface will be viewed. Typical deviations in verticality for normal work will be 20 mm from a grid line for a 3 m high wall. More information is available in Section 2.6 of the Formwork Guide (CS, 2011; Section 2.6).

23.6.   Formwork materials

23.6.1   Face contact material

Perhaps the most common sheet material which is used as face contact material is plywood. Plywood is a layered material made up of sheets which are normally 1.22 m × 2.44 m (i.e. 4 ft × 8 ft), with properties related to the direction of the face grain of the outer ply layer. They are generally used in 17.5 mm, 19 mm or 25 mm thicknesses. The Formwork Guide (CS, 2011) gives details of working properties taken from the previous British Standard and for various plywood and other wood-based panel materials, together with details for other commercially available sheet materials. Plywood has different properties depending on the direction of the face grain; some plywoods have less than 50% capacity if used the wrong way round! Economic design is based on the plywood spanning in its 'strong' direction and it is important that it is fixed in the correct orientation.

The use of expanded metal steel products (Hy-rib) in construction joints, in place of plywood, almost eliminates the need for scabbling (i.e. removes the risk problems associated with vibration known as 'white finger') since the metal is left in place. Trials by the British Cement Association have shown that there is a significant reduction in concrete pressure when expanded metal products are used. See details in the Formwork Guide (CS, 2011).

The use of fabric such as Zemdrain on the face contact material introduces control over the permeability. This is known as controlled permeability formwork (CPF); see CIRIA Report C511 (CIRIA, 2000). By allowing the pressure of the concrete to force the surplus pore water and any air into the fabric and to be drained away, there is an almost complete elimination of blowholes on the concrete surface. The face strength of the concrete is increased by 30% in the critical cover zone of the concrete. A recent development is the use of composite sheets having a foamed polystyrene core with a synthetic thermoplastic material face to both sides or, for wall formwork, with a thin reinforcing sheet of aluminium to both sides. Repair techniques on such sheets are specialised.

23.6.2 Bearers

In wall formwork, bearers are typically aligned horizontally supporting the face contact material; in such cases they are often referred to as 'walings'. They are often softwood constructional timber using strength classes C16, C24 or C27. Site conditions, such as exposure to wetting, affect the strength of timber. The duration of loading and facility for load sharing will also affect the apparent strength of the timber, as will the depth of the timber section used. The Formwork Guide (CS, 2011) provides details of safe working properties for various commonly used timber section sizes.

Alternatively, proprietary beams fabricated from timber, aluminium or steel can be used. Many of the European systems of formwork incorporate proprietary timber bearers fitted vertically. They should be used in accordance with the manufacturers' instructions at all times.

23.6.3 Soldiers

Soldiers can be timber or proprietary beams; in Figure 23.1, the soldiers have central slots for the positioning of tie rods. The soldiers support the bearers which span horizontally between them, either using design properties given in the Formwork Guide (CS, 2011) or using information from manufacturers.

Alternatively, proprietary beams or 'soldier-type' members may be installed horizontally to support vertically-fitted bearers.

23.6.4 Formwork ties

To resist the bursting effect of the pressure of the concrete, the opposing faces of wall formwork (in double-faced formwork) are connected by tie rods. The most common type of tie rod is the through tie. A typical through-tie system is depicted in Figure 23.2, comprising a high-strength threaded bar (generally 15 mm diameter) passed through an expendable plastic tube. Simple plastic cones are fitted at the ends of the tube.

After use, the bar is removed and re-used. The safe load taken by the bar can be large (of the order 110 kN) and waler plates of sufficient size will be required to spread the load into the soldiers or bearers. The Formwork Guide (CS, 2011) recommends that, when designing with these recoverable tie assemblies, a minimum factor of safety of 2 is adopted based on the minimum guaranteed ultimate strength of the bars used. Alternatively, safe working loads may be supplied by the tie manufacturer.

Other types of tie rods include taper ties, lost ties, wire ties, coil ties, mild steel all-thread ties, etc. The lost-tie system utilises tapered-ended 'she-bolts' screwed to each end of threaded tie rods. This allows the entire assembly to be placed through the wall form from one side during erection and permits the she-bolts to be subsequently removed,

Figure 23.2 Typical through-tie assembly
Courtesy of RMD Kwikform (UK) Ltd

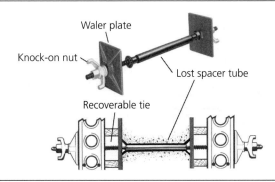

leaving the tie rod embedded in the concrete. The length of the lost tie rod is specified to suit the wall thickness and the cover required to the reinforcement.

It is important to note that suppliers of tie-rod systems will state recommended safe working loads for the ties *used in tension* in wall formwork. Whenever used in other applications, the safe loads will alter as the factors of safety increase, and reference must be made to the tie-rod supplier.

23.6.5 Proprietary panels

Proprietary panel systems are now common and, typically, have plywood face contact material fitted within a steel or aluminium frame; a typical example is shown in Figure 23.3.

Formwork comprising proprietary panels gives a greater potential for re-use for the plywood by reducing damage during handling. Panels are either small enough for manual handling (say 1200 mm × 600 mm), or they may be large crane-handled panels (up to 2400 mm × 2700 mm). The main advantage is the speed of initial use, with little 'make-up' time. It should be noted that such panel systems, when on hire, will generally give 'ordinary' finish (Class F2, suitable for rear, unseen faces of retaining walls), rather than 'plain' finish (Class F3, F4, F5, suitable for quality surfaces to walls). They will often have far fewer components and they have the significant benefit of being available on hire.

23.6.6 Release agents

To obtain satisfactory finishes it is very important that the release agent used on the formwork is suitable. A satisfactory finish will not be achieved if an incorrect release agent is used. It should be stored, used and applied in accordance with the recommendations of the supplier. Any subsequent treatment to the concrete surface may be affected and the supplier's recommendations on compatibility should always be sought. Release agents are classified by numbered Categories. A fuller treatise is given in section 3.10.2 of the Formwork Guide (CS, 2011) but the following should be taken into consideration with regard to chemical and vegetable release agents.

Figure 23.3 Typical proprietary panel formwork system
Courtesy of Jim Murray, PERI (UK) Ltd

23.6.6.1 Chemical release agents

Chemical release agents (Category 5) are various blends of chemicals in suspension in light oil solvents. Coverage rates are 35–50 m^2/l. On being sprayed on to the formwork, the light oil evaporates leaving a chemical to react with the cement to form the barrier. They are of a 'drying' nature, suitable for plywood, timber, steel, etc. and most forms. However, over-application resulting in build-up on the forms can lead to dusting of the resultant concrete surface. There are inherent Health and Safety implications, as the chemicals are dissolved in oils; disposal needs careful consideration.

23.6.6.2 Vegetable oil release agents

Vegetable oil release agents (VERAs; Category 7b) are finding increased usage in construction. Being non-toxic biodegradable vegetable oil (generally based on rapeseed oil), they are suitable for use in confined spaces and for all formwork. Some are supplied in plastic bags, to be dissolved and diluted with water for use.

23.7. Concrete pressure calculation
23.7.1 General

The pressure exerted by the concrete influences the choice of face contact material, as well as dictating the design of the formwork. Correct calculation of the pressure is very important in designing formwork for walls and columns. The magnitude of the design pressure for a particular formwork arrangement should be communicated to

Figure 23.4 Fluid pressure on vertical formwork

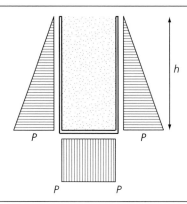

the site team so that those placing the concrete will be able to limit the rate of placing the concrete such that the design pressure is not exceeded. Drawings of formwork should state the maximum pressure in units of kN/m^2, and users of proprietary panels should be aware of the limiting design pressure for their particular arrangement. Changing the tie-rod diameter and/or locations can affect the limiting pressure on the proprietary panel system. Whenever a fluid such as wet concrete is placed in a vessel, the pressure exerted by the fluid at any depth P (Figure 23.4) is defined:

$$P = h \times D$$

where P is the pressure (kN/m^2); h is the depth (m) and D is the density (kN/m^3). For concrete, the density is taken as $25\,kN/m^3$. Under 3 m head of fluid concrete, the pressure is therefore $75\,kN/m^2$.

The pressure always acts at right angles to the face. The force on the formwork can therefore be calculated as pressure × area acted upon.

23.7.2 Effect of stiffening of the concrete

Concrete does not always act as a fluid because, with time, it starts to stiffen and become a solid. For concrete, pressures may be reduced if stiffening occurs during the placing operations, as shown in Figure 23.5. The full fluid pressure head is not realised on the vertical faces of the lower part of the formwork. It should be noted that the soffit form has applied to it the full vertical weight of concrete without stiffening (i.e. the mass). It is obviously more economical to design the wall/column formwork to the limiting value of concrete pressure, P_{max}. There are many factors which affect the concrete pressure, including the temperature of the concrete and whether or not retarding admixtures, pulverised fuel ash (PFA) or ground-granulated blast furnace slag (GGBS) are incorporated.

For the pressure imposed by concrete on formwork, basic research was published in CIRIA Report R108 (Harrison and Clear, 1985). Since then, there have been changes

Figure 23.5 Effect of concrete stiffening on vertical formwork

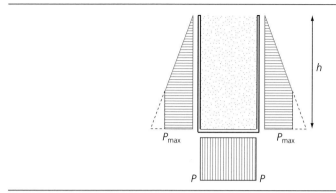

to the types of cement and to concrete specifications (to suit BS EN documents, etc.). University of Dundee research (Dhir *et al.*, 2004) concluded that the methods adopted by CIRIA R108 were safe for use, subject to understanding of the type of concrete used. Concrete mixes using different cement combinations were first classified into three groups for purposes of concrete pressure determination by Pallett (2009). The groups are

- Group A: basic concrete
- Group B: retarded concrete
- Group C: heavily retarded concrete.

23.7.3 The pressure of concrete on formwork

When designing formwork for parallel-sided walls up to 10 m tall or columns up to 15 m tall, Tables PAA, PBB and PCC in section 4.4.3 of the Formwork Guide (CS, 2011) provide concrete pressures linked to rates of rise of the concrete within the form, for various concrete temperatures and for the three concrete groups. The rate of rise is the speed of the rise of the concrete vertically up the forms (in m/hr) and, for parallel-sided forms, is assumed reasonably uniform. The concrete temperature used is *not* the ambient air temperature; for UK work it is likely to be 5°C in winter, 15°C in summer and 10°C in autumn and spring. An example of a table of the maximum concrete pressure P_{max} is reproduced in Tables 23.2 and 23.3. Note in particular the significant change in concrete pressure as the temperature reduces.

For the specified concrete, temperature, form height, required rate of rise of the concrete within the form and the maximum concrete pressure P_{max} can be determined. On site, the formwork arrangement is known, the limiting concrete pressure P_{max} is known (from drawings or from suppliers' data sheets) and the concrete group is known, but the concrete temperature can vary from day to day. To limit the maximum design pressure, the rate of rise of the concrete within the form must be determined so that the required rate of delivery of the concrete can be arranged. There are two ways to determine the rate of rise where the value of P_{max} is known: either use the pressure tables or, more

Table 23.2 Example of concrete pressures for Group A Basic concrete
Data courtesy of the Concrete Society

Walls and bases: A wall or base is a section where at least one of the plan dimensions is greater than 2 m

Conc. temp.: °C	Form height: m	Rate of rise in m/hr						
		0.5	1.0	1.5	2.0	3.0	5.0	10.0
5	2	40	45	50	50	50	50	50
	3	50	55	60	65	70	75	75
	4	60	65	65	70	75	85	100
	6	70	75	80	80	90	100	115
	10	85	90	95	100	105	115	135
10	2	35	40	45	45	50	50	50
	3	40	45	50	55	60	70	75
	4	45	50	55	60	65	75	90
	6	50	55	60	65	75	85	105
	10	60	70	75	80	85	95	115
15	2	30	35	40	45	50	50	50
	3	35	40	45	50	55	65	75
	4	35	45	50	50	60	70	90
	6	40	50	55	60	65	75	95
	10	50	55	60	65	75	85	105

Columns: A column is a section where both plan dimensions are less than 2 m

Conc. temp.: °C	Form height: m	Rate of rise in m/hr				
		2.0	4.0	6.0	10.0	15.0
5	3	75	75	75	75	75
	4	85	100	100	100	100
	6	95	115	125	145	150
	10	115	135	145	170	190
	15	130	150	165	190	210
10	3	65	75	75	75	75
	4	75	90	100	100	100
	6	80	100	115	130	150
	10	95	115	130	150	175
	15	105	125	140	165	190
15	3	60	75	75	75	75
	4	65	85	95	100	100
	6	75	90	105	130	150
	10	80	100	115	140	165
	15	90	110	125	150	175

Note: Concrete Group A Basic Concrete comprises

(i) Concretes without admixture: CEM I, SRPC, CEM IIA with silica fume or metakaolin

(ii) Concretes with any admixture except with retarding properties: CEM I, SRPC, CEM IIA with silica fume or with metakaolin (formerly Groups 1 and 2)

Table 23.3 Example of concrete pressures for Group B retarded concrete
Data courtesy of the Concrete Society

Walls and bases:
A wall or base is a section where at least one of the plan dimensions is greater than 2 m

Conc. temp. °C	Form height m	Rate of rise in m/hr						
		0.5	1.0	1.5	2.0	3.0	5.0	10.0
5	2	50	50	50	50	50	50	50
	3	65	70	75	75	75	75	75
	4	75	80	85	90	95	100	100
	6	95	100	105	105	110	110	135
	10	120	125	130	130	140	150	165
10	2	40	45	50	50	50	50	50
	3	50	55	60	65	70	75	75
	4	60	60	65	70	75	85	100
	6	70	75	80	80	90	100	115
	10	85	90	95	100	105	115	135
15	2	35	40	45	45	50	50	50
	3	40	45	50	55	60	70	75
	4	45	50	55	60	65	75	90
	6	50	60	65	65	75	85	105
	10	65	70	75	80	85	100	120

Columns:
A column is a section where both plan dimensions are less than 2 m

Form height m	Rate of rise in m/hr				
	2.0	4.0	6.0	10.0	15.0
3	75	75	75	75	75
4	100	100	100	100	100
6	120	130	140	150	150
10	145	160	175	195	215
15	170	190	205	225	245
3	75	75	75	75	75
4	85	95	100	100	100
6	95	110	125	145	150
10	115	130	145	170	190
15	130	150	165	190	210
3	65	75	75	75	75
4	75	90	100	100	100
6	80	100	115	135	150
10	95	115	130	155	175
15	105	125	140	165	190

Note: Concrete Group B Retarded Concrete comprises
(i) Concretes without admixture: CEM IIA, CEM IIB, CEM IIIA; (ii) Concretes with admixture that does not have retarding properties: CEM IIA, CEM IIB, CEM IIIA; (iii) Concretes with admixture that retards: CEM I, SRPC, CEM IIA with silica fume or with metakaolin (formerly Groups 3, 4 and 5)

accurately, use the Rate of Rise Tables RWA, RCA, RWB, RCB, RWC and RCC published in the Formwork Guide (CS, 2011; section 4.4.3).

Note that where pour heights are small (such as in building work), if the formwork is designed for full fluid head (Figure 23.4) then there is no limit to the speed of concreting as it is not possible to generate a pressure larger than fluid head. Designing a 3 m column form for maximum 75 kN/m² pressure would therefore not require control of the rate of rise at any concrete temperature or type of concrete mix.

23.8. Wall formwork design
23.8.1 Double-faced formwork
Having established the design concrete pressure for the formwork (which always acts at right angles to the face), the formwork is designed in five basic steps. Whether the bearers are horizontal (Figure 23.6a) or vertical (Figure 23.6b) or whether a proprietary form-work system is being used, the basic principle is *follow the load*. Start at the formwork face and follow the forces designing through to the restraint which, in double-faced forms, is provided by the tie rods. This is described in the 5 steps below.

1   Check the safe span of the face contact material or plywood. This is usually derived from tables plotting pressure against span. This obviously gives the maximum spacing for the bearers fixed horizontally (Figure 23.6a) or vertically (Figure 23.6b). The span of the face contact material is taken as being the spacing of the centres of the bearers/walings.
2   Check the safe span of the bearers. This can also be derived from tables but more economic designs will be produced by analysing the bearers as continuous beams (where appropriate). It is good practice to design the bearers to project past the last support by a maximum of 1/3rd of the adjacent span, since this improves the economy of the design. The span of the bearers when used horizontally as walings is taken as being the spacing of the centres of the soldiers (or of the stiff horizontal members when the bearers are fixed vertically).

Figure 23.6 Follow the load
Courtesy of Pallett Temporary Works Ltd

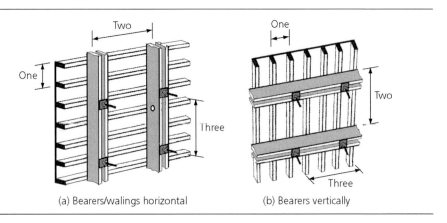

(a) Bearers/walings horizontal   (b) Bearers vertically

3   Check the design of the soldiers. The tie rod spacing determines the span requirements for the soldiers but additional checks may be required if, for example, there are joints in the soldiers. As the design pressure reduces near the top of the wall, fewer ties are required (see Figure 23.7). The layout of ties (and therefore the soldiers) may have been specified by the Permanent Works Designer to suit, for example, a particular surface finish with a regular pattern. The span of the soldiers is taken as being the spacing of the tie rods.
4   Check the capacity of the tie rods for the chosen arrangement of soldiers.
5   Check the deflection of the face of the forms. With such large pressures being imposed on the formwork system, the design should take careful account of deflections with reference to the acceptable tolerances (see Section 23.5). It should be remembered, however, that the deflection limit (normally 1/270th of the span) is applied individually to the face contact material, to the bearers and then to the soldiers; it is not cumulative.

Other considerations to be observed during the design process will include safety issues (working platforms for placing the concrete, CDM Regulations, Work at Height Regulations) and handling of the formwork (weight limit for manual handling and crane or traveller capacity for mechanical handling). See Chapter 1 on safety and the section on mechanical handling of formwork in the Formwork Guide (CS, 2011; section 5.9).

23.8.2   Stability of formwork

A check will be needed on the stability of the formwork (and any required propping designed for a minimum factor of safety) against overturning, considering the most adverse conditions. The minimum factor of safety on overturning is 1.2. A typical double-faced wall formwork arrangement with a single inclined push-pull prop, connected to a kentledge block, is shown in Figure 23.7.

Figure 23.7 Cross-section of double-faced formwork to wall with propping
Courtesy of RMD Kwikform (UK) Ltd

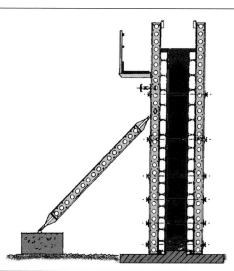

Stability checks are carried out for overturning caused by

1   'maximum wind', plus overturning from a nominal load on any platforms
2   'working wind' (upper limit at which plant may be operated on site) on the day of concreting, plus overturning from the full load on the platforms
3   'minimum stability force' (10% of the total self weight of both faces of the formwork) acting three-quarters of the way up the form plus any overturning from the full load on the platforms.

A simplified method to establish the wind forces (both 'maximum' and 'working') on freestanding wall formwork can be found in the Formwork Guide (CS, 2011; section 4.5.1).

23.8.3   Single-faced formwork

In certain conditions, it is not possible to have two faces of formwork. Examples are walls cast against existing secant pile walls or diaphragm walls. Only one face of formwork can be erected and tie rods cannot be used. These single-faced wall forms will have the same concrete pressures imposed on them as double-faced formwork. The design process is similar with the exception that the final restraint cannot be provided by tie rods and must, therefore, be provided externally. Single-faced formwork always requires particularly careful attention to detail; it must be remembered that the force generated by the concrete pressure will be horizontal when using vertical formwork.

The most common method of support for small single-faced formwork is to use inclined props as shown in Figure 23.8. Because of the inclined props, there will always be a

Figure 23.8 Typical arrangement of single-faced formwork using soldiers
Courtesy of Pallett TemporaryWorks Ltd

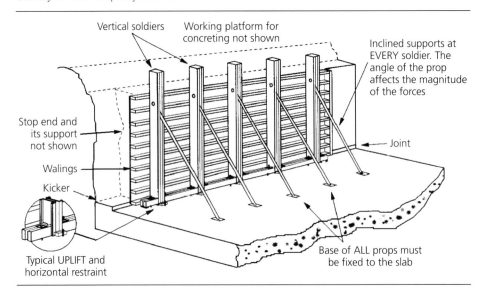

Figure 23.9 Typical arrangement of single-faced formwork using frames
Courtesy of Pallett Temporary*Works* Ltd

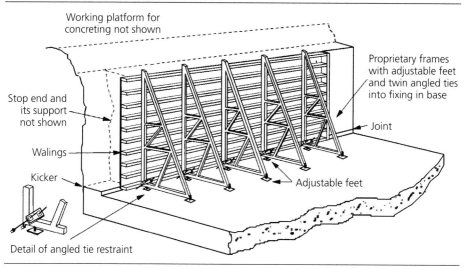

corresponding and significant uplift force at the base of the form. This introduces the need for fixings into the existing slab to provide restraint against the uplift, as well as providing the necessary horizontal restraint.

An alternative method of support for single-faced formwork is the use of proprietary large frames. These incorporate a single connection between the frame and the existing slab providing both vertical and horizontal restraint to the form; a typical detail is shown in Figure 23.9. It is important to install the ties accurately and at the correct angle to prevent them being incorrectly loaded, which may cause them to fail.

Control of movement of the top of the single-faced formwork is always difficult. Care is required to ensure that the specified tolerances are not exceeded. Loads imposed on the existing slab by the anchors, fixings and props are significant; approval from the Permanent Works Designer should always be sought.

23.9. Column formwork design

Because of their comparatively small cross-section and relatively high rates of rise, column forms are subject to higher concrete pressures than walls. Due to the confined space into which the concrete is placed, tall and inclined columns may require pockets or windows at intervals to facilitate placing and compacting of the concrete (CS, 2011; section 5.5).

Columns may have circular, square, rectangular or other irregular cross-sections. These irregular cross-sections can often be formed by placing inserts or box-outs within standard square or rectangular column moulds. Circular column forms are available made from steel, GRP or single-use cardboard forms; the latter is particularly useful if only a few columns are required. Steel and GRP column forms can incorporate splayed column heads.

Variations in column shapes and sizes, particularly on the same project, should be kept to a minimum. Ideally, column sizes should be selected in modular increments of 75 mm (e.g. 300, 375, 450, etc.) enabling both the designer and the builder to standardise (and hence economise).

A range of column forms using proprietary panels is available, with some designed to cater for varying rectangular shapes by adjustment on site using 'universal panels' arranged in a 'windmill' pattern. As panel formwork is designed for a specific limiting concrete pressure, it may be beneficial to sequence the construction of the columns with other site concreting work and/or to pour multiple columns simultaneously to reduce the risk of overloading the column formwork. Restricting the pour rate so that the allowable pressure on the forms is not exceeded may not always be a workable solution, and specifically designed formwork may be more appropriate.

23.10. Striking vertical formwork

The time at which striking of vertical formwork can be carried out should be carefully controlled. BS EN 13670 states that 'Formwork shall not be removed until the concrete has gained sufficient strength, and can resist any damage caused by striking' (BSI, 2009).

A minimum value of in situ concrete cube strength of $2\,\mathrm{N/mm^2}$ is recommended in all cases when striking vertical formwork; see the NCSC guidance (ConStruct, 2010). The informative annex C.5.7 of BS EN 13670 (BSI, 2009) suggests a concrete strength of 5 MPa (equivalent to $5\,\mathrm{N/mm^2}$) to resist damage when a value is not given in the project specification.

The Formwork Guide (CS, 2011) recommends a minimum strength of $2\,\mathrm{N/mm^2}$ to reduce the risk of mechanical and frost damage for striking plain and special concrete finishes (Classes F3, F4 and F5; BSI, 2009).

A lower criterion is generally possible for striking forms with basic or ordinary concrete finish (Classes F1 and F2; BSI, 2009), usually related to the maturity of the concrete. In practice, provided the mean concrete temperature is above 10°C overnight, the vertical formwork can be struck next morning. If the mean air temperature is above 10°C, it can safely be assumed that the concrete temperature was above 10°C. Where the newly struck concrete may be exposed to frost, a minimum in situ concrete equivalent cube strength of $2\,\mathrm{N/mm^2}$ is recommended.

Note that certain project specifications, for example, the Specification for the Water Industry (CESWI, 2011), may require higher strengths prior to removal of formwork.

23.11. Workmanship/checking

To produce concrete of a high standard of appearance and precision, a high standard of site workmanship is required; this will apply even if formwork is specially constructed for the job in question. Where the amount of work does not justify the use of specially designed and fabricated formwork, the degree of success in achieving the required result will depend solely on the skill and expertise of the site operatives. In a few cases, the economic solution may be to fabricate a high-quality form for only one or two uses.

There are cases, however, when good-quality work can be achieved with less skilled labour. These will normally be where work is simple, of a highly repetitive nature and where the size of the job justifies the use of sophisticated special-purpose formwork which is designed for simplicity. A considerable amount of the work carried out on site does not demand good appearance or close tolerances, although appreciable skill and experience is still necessary to ensure that the formwork is stable, safe and to the required standard.

All blemishes in the formwork will appear on the surface of the finished concrete. Blemishes will obviously not become apparent until the formwork is struck, by which time the concrete has hardened making the repairs difficult.

When using proprietary systems, it is important that site management ensure that the operatives construct the systems correctly using the manufacturer's approved components. Once the forms have been constructed the site must ensure that the concrete placement methods are appropriate for the system being used, and are being used within the pressure limits set by the manufacturer and/or formwork designer (see also Chapter 2).

Checking of formwork should be carried out systematically, as stated in Section 23.8.1. The axiom 'follow the load' also applies to checking of formwork. Two useful guides are *A Guide to the Safe Use of Formwork and Falsework* (ConStruct, 2008) and the Concrete Society Checklist for the Assembly, Use & Striking of Formwork (CS, 2003).

REFERENCES

BRE (Building Research Establishment) (2007) Formwork for Modern, Efficient Concrete Construction. BR 495. HIS BRE Press, Bracknell.
BSI (2009) BS EN 13670: Execution of concrete structures. BSI, London.
CESWI (Civil Engineering Specification for the Water Industry) (2011) *Civil Engineering Specification for the Water Industry*, 7th edition. WRc plc, Swindon.
CIRIA (Construction Industry Research and Information Association) (2000) Controlled Permeability Formwork. Joint Report CIRIA/Concrete Society, Report C511, London.
ConStruct (Concrete Structures Group) (2008) A guide to the safe use of formwork and falsework. Ref: CSG/005. Concrete Society, Camberley.
ConStruct (2010) *National Structural Concrete Specification for Building Construction*, 4th edition. Ref. CCIP-050. Concrete Society, Camberley.
CS (Concrete Society) (1999) Plain Formed Concrete Finishes: Illustrated Examples. Concrete Society Technical Report No. 52, Crowthorne.
CS (2003) Checklist for the assembly, use & striking of formwork. Ref. CS144. Concrete Society, Crowthorne.

CS (2011) *Formwork: A Guide to Good Practice*, 3rd edition. Special Publication CS 030. Concrete Society, Camberley.

Dhir RK, McCarthy MJ, Caliskan S and Ashraf MK (2004) Design formwork pressures for the range of new cement, superplasticised and self-compacting concretes. DTI research contract No. 39/3/739 (CCC2399) University of Dundee Report CTU/3004.

HA (Highways Agency) (2004) *Manual of Contract Documents for Highways Works. Volume 1 Specification for Highways Works.* HMSO, London.

Harrison TA and Clear C (1985) Concrete pressure on formwork. Construction Industry Research and Information Association, Report 108. CIRIA, London.

NBS (National Building Specification) (annually) Formed finishes, Section E20. National Building Specification Ltd, Newcastle-upon-Tyne.

Pallett PF (2009) Concrete groups for formwork pressure determination. *Concrete* **43**(2): 44–46.

Useful web addresses

http://www.concrete.org.uk
http://www.construct.org.uk
http://www.temporaryworks.info

306

Temporary Works: Principles of Design and Construction
ISBN 978-0-7277-4177-6

ICE Publishing: All rights reserved
http://dx.doi.org/10.1680/twpdc.41776.307

Chapter 24
Soffit formwork

Peter F. Pallett Pallett Temporary*Works* Ltd

The support to the underside of in situ concrete, flat or inclined, requires formwork to contain and mould the concrete to the desired shape. Often supported on foundations by means of falsework, the soffit formwork is an important part of temporary works. The supports can only be removed when the concrete has gained sufficient strength, so the procedure and sequence for striking needs to be understood and approved before concreting.

24.1.   Introduction

The forming of the underside of concrete structures while the concrete gains strength utilises soffit formwork, either inclined or nominally level. Unlike vertical formwork (discussed in Chapter 23), the concrete has to have gained sufficient strength before the structure can support itself thus allowing the formwork to be removed. Generally, in situ concreting on soffit formwork will have some supporting falsework (see Chapter 22 on falsework) to transfer the load to suitable foundations. In certain cases, such as permanent formwork or in the case of cantilever soffit formwork, supporting falsework may not be required and the loads are transferred directly to the permanent works.

Soffit formwork is found in civil structures and to the undersides of bridge decks, beams and parapets. In building it is used to form the underside of slabs: ideally flat slabs or, with moulds, slabs with downstands. It is also used to form the underside of beams and in a wide variety of situations. A typical arrangement of soffit formwork to a structure with supporting falsework is depicted in Figure 24.1.

The increasing use of proprietary components such as formwork panels, proprietary timber and aluminium bearers as well as lightweight aluminium falsework components has seen a movement away from traditional plywood and timber soffit formwork (as exemplified in Figure 24.1) to the use of proprietary solutions. Soffits may support voided slabs such as trough or waffle floors or bridge decks incorporating square or circular voids.

This chapter provides information about the different philosophies of design and use of soffit formwork for both civil and building applications. It includes bridge and slab formwork, cantilever soffits and the latest considerations for striking of soffit formwork in the UK.

Figure 24.1 Typical arrangement of soffit formwork and falsework
Courtesy of Pallett TemporaryWorks Ltd

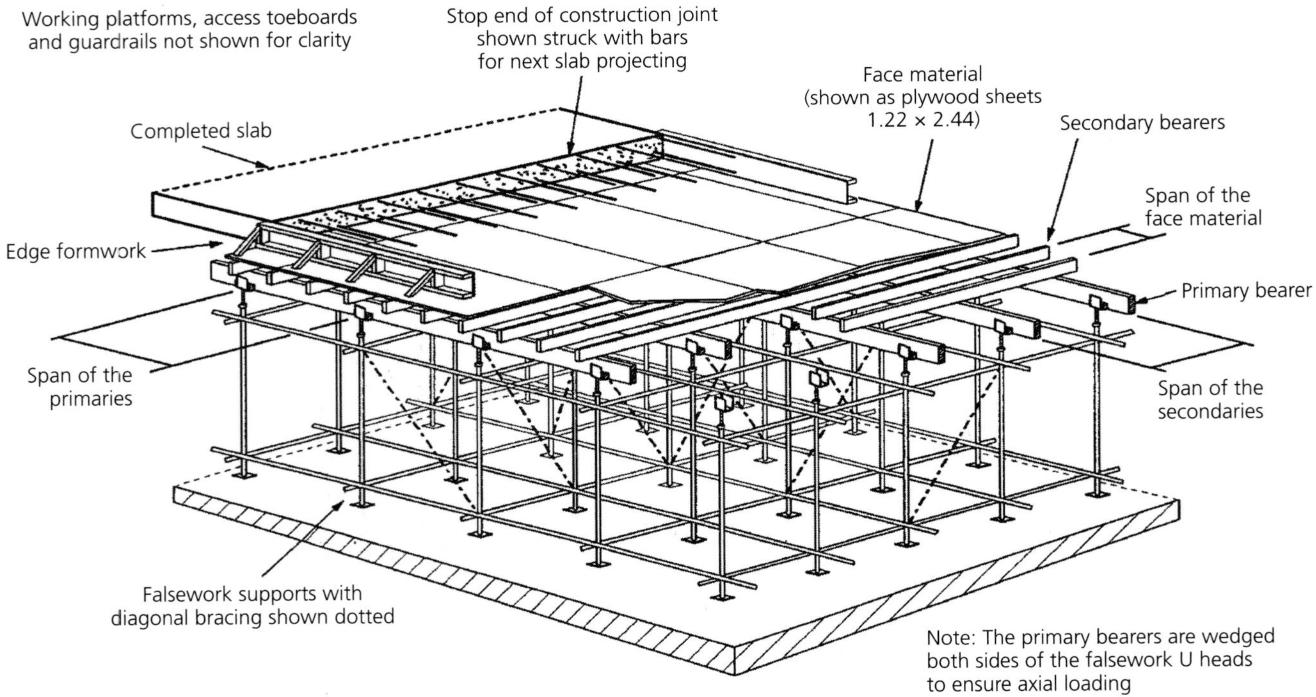

Working platforms, access toeboards
and guardrails not shown for clarity

Stop end of construction joint
shown struck with bars
for next slab projecting

Span of the
face material

Primary bearer

Secondary bearers

Span of the
secondaries

Face material
(shown as plywood sheets
1.22 × 2.44)

Completed slab

Edge formwork

Span of the
primaries

Falsework supports with
diagonal bracing shown dotted

Note: The primary bearers are wedged
both sides of the falsework U heads
to ensure axial loading

24.2.   Preamble to soffit form design

24.2.1   General

The main sources of information for soffit formwork and its supporting falsework are the Concrete Society's *Formwork: A Guide to Good Practice* (FGTGP) (CS, 2011), ConStruct's *Guide to Flat Slab Formwork and Falsework* (2003) and the British Standards on falsework, namely BS 5975 (BSI, 2011) in permissible stress and BS EN 12812 (BSI, 2008) in limit state terms.

Consider the components of soffit formwork. The face contact material in contact with the concrete could be plywood, wood-based panels (particleboard or oriented strand board), plastic composites, steel or a proprietary panel system. These are usually supported on bearers known as secondary bearers. In turn, the secondary bearers are supported on more substantial bearers, known as primary bearers. The primary bearers fit on to the falsework uprights, usually centralised in adjustable forkheads. The primary bearers may be considered as part of the formwork and designed using the Formwork Guide (FGTGP) (CS, 2011) or as part of the falsework (BSI, 2011); for example, if the primary bearers are constructional softwood the safe load tables are identical in FGTGP and BS 5975.

24.2.2   Specification and finishes

The contract documents will specify the standard of finish required for the concrete surface of the soffit and this will affect the selection of material used to create the face that will form the visible surface finish.

British Standard BS EN 13670 *Execution of concrete structures* (BSI, 2009) defines the generic surface finishes. The two main UK specifications are the National Structural Concrete Specification for Building Construction (NSCS) (ConStruct, 2010; section 8.6) and the Highways Agency specification (HA, 2006; volume 1, clause 1708). Table 23.1 in Chapter 23 provides a comparison of the two specifications. Other specifications used include the UK Water Industry Research document *Civil Engineering Specification for the Water Industry* (CESWI, 2011; clause 4.28) and the National Building Specification Formwork for in situ concrete (NBS, 2011; section E20).

Particular care is necessary in specifying the surface finish for bridges, especially for their parapets. The CIRIA report R155 *Bridges: Design for improved buildability* (CIRIA, 1996) recommends that the HA Class F3 finish be limited to small vertical areas of the parapet, such as those visible from the highway. Unfortunately, if specified for the entire parapet edge and soffit, the 'no-tie' requirement of Class F3 makes restraint of such soffit formwork extremely complex and unnecessarily expensive, and often leads to grout loss at connections with unsightly marks. The solution is to specify Class F4 for most of the parapet, leaving the small vertical upstand (visible) face as Class F3 finish. Realistic specifications will produce better results.

24.3.   Loading on soffit forms

24.3.1   Vertical

The soffit formwork not only has to carry its self weight and the weight of the wet concrete being supported (note that wet concrete is an imposed load, not a dead load), but also the two construction operations loads (see Chapter 22). These are (1) the working area load distributed over the whole working area of 0.75 kN/m^2 (i.e. Service Class 1) and (2) the variable transient in situ loading allowance applied over an area $3 \text{ m} \times 3 \text{ m}$, which varies from 0.75 kN/m^2 for slabs up to 300 mm up to a maximum of 1.75 kN/m^2 for solid slabs greater than 700 mm. Intermediate thicknesses are designed on 10% of the slab self weight (BSI, 2011; clause 17.4.3.1).

24.3.2 Horizontal
In addition to vertical forces, soffit formwork can have applied horizontal forces. These could be from surges in concrete pump lines, impact forces and possibly from arrangements of the stop-ends. All slabs will have stop-ends and/or construction joints. Particular care is necessary on all slab/deck stop-ends greater than 400 mm depth.

When casting a slab against an existing structure or against a previous cast section, there will be a lateral force generated from the reaction to the pressure of concrete (i.e. the fluid head of concrete on the connection) acting on the existing face. For example, a 900 mm slab cast against an existing slab generates a lateral force of about 10 kN per metre run of joint.

A common site error is to ignore discontinuities in the soffit formwork. Where there is a discontinuity in the formwork, a lateral force (equivalent to the fluid head of concrete at that point) exists laterally and attempts to move the forms apart. Generally the arrangement of staggered bearers supporting the face material will provide the restraint, but where a section of falsework and formwork is not connected (e.g. between tables of formwork) or where the falsework is staggered to allow for changes in levels, discontinuities can be formed. The solution is usually quite simple: join the sections of falsework together below the soffit formwork. This is discussed in more detail in both the Formwork Guide (FGTGP) (CS, 2011) and BS 5975 (BSI, 2011).

24.3.3 Notional Force
One of the topics discussed in Chapter 22 is the use of the soffit formwork to provide the stability of the falsework, known as top-restrained falsework. Where this occurs, the soffit forms will have to transmit the relevant lateral notional forces to suitable restraint with the soffit formwork acting as a plate. This is discussed in more detail in BS 5975 (BSI, 2011; clause 19.3.2.4). Designers need to consider the forces in all directions, so that both tension and compression will apply to the soffit forms.

24.4. Design
The design of soffit formwork is different from that for walls as discussed in Chapter 23; the loads are usually less. For example, a 900 mm thick in situ concrete bridge deck imparts an imposed load of 22.5 kN/m^2 on the soffit and a 250 mm slab only 6.25 kN/m^2, compared to the pressures on the face of wall and column forms in the order of $60–130 \text{ kN/m}^2$. As a result, the supporting members will often safely span greater distances although this will lead to larger deflections in the bearers. Often it is the deflection criteria that will govern the span.

Figure 24.2 Beam reactions for one, two or three spans with distributed load

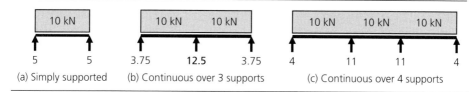

(a) Simply supported   (b) Continuous over 3 supports   (c) Continuous over 4 supports

The basic design principle is that the loads are transferred from the face to the supporting falsework. Refer to Figure 23.5 (Chapter 23) and consider the similar arrangement turned through 90° to become a soffit.

The distribution of load into the vertical members from the soffit formwork bearers will often be very random. The face contact material, the secondary bearers and often the primary members in the forkheads will be continuous over several supports, giving rise to increased reactions at internal supports from their elastic reactions. The support reactions of beams change when they are continuous over more than two supports, and this applies to all types of members used as beams.

Figure 24.2 shows the support reactions caused by a distributed load on each equal span of 10 kN per span for one, two or three spans. The designer's worst case is a single beam continuous over two spans, i.e. with three supports (Figure 24.2b), giving a central reaction of the static load times 1.25 for continuity, i.e. a staggering 25% increase in load. The '10% continuity rule' in BS 5975 (BSI, 2011; clause 19.3.3.2) accepts that, in the case of falsework comprising random bearers with the formwork and falsework all in various lengths, the vertical load is calculated on the area supported by the standard plus 10% to allow for continuity. (Note that the 10% is added once, not for each level of bearers.) In certain cases, for example, over two spans, a more precise calculation may be justified. Certain proprietary systems incorporate simply supported beams and this 'rule' may not apply.

In the UK, most contractors will use table systems for flat slab construction; generally, with aluminium beams in both directions at the top. A typical example is shown in Figure 24.3. Table systems comprise large diameter aluminium props (typical diameters are 100–150 mm) with long threaded sections to allow for adjustment, connected together with ledger frames and/or cross-bracing.

The stiffness of the assembly is derived from long lengths of aluminium primary beams. These tend to limit the lengths of table handled to 12 m with standard components, but longer lengths are possible. Tables have the benefit that once made up they enable rapid construction, and the benefits increase with repetitive use. They can be used with cross-wall construction or columns, but are most economic when there is access to opposite faces of the building for direct removal of the tables. Table systems ideally suit flat slab and repetitive construction and become economic at over eight uses. Cycle times as short as 4 days have been achieved with careful planning; see the flat slab guide (ConStruct, 2003).

Figure 24.3 Typical aluminium table with ledger frames
Courtesy of Jim Murray, PERI (UK) Ltd

Tables need space to be 'flown' out of the building (either to one side or to both sides), with a minimum end allowance of 500 mm for clearance from the building to adjacent structures/objects and to allow for cantilever access platforms. A minimum clearance to columns/walls of 40 mm per side should be allowed to the sides of each table; some infill support is therefore necessary at arises when used with crosswall construction.

The various methods of handling tables are outside the scope of this book; see the Formwork Guide (FGTGP) (CS, 2011) for detailed information. Consideration must be given to the handling and operation of the system. For example, if handled as individual tables, the lengths of aluminium bearers become critical in striking out after pouring. Physically removing long lengths is extremely hard and places unnecessary risk on the operatives. Note that BS 5975 (BSI, 2011; clause 19.1.13) recommends that, when handling individual units, a working platform of about 2 m below the underside of the soffit should be fitted.

24.5. Cantilevered soffits

A common method for casting the concrete parapets of bridges that are constructed with pre-cast concrete or steel beams is to project beams out either below or above the parapet to be supported; typical arrangements are depicted in Figure 24.4. Known as cantilevered soffits, they have to be designed for the actual loads including any side forces from edge forms. Allowance has to be made for deviations caused by the

Figure 24.4 Typical cantilever soffit arrangements
Courtesy of Pallett Temporary*Works* Ltd

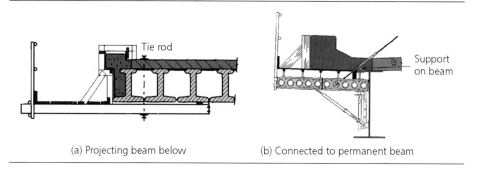

| (a) Projecting beam below | (b) Connected to permanent beam |

method adopted, such as deflections caused by the elastic extension of the tie rods, etc. The effective length of cantilevered beams is given in BS 5975 (BSI, 2011; table K.3) where, for example, when the tip of the cantilever is free to rotate with the applied load, the effective length is 7.5 times the actual length. Design is not easy, and consideration of differential deflections and subsequent movements can become complicated. Further guidance is given in the Formwork Guide (FGTGP) (CS, 2011).

24.6. Striking soffit formwork
24.6.1 General
The time at which soffit forms can be removed and the exact procedure for striking the forms requires detailed consideration. Without such consideration, there is a real risk of damaging the permanent works and possibly initiating an accident. The specification should define any requirements for striking taking into account considerations of frost and mechanical damage, reduction in thermal shock and limiting excessive deflections. Detailed guidance on use of fast track equipment for early striking procedures is given in the Flat Slab Guide (ConStruct, 2003) and criteria are listed in Table 24.1.

Unlike wall formwork, in order to remove soffit formwork the structure has to be capable of carrying its own weight plus any imposed load at the time of striking. The

Table 24.1 Striking soffit forms: slabs and beams, etc.

Finish description	Criteria for striking soffit formwork
Basic, ordinary, plain or special finish	Use specifications, codes of practice or tables (e.g. CIRIA R136, 1996)
HA all classes	Assess the concrete strength at time of striking knowing the maturity, and concrete mix, etc. using either a method based on pro rata the strengths or, for flat slabs, an assessment based on crack width

total service load on the member at the time of striking will depend on the sequence of construction and, in multi-storey construction, whether there is any backpropping. The load can include the following.

- Self weight of the member: it is usual to assume a concrete density of 24 kN/m^3 in building and the higher value of 25 kN/m^3 in civil works.
- Formwork self weight from any further construction: usually about 0.50 kN/m^2
- Falsework self weight from any further construction: usually 0.10–0.15 kN/m^3
- Working area load for access: minimum 0.75 kN/m^2 (service class 1 loading).
- Stored materials: should be avoided on newly struck slabs.

Particular consideration should be given to the striking of suspended slabs which are designed for light imposed loads; examples are roof slabs and reservoir roofs which will not have earth cover. In these cases, the self weight may be the predominant load and the construction operations load will represent a load very similar to the Permanent Works Designer's imposed load. For such slabs with very low design imposed loads, it may not be possible to strike until the concrete approaches its characteristic strength. Instances of early cracking and excessive deflections on reservoir roofs have been attributed to incorrect early striking. The permanent works slab or beam will generally be allowed to take up its instantaneous deflected shape before other loads are applied.

Some proprietary systems actually have quick strip arrangements, allowing the expensive formwork face components to be struck early (normally at a minimum concrete strength of 5 N/mm^2 to avoid damage) while leaving the main slab supported until approval to strike is received. The management and control of such soffit schemes is discussed in Chapter 2.

24.6.2 Striking bridge soffits
The Highways Agency specification (HA, 2006; volume 1, clause 1710.4) limits striking to either 10 N/mm^2 concrete strength or three times the stress to which the member is subjected. This is discussed in detail in the Formwork Guide (FGTGP) (CS, 2011; section 5.3.6.1). The criteria for striking should be agreed with the Permanent Works Designer.

24.6.3 Striking slabs up to 350 mm thick
The Formwork Design Brief (CS, 2011; appendix A) will have identified the method of strength assessment for striking, the design service loads on the structure and the characteristic strength of the concrete.

24.6.3.1 Ratio of loads method
Methods of striking soffit and beam formwork have traditionally been based on considering the ratio of the loads on the slab at time of striking and the designer's known service load. This method assumes that the slab is elastic, i.e. if you double the total load then the bending moment, deflection, etc. are also doubled. Striking may therefore commence if the ratio of the loading on the slab at the time of striking compared to

the design service load is similar to the ratio of concrete strength at the time of striking to the characteristic concrete strength.

24.6.3.2 Crack width method

The research work carried out at the start of the twenty-first century has showed that faster and safe construction methods are possible using crack width and not ratio of loads as the criterion. This was fully researched at the European Concrete Building Project (ECBP).

The assumption for loading a concrete slab is that the crack width is proportional to the stress in the steel reinforcement which, in turn, is proportional to the load. Hence if load is removed or added, there will be a proportional reduction/increase in crack width. Although the slab is designed for the ultimate limit state, the actual maximum load on the slab at the time considered will be the summation of the unfactored loads because the consideration of crack width is at serviceability limit state, not ultimate. The load applied to a slab during any stage of construction should not be greater than the designer's unfactored design service load. Obviously if the concrete slab is struck earlier than intended, then the structure may be permanently damaged.

This method was first published by the BRE in BR 394 (Beeby, 2000) and is fully detailed in the Formwork Guide (CS, 2011; section 5.3.7.2). Using this method of evaluating crack width criteria will give a faster method for safely striking flat slabs than that derived from the ratio of loads.

The method relies on accurately evaluating the actual concrete strength of the new concrete. This subject is covered in more detail in both the Formwork Guide (CS, 2011) and the Flat Slab Guide (ConStruct, 2003). Cube strengths at an early age (say 19 hours) can be unrealistic and alternative methods of strength assessment at early age (e.g. LOK test, maturity measurements or the Capo test) are preferred.

Where there are several other levels of construction, there may also be a requirement to support additional loads. There will be occasions in multi-storey construction when the slab immediately below the level to be supported has not achieved full maturity, and construction loads will require to be supported through several levels. This is known as backpropping; see BS 5975 (BSI, 2011).

24.6.4   Sequence of striking

The sequence for striking the supports should be agreed before any striking commences. On complex structures, this may be specified by the Permanent Works Designer. The following procedure should generally be adopted

1   slabs spanning between walls: commence striking at the middle, working towards the walls
2   slabs supported on beams: strike the slabs commencing at the middle, working towards the beams, then after slabs are fully struck strike the beams commencing at the middle, working towards the columns
3   cantilevers: commence at the tip and strike towards the support.

24.7. Checking and inspection

Useful guides to aid checking and inspection of soffit formwork are *A Guide to the Safe Use of Formwork and Falsework* (ConStruct, 2008) and CS 144 *Checklist for the Assembly, Use & Striking of Formwork* (CS, 2003).

REFERENCES

Beeby AW (2000) A radical redesign of the in-situ concrete frame process, Task 4: Early striking of formwork and forces in backprops. The University of Leeds, Building Research Establishment Ltd. Report BR 394, London.

BSI (2008) BS EN 12812: Falsework: Performance requirements and general design. BSI, London.

BSI (2009) BS EN 13670: Execution of concrete structures. BSI, London.

BSI (2011) BS 5975: 2008 + A1: 2011 Code of practice for temporary works procedures and the permissible stress design of falsework. BSI, London.

CESWI (Civil Engineering Specification for the Water Industry) (2011) Civil Engineering Specification for the Water Industry, 7th edition. WRc plc, Swindon.

CIRIA (Construction Industry Research and Information Association) (1995) Formwork striking times: Criteria, prediction and methods of assessment. Report R136. CIRIA, London.

CIRIA (1996) Bridges: Design for improved buildability. Report R155. CIRIA, London

ConStruct (Concrete Structures Group) (2003) Guide to Flat Slab Formwork and Falsework. Ref No. CS 140. Concrete Society, Camberley.

ConStruct (2008) A guide to the safe use of formwork and falsework. Ref: CSG/005. Concrete Society, Camberley.

ConStruct (2010) National Structural Concrete Specification for Building Construction, 4th edition. Ref. CCIP-050. Concrete Society, Camberley.

CS (Concrete Society) (2003) Checklist for the assembly, use & striking of formwork. Ref. CS144. Concrete Society, Crowthorne.

CS (2011) Formwork: A Guide to Good Practice, 3rd edition. Special Publication CS 030. Concrete Society, Camberley.

HA (Highways Agency) (2006) Specification for Highway Works, Manual of Contract Documents for Highway Works. HMSO, London.

NBS (National Building Specification) (2011) National Building Specification. NBS Building, Newcastle-upon-Tyne.

Useful web addresses

http://www.nasc.org.uk
http://www.construct.org.uk
http://www.temporaryworks.info
http://www.concrete.org.uk
http://www.twforum.org.uk

Temporary Works: Principles of Design and Construction
ISBN 978-0-7277-4177-6

ICE Publishing: All rights reserved
http://dx.doi.org/10.1680/twpdc.41776.317

Chapter 25
Climbing and slip forms

Jim Murray Engineering Director, PERI Ltd

Climbing and slip forms are systems for the construction of in situ reinforced concrete vertical wall elements, several lifts high, that do not rely on support or access from other parts of the permanent works. A combined formwork assembly and access platform is either supported on anchors/tracks bolted to the previous section of wall or, for continuous pouring, supported on climbing rods cast into the concrete. Protection screen systems, either for use with climbing formwork or as separate entities, have similar design considerations. The type of structure and suitability on repetitive wall elements affects the economy of these systems.

25.1. Introduction

The operation of climbing formwork, often referred to as 'jump form', involves individual pours with the formwork moved between the pours; alternatively, the operation of slip form requires the concrete to be poured continuously and the forms are raised to suit the speed of placing concrete.

Climbing or jump-form formwork (see Section 25.3) typically comprises the formwork and safe working platforms for cleaning/fixing of the formwork and access for fixing reinforcement and concreting works. Unlike conventional formwork discussed in Chapter 23, it supports itself on the previously cast concrete and does not rely on support or access from other parts of the structure or permanent works.

Climbing formwork is suitable for vertical elements in high-rise structures such as bridge piers/columns or stair/lift shafts, core walls, shear walls, etc. in buildings. These are constructed in a staged process. It is a highly productive system designed to increase speed and efficiency while minimising labour and crane time. Systems are normally modular and can be joined together to form long lengths to suit varying construction geometries. Further detailed guidance on use of climbing formwork is given in *Formwork: A guide to good practice* (CS, 2011; section 6.2).

Slip forming (see Section 25.4) is a system whereby the entire formwork system with its safe access platforms are incrementally jacked upwards as the reinforcement and concrete is placed. Slip forming is used for constructing chimneys, silos, water tanks and shaft linings as well as towers, lift shafts and bridge piers. There are no construction joints, which is particularly important for leak-free structures. Fast rates of production can be achieved, but these systems require more initial site preparation and are generally carried out by specialist subcontractors. See also the *Good Concrete Guide 6* (CS, 2008).

25.2. Climbing and slip form viability assessment

25.2.1 General

Jump form, where the formwork assemblies are moved from position to position with the aid of a crane, are widely used in high-rise buildings (typically in excess of 5 storeys). The complexity of the system increases with the height of the structures with fully self-climbing systems, independent of craneage, becoming viable in excess of 20 storeys. However, a combination of crane-handled and self-climbing platforms can be viable on lower structures.

Self-climbing formwork offers the advantage of considerably reducing the requirement for crane time, thus allowing the crane to be used for other construction work. Another advantage is that climbing formwork can be designed to operate in high winds when required (where the use of a crane may become limited), thus lessening the risk of delays in the construction program.

Slip-form formwork has a longer initial set-up time than climbing or jump forms and will be more expensive per square metre of formwork, but the resulting equipment cost per square metre of slip-formed surface will be much lower. As it is often a 24 hour process in shifts, the labour costs can be higher but production rates will be faster. Slip-forming will usually suit tall structures that are not less than 20–25 m tall and which do not have frequent plan changes. Slip-forming may be economic for structures as low as 12 m tall, or even lower if several identical structures can be constructed in sequence.

Whether it is a crane-dependent, fully self-climbing or slip-form system which is selected, the general principle is the same. The formwork is independently supported, relying on the concrete which has been cast earlier so that core walls, for example, can be completed ahead of the rest of the main building structure (see Figure 25.1).

The construction in advance of such core/lift shaft walls can provide stability to the main structure during its construction and can have the beneficial effect of taking the core off the project critical path. This then permits different phases of work to be carried out concurrently without interference.

25.2.2 Economy of construction

The economy and speed of construction are key factors in deciding whether or not to select climbing formwork or slip form. For bridge piers/columns and similar structures the question is not so much whether to climb, but how to climb. In high-rise buildings, the decision-making process is not so straightforward and can depend upon many factors. With an ever-growing emphasis being placed on improvements in safety and productivity, together with the increasing complexity of structures and limited building footprints on congested city sites, climbing has become the preferred solution more often than not. The vertical elements can be progressed quickly in advance of the floors, thus taking a significant part of the overall structure off of the critical path.

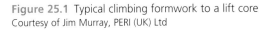
Figure 25.1 Typical climbing formwork to a lift core
Courtesy of Jim Murray, PERI (UK) Ltd

The benefits of reduced demand on the use of cranes and the efficient construction method achieved due to the repetitive nature of the construction method leads to fast cycling times. Where sites have sufficient ground level space and a well-considered construction program linked with good site management and experienced operatives, using more traditional techniques can be just as effective.

25.2.3 Assessment/suitability of structure

The first point to consider when investigating the feasibility of using climbing formwork or slip-form techniques is the structure itself. All systems require that the permanent wall under construction be sufficiently strong and have sufficient stability in the temporary condition to support it.

The Permanent Works Designer (PWD) is the only person who has sufficient knowledge of the structure to assess whether it can withstand the loading induced, particularly by the climbing formwork system. The Construction (Design and Management) (CDM) coordinator has a duty to ensure that the permanent works and temporary works designers (TWD) cooperate, and that the permanent structure can withstand the loads applied to it by the temporary works (see Chapter 2 on management). The temporary works coordinator (TWC) has an important role at this stage, as it is highly probable that the use of climbing formwork as a method of construction was not considered during the structural design phase. The PWD should verify whether the vertical elements can support climbing formwork, albeit within defined constraints (e.g. under extreme wind conditions). However, it is the responsibility of the PWD to review their design and liaise with the contractor's TWD team.

The PWD also has a role to play when the contractor is considering the climbing cycle or rate of slip. The concrete mix design and the early age strength of the concreted section both have a significant impact on whether a short cycle time/climbing rate is achievable. The cycle time can be a critical factor on the effectiveness of the system. For example, if the climbing system cannot be climbed after 4 days it may not be a viable solution in relation to the costs involved, particularly when large systems utilising hydraulics are proposed. When slip-forming, materials such as concrete, reinforcement, hoist extensions, etc. must suit the rate of construction envisaged. Changes to the design, such as increased reinforcement or improved concrete mix for early higher strength, may be viable to produce the output required for a given site.

Openings, features or cast-in components in the permanent structure can significantly affect slip-forming and, in certain cases, make it unfeasible. The resulting surface finish is always an important aspect when considering the use of slip-form techniques. It should be pointed out that final tolerances of slip-formed structures will be similar to other construction methods.

The proprietary supplier will provide details of the loads being imposed onto the structure by the system proposed and how the brackets then transmit the loads into the structure. The ability of the structure to resist the applied forces is equally as important as the concrete strength local to the anchor. To be able to check these conditions requires a detailed knowledge of the concrete structure and associated site activities. The TWC has a duty to ensure that the PWD is satisfied in the ability of the structure to withstand the loads being imposed and remain in accordance with the design specification. Working together with the contractor's TWD team, they can then consider an appropriate lifting cycle.

25.2.4 Design
The design of climbing formwork and slip-form operations is generally carried out by the design offices of the proprietary supplier or specialist subcontractor, as they have the product knowledge, competency and expertise. With the reduction in contractor's temporary works departments, contracts increasingly rely on proprietary suppliers to provide relevant designs with equipment. Those contractors who still have a design capability should be able to understand and produce designs for climbing jump-form formwork systems (see Section 25.3.2). However, it is recommended that design responsibility for the specialised design of rail climbing formwork systems and slip form should remain with the proprietary suppliers and/or specialist subcontractors, due to their in-depth knowledge of and familiarity with the systems.

25.3. Climbing formwork
25.3.1 System selection
In their most basic form, climbing formwork systems can be used simply as working platforms for personnel. In many cases such as city centre sites, where available space

within the site compound is limited, the platforms can be pre-assembled off site with integral guard rails, toe-boards and lifting points. They are generally used to allow steel fixers access to the reinforcement, access to the finished concrete face of a structure and to fix soffit edge formwork. They can be designed to provide a continuous deck around outside corners and can be easily adapted to suit buildings with geometrically complicated shapes.

Climbing formwork is compatible with a variety of formwork systems and allows incremental vertical segments of structure to be poured, commonly to a storey height of between 3 m and 4 m. The three types of system in common use are as follows.

- Climbing jump-form formwork: units are individually lifted off the structure and relocated at the next construction level using a crane (see Figure 25.1).
- Rail-guided climbing formwork: units are connected to a rail/anchor configuration attached to the structure which offers greater safety and control during lifting operations. The proprietary systems available differ in that some have a fixed sectional rail attached onto the structure which the units climb up, recycling the rail as they climb, while others have an 'anchor and shoe' assembly attached to the structure which the rail climbs by recycling the 'shoe' as it climbs.
- Rail-guided self-climbing formwork: hydraulic jacks are introduced to climb the units up the structure, avoiding the requirement of using a crane. This can be done either with portable hydraulics resulting in platforms being raised sequentially or, alternatively, with hydraulics positioned at every rail and the platforms lifted in unison. The latter option is more expensive; it only becomes viable on structures of significant height or of a complex plan layout.

25.3.2 Climbing/concreting cycle

Most formwork systems are supported from anchor assemblies cast into the preceding section of wall. A typical sequence for a jump form is shown in Figure 25.2. Anchors are attached to the formwork (see Figure 25.2a) and are cast-in with the concrete pour, but the anchor cone and the mounting device are recoverable. Note that a wind brace in tension is fitted to stabilise the assembly from clockwise rotation from the wind. A nailing disc is used to secure the anchor assembly to the wall formwork to ensure it is held in the correct position. Once the section of wall has been cast (see Figure 25.2b) and adequate concrete strength has been verified, the formwork can be struck off the wall. The system anchor assembly for the next cycle can be fitted (see Figure 25.2c) and the formwork cleaned and release agent applied in readiness for next use. Shortly before moving, the wind brace is disconnected and the whole assembly is then lifted off its anchors (see Figure 25.2d) by a crane and refitted onto the anchors in the next position, usually by moving vertically upwards. The wind brace is replaced, and reinforcement fixing can now commence. The cycle then repeats.

The operation must be carefully planned and coordinated. Access to the working area during lifting should be restricted to essential personnel since unprotected edges are created between the individual platforms when they are being moved; this presents a significant safety risk and must be cordoned off.

Figure 25.2 Typical climbing sequence of a 'jump-form' proprietary system
Courtesy of Jim Murray, PERI (UK) Ltd

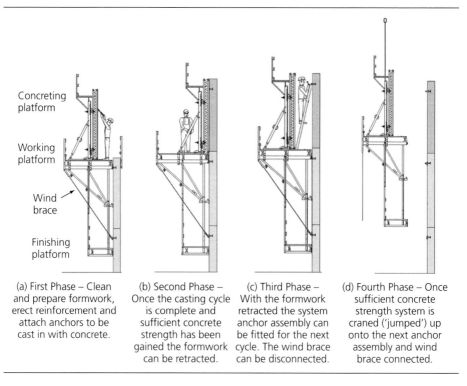

| (a) First Phase – Clean and prepare formwork, erect reinforcement and attach anchors to be cast in with concrete. | (b) Second Phase – Once the casting cycle is complete and sufficient concrete strength has been gained the formwork can be retracted. | (c) Third Phase – With the formwork retracted the system anchor assembly can be fitted for the next cycle. The wind brace can be disconnected. | (d) Fourth Phase – Once sufficient concrete strength system is craned ('jumped') up onto the next anchor assembly and wind brace connected. |

The process for rail-mounted systems is similar, although the system is fixed to a rail and therefore does not leave the wall once attached until construction is complete. Often such systems incorporate devices to strike the formwork laterally on the working platform to facilitate cleaning, fixing anchors, etc.

25.3.3   Design considerations

To achieve a viable and cost-effective climbing formwork solution, it is necessary to strike a balance between several governing factors. This primarily involves maximising platform size while maintaining the ability to climb the system with minimal limitations, for example, during periods of high winds.

Different systems provide the option of varying platform widths. Wider platforms provide the space to allow the associated wall formwork to be fully retracted when struck, thus allowing clear access for cleaning and fixing reinforcement. Whereas, narrower platforms generally incorporate a tilting mechanism for access to the formwork face. Self-climbing systems can be designed to incorporate additional platform levels above the main construction level. This enables multiple operations to be performed simultaneously, for example, fixing reinforcement for a wall prior to casting concrete at a lower section, which offers the potential for realising shorter construction cycle times.

The achievable platform length is governed by the spacing of anchors and the associated wind parameters to be considered. The longer the platform, the higher the load on the anchors; this then has an impact upon the height and width of the associated wall form-work. All of these factors will dictate the allowable operational wind speed at which the climbing system can be safely worked on and moved. If this is misjudged, then part of the reason for selecting a climbing system from the outset may be compromised.

25.4. Slip forms
25.4.1 General
Slip-forming is the process of continuous concrete construction, and is normally carried out vertically with a constant cross-section. The forms are raised and the concrete placed at such a rate that the concrete achieves sufficient strength before the forms expose it. Rates of rise of 80–300 mm per hour can be achieved, and construction usually continues around the clock. Dayshift-only working (involving slip-forming for approximately 10 hours and then stopping) with controls is possible, but will affect surface finishes. It does, however, have the advantage of not requiring night working and eliminates supply of small amounts of concrete throughout the night from commercial batching plants.

A typical slip-form example is shown in Figure 25.3. Vertical slip-forming can involve large volumes of concrete, generally of high-strength low-water to cement ratio with significant admixtures to suit the consistency necessary for placing, but supplied in

Figure 25.3 Typical slip-form construction to building cores
Courtesy of Slipform International Ltd

small amounts continuously. The upward form movement speed can be adjusted to a significant degree by varying the admixture dosage. The concrete surface finish is peculiar to the process.

The layout is normally simple. It is possible to vary the wall thickness and layout over the height, although each complication will increase the overall cost. The ideal structure should have significant dimensions in both major axes to ensure stability. Variants of the process can operate horizontally and on sloping structures.

Slip-forming is a highly specialised process and advice should be sought from people with the relevant experience. A useful guide is the Concrete Society Good Concrete Guide 6 (CS, 2008).

25.4.2 Design considerations

The typical arrangement of slip-forms comprises two panels held in position by a yoke with two legs and a cross-member over the top, as shown in Figure 25.4. A jack is fixed to the cross-member, which climbs a rod whose base is in the structure. The

Figure 25.4 Typical diagram of slip form
Courtesy of Slipform International Ltd

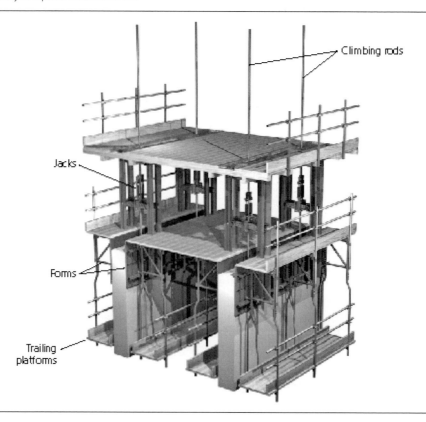

jacking rods are either left in place or subsequently withdrawn from the concrete by reversing the jacks. The various walls are braced together, and working areas and access scaffolds are added. The PWD has an important role in ensuring that reinforcement is detailed to suit the method.

The forms are generally only 1.2 m high and are set up with a slight taper to prevent the form gripping the concrete and lifting it at the trailing edge. It is set up with the correct wall thickness at approximately mid-height. The face contact material will most likely be steel panels although, where vertical striations are needed, film-faced plywoods with hardwood features have been used. Trailing platforms can be used to carry out any remedial or finishing work on the concrete.

Openings can be formed by using inserts narrower than the wall, thus avoiding displacement of the former vertically as sliding proceeds. An allowance of 18 mm less than the nominal wall thickness will clear any build-up of hardened concrete on the upper edge of the form.

Sufficient ancillary plant as standby equipment is recommended. Detailed consideration of access to the continuously changing slip-form location has to be planned, and any material/passenger hoists and concrete-pumping boom extensions must keep pace with construction. Detailed planning is important as stoppages on slip-forming should be avoided. Clearly a plan should be in place for stopping the system, but this should be a last resort.

25.5. Climbing protection screens
25.5.1 General
Protection screens create an enclosure through which a covered working area is formed to provide protection from wind and other adverse weather conditions while working at height, and to provide protection from falling objects. A typical example is shown in Figure 25.5. As with climbing formwork systems, protection screen systems have commonly been deployed on structures which are in excess of 10 storeys high. With the inherent benefits these systems offer their use within the construction industry is becoming more widespread, offering benefits of full-height protection on structures over one storey in height. Further guidance on protection screens is included in *Formwork: A Guide to Good Practice* (CS, 2011; section 7.6.3). The intended use of protection screens should be stated in the temporary works design brief so that the TWD can take full account of the effects of wind on the system.

25.5.2 Types of screens
The basic principles are similar to climbing formwork systems. The screens climb in advance of the floors being constructed, enclosing a number of levels to provide protection to site operatives up to and including the top level of construction.

Screens can be clad in either solid panels (e.g. plywood) or with perforated mesh or netting and are supported on rails attached to the already cast slabs of the permanent structure. Commonly perforated mesh is chosen, as it provides a balance between

Figure 25.5 Typical protection screen system
Courtesy of Jim Murray, PERI (UK) Ltd

protecting those below who may be struck by falling debris while still permitting natural light to enter each working level. Some screens can incorporate working platforms; this can be of benefit where post-tensioning work is required or to provide space for following trades undertaking work on the façade.

25.5.3 Design considerations

Similar criteria to that examined when determining the suitability of a climbing form-work system are equally applicable when deciding upon the suitability of a protection screen system. The capacity of the permanent structure to withstand the imposed loads induced (in particular from wind forces), access requirements and method of climbing must all be evaluated in the same manner. Again, the CDM coordinator must ensure that the PWD and TWD cooperate and that the permanent structure can withstand the loads applied to it by the temporary works.

Wind effect is often the governing factor to be considered when designing protection screens, as they often travel up to two levels in advance of the construction works thus generating significant cantilever forces (especially if solid cladding panels are used). Anchor spacing is directly affected by wind load which in turn determines the spacing of slab rail supports. Additional propping may even be required, in particular at corner sections which induce even higher loads as described in *Formwork: A Guide to Good Practice* (CS, 2011; section 4) and the British Wind Standard BS EN 1991-1-4 (BSI, 2009).

25.6. Checking and inspection

Suppliers and importers have a duty to provide information and user guidance about their products, for example, project drawings, parts lists, safety instructions, etc. (CS, 2011; section 3). The TWC should gather such information and ensure that all those working with the proprietary system are familiar with the content of the relevant instructions and safety information for their particular application. All operatives should be trained in the use of the system, and be aware of the precise procedure of using the system. Toolbox talks and similar on-site familiarisation with the equipment are an essential prerequisite for safe operation of these systems. Due care and attention are required to assess that no additional guidance is required as a result of any site-specific conditions encountered. Precise guidance will be available from the manufacturer for all working operations, climbing operations and non-operational conditions. Periods of high winds or the application of sheeting to handrails, for example, may result in design loads being exceeded and necessitate a review of the working parameters provided.

Slip-forming requires a continuously controlled inspection regime and needs a small but highly skilled workforce on site; this requires team effort and there is no place for restrictive working practices on slip-form operations. For this reason, specialist subcontractors are often employed to carry out the slip and the various responsibilities are established before slip-forming commences.

Each stage of a climbing sequence, such as a climbing sequence for jump forms as described in Section 25.3.2, will result in load being transferred into the supporting permanent structure. The TWD must pass on all relevant information to ensure that stability is considered at every stage and that permissible imposed loads are not being exceeded.

REFERENCES

BSI (2009) PD 6688-1-4. Background Information to the National Annex to BS EN 1991-1-4. BSI, London.

CS (Concrete Society) (2011) Formwork: A Guide to Good Practice, 3rd edition. Special Publication CS 030. Concrete Society, Camberley.

CS (2008) Good Concrete Guide 6: Slipforming of vertical structures. Ref. CS162. Concrete Society, Camberley.

FURTHER READING

BRE (Building Research Establishment) (2007) Formwork for Modern, Efficient Concrete Construction. BR 495. HIS BRE Press, Bracknell.

ConStruct (Concrete Structures Group) (2010) National Structural Concrete Specification for Building Construction, 4th edition. Ref. CCIP-050. Concrete Society, Camberley.

CS (2003) Checklist for the assembly, use and striking of formwork. Ref. CS144. Concrete Society, Crowthorne.

Useful web addresses

http://www.concrete.org.uk
http://www.construct.org.uk
http://www.temporaryworks.info

Temporary Works: Principles of Design and Construction
ISBN 978-0-7277-4177-6

ICE Publishing: All rights reserved
http://dx.doi.org/10.1680/twpdc.41776.329

Chapter 26
Temporary façade retention

Ray Filip Consultant
Stuart Marchand Director, Wentworth House Partnership

The work involved in supporting existing façades or party walls for renovation, during rebuilding or after damage is a specific type of temporary works with different risks, durations and types of loads than the temporary structures of falsework and scaffolding. Although similar equipment is used, the philosophy, procedures and relationship to the permanent works are different. Unlike formwork and falsework, the structure to be supported already exists; it may be old, in poor condition or not vertical. Procedures will need to reflect the status stressing the importance of initial surveys and possible extensive monitoring during use to reduce the risks. Permanent works designers have an important role in the management and control of façade retention schemes.

26.1. Introduction

The elevations of a building are generally known as façades and the front façade is often highly decorative. Building façades are retained because they are considered to be of architectural, historical or visual importance. Behind the façade, the interiors may have deteriorated or simply may not meet the requirements of modern usage. To meet with planning restrictions and conservation orders (listed buildings), the interiors are rebuilt behind the retained façade using modern methods and materials such as steel frame or reinforced concrete. A shoring (façade retention) scheme is generally required to support the façade and protect workers (and the general public) while the work is carried out. The shoring scheme must be designed and installed with care. The façade will eventually be connected and supported by the new internal structure. Occasionally other external walls (not just the front elevation), internal walls, floors and roof structure will be retained and restored. Emergency unplanned retention may also be required after fire or explosion to make the remaining structure safe for rebuilding or safe demolition, if deemed beyond repair.

The authoritative guidance document is the CIRIA Report C579 *Retention of Masonry Façades: Best Practice Guide* (CIRIA, 2003a), which gives information for all the parties involved in the planning, design and construction of façade retention schemes. For specific site guidance, CIRIA C589 *Retention of Masonry Façades: Best Practice Site Handbook* (CIRIA, 2003b) is recommended. Both documents highlight the importance of appointing a competent temporary works coordinator as recommended in BS 5975 (BSI, 2011); see also Chapter 2 on management.

This chapter gives information about the types of façades and the important differences in design principles relative to other temporary works.

26.2. Philosophy of façade retention
26.2.1 Major alternative
The first consideration is: does the façade actually have to be supported? Dismantling the façade as a whole, restoring the stonework, masonry or bricks and rebuilding using traditional methods might be more appropriate.

26.2.2 General principles
Many of the building façades (and other parts of the building) being retained would not conform to modern building techniques and codes of practice, hence significant engineering judgement and experience is required of those involved.

When considering façade retention schemes, the following philosophy and sequence should be adopted.

- *Planning*: desk study to establish the age of the building, neighbouring properties and their owners, history and previous usage of the building and listing issues. Visual inspection to identify potential hazards, existing services, working restrictions, other site constraints, etc. CDM coordinators (appointed by the client) have a duty to be involved at this stage so that conceptual design for the temporary works and new permanent works can demonstrate that the works can be built safely. Relevant permissions may be needed and other statutory obligations may have to be carried out.
- Secure the site: public protection, protection of neighbouring properties and safe means of access, etc. should be provided.
- Understand how the building works: never underestimate the importance of this and a full structural investigation and dimensional survey (which should include ground conditions, groundwater levels and foundations) should be carried out. How stability is achieved and the position of load-bearing elements should be established. The CIRIA Report R111 *Structural Renovation of Traditional Buildings* (CIRIA, 1986) is a useful guide on how old buildings may have been constructed. Particular attention should be paid to areas of obvious distress such as cracks, bowing or ingress of water (signs of poor maintenance) and to any area where repairs or alterations have previously been carried out. The façade may not necessarily be of solid construction; it may be stone faced on brickwork backing or rubble in-filled stone walls. The surroundings should be investigated, including pavement vaults, cellars, services and the condition of nearby pavements and roads. Preliminary shoring and propping may be necessary. Surface finishes may need to be removed to expose brickwork and embedded steel or timber and their condition assessed. Floorboards may also have to be removed to assess floor capacity.
- Unstable areas should be made safe: temporary supports should be installed to allow repairs to be carried out or to remove hazardous items (such as asbestos). Chimney stacks are prone to weathering and can be removed. If laid with lime mortar, the bricks can be re-used for rebuilding (or the chimneys will require

shoring). Existing foundations may need to be underpinned and existing services diverted or made safe. Delicate items that are to be retained may need to be protected from accidental or weather damage, or they may be dismantled for safe storage during the works and then re-instated.

■ Design the retention scheme: designers should carry out risk assessments and any residual risks clearly communicated. A sequence of works should be provided and provisions made for unexpected items. Structural surveys cannot consider every part of the structure as many structural items are unseen until demolition commences. The retention scheme should allow the new structure to be constructed as easily as possible. Although the design may be carried out by the client's engineer, the principal contractor or by a specialist equipment supplier or specialist subcontractor, the design interfaces should be established along with the design check category (BSI, 2008). Possible modes of failure should be considered and adequate support provided for each eventuality or the risks eliminated (e.g. the risk of swinging loads impacting the façade retention scheme may be reduced by specifying lifting and craneage zones).

■ Install the retention scheme: this should be carried out carefully by competent persons to prevent damage to the existing structure. Some partial demolition or minor shoring may be necessary to allow access, so that the main retention scheme can be installed and connected to the façade it is supporting.

■ Carry out the main demolition of the internal structure to an agreed sequence: this should be completed carefully and in a systematic manner, avoiding damage to the retained structure and retention scheme. Checks should be made on the façade during and after demolition is completed (monitoring is discussed later). Weather protection may be needed to any exposed party walls and to the rear of the façade where water could cause deterioration (i.e. to lime mortar, embedded steel or timber).

■ Carry out the new works to an agreed sequence: monitoring, inspection and maintenance of the retained structure, retention scheme and surroundings should be carried out throughout the works.

■ Load transfer: the new works are designed to restrain and sometimes support the existing façade. Where the weight of the façade is supported on the new structure, consideration must be given to the means of load transfer from the temporary support to the permanent structure. Unless the façade is to continue as load bearing, then the connections should allow for differential movement between the façade and the new construction.

■ Removal of the temporary works: this may be progressive removal as the permanent structure is completed.

It is important to realise that the building has achieved a state of equilibrium over many years and, by changing the support conditions, this equilibrium can be jeopardised; the designer must consider this. Deflection is one of the main criteria for the design, and the support system should be sufficiently stiff to limit the deflection.

Some of the above points may be given lower priority or even be bypassed in the case of emergency retention schemes. Emergency schemes will be selected on availability of materials, ease and speed of assembly.

26.2.3   Party walls

The support of walls which form part of a building, yet stand partly on land with different owners, is known as a party wall. Temporary retention systems can be used to support party walls. The legislation is complex and beyond the scope of this book. Party walls can generally only fall in the direction of the previously demolished building, but stability of any structures isolated by demolition must be considered. However, if it can be shown beyond doubt that the party wall is adequately tied into the structure beyond, then support will not be required. This may be the case in a row of terraced properties when demolishing a newer property back to a previous end-of-terrace property. If there are any concerns about the adequacy of the tied connection, then additional fixings may be considered as an alternative to a retention scheme. For a party wall, the effects of deflection need careful consideration as limits provided in C579 (CIRIA, 2003a) may be inappropriate. Always seek professional advice when dealing with party wall support and its legislation.

26.2.4   Surveying the existing building

The importance of an early thorough investigation of the existing façade is critical to the successful completion of all temporary works façade support systems. When it is unlikely that 'as built' drawings were produced, some of the major issues that need to be addressed are discussed in detail in Reports C579 (CIRIA, 2003a) and 111 (CIRIA, 1986).

Are there any hazards (e.g. asbestos)? How is vertical and lateral stability achieved? Are neighbouring properties affected by the new works? What is the form of construction? Particular attention should be paid to cracks and signs of damage. Chimneys should be thoroughly investigated (e.g. position of flues). Verticality of the façade (out of plumb of more than 10% of the wall thickness is a matter of concern).

Are there any basements or pavement vaults? What is the position and nature of existing services? Is the building listed or part listed or is it in a conservation area? Are there any tree preservation orders (TPOs)? Soil conditions, groundwater level and existing foundations must all be considered. As part of the survey, some materials testing may be necessary to establish strength, etc.

26.3.   Types of temporary façade retention schemes
26.3.1   Timber shoring

Timber shoring has previously been commonplace, however, nowadays it is rare apart from minor retention schemes.

26.3.2   Scaffolding

Scaffolding in tube and fitting (see Chapter 21 on scaffolding) is suitable for relatively low-level façades (up to 3–4 storeys with sufficient space around the base of the façade for installation, approximate width required will be 50–100% of the height; CIRIA, 2003a). Above this height the quantity of scaffolding involved and labour costs may make installation, inspection, rebuilding and removal challenging. A typical example is depicted by Figure 26.1a.

Figure 26.1 Comparison of 3-storey temporary façade retention schemes
Courtesy of RFK Consult Ltd

(a) Typical using scaffolding

(b) Typical using proprietary equipment

26.3.3 Proprietary equipment

Proprietary equipment with formwork soldiers and ties may be suitable for higher façades as the number of components is reduced (compared to scaffolding) and each component is stronger and stiffer (see Figure 26.1b). Proprietary equipment has the advantage that components can be easily joined together with push-pull props and tie rods and easily adjusted to remove 'slack' from the system.

26.3.4 Fabricated steelwork

Fabricated steelwork may prove an economic solution for long-term retention schemes where the cost of hiring proprietary equipment may be prohibitive; however, manufacturing and installation costs may be higher. Combinations of equipment are often used.

23.3.5 Vertical towers

Vertical towers (Figure 26.2a and b) comprising proprietary equipment (soldiers, push/pull props, tie rods) or fabricated steelwork with tie rods clamping the façade are a common solution (approximate width required 16–20% of height; CIRIA; 2003a). Substantial kentledge blocks (or compression/tension piles) are required to resist over-turning and sliding forces; they can also act as foundations to spread the vertical loads. The self weight of the façade can be utilised as part of the kentledge required.

To minimise disruption to the internal rebuilding, vertical towers are installed to the external face of the façade (where practicable). The frame acts as a vertical cantilever with wind loads transferred to the foundations through bracing. Deflection of the frame is usually the critical design consideration to prevent damage to the façade (through cracking). Push-pull props or tie rods are used for bracing. Horizontally spanning waling beams, which are tied together through window openings (to minimise drilling though the façade), are placed internally and externally, 'sandwiching' the façade. The towers are connected to the waling beams.

It is important to consider the combined vertical and horizontal loads on the foundations as the uplift (due to the overturning moment) will reduce the horizontal capacity. The greater the width of the frame (i.e. greater lever arm), the smaller the uplift will be. An allowance may need to be made for pedestrian access. Portal frames are utilised for this purpose, as shown in Figure 26.2b. Particular attention is required in the design of such schemes, as the eccentric loading from the self-weight onto the portal structure induces lateral sway deflection in the portal. Vertical towers can also be utilised where party walls are to be retained.

26.3.6 Horizontal frame arrangements

Where vertical towers are impracticable and adequate buttress walls exist, horizontally spanning trusses can be installed. These will have diagonal wind braces, waling beams as described above and vertical column supports or supporting braced towers as shown in Figure 26.3. When using internal frames (Figure 26.3b), the temporary frames must be positioned in order to avoid clashing with the new floor construction. The frames are positioned so they can be installed by operatives standing on the existing

Figure 26.2 Typical vertical tower arrangements
Courtesy of Pallett Temporary*Works* Ltd

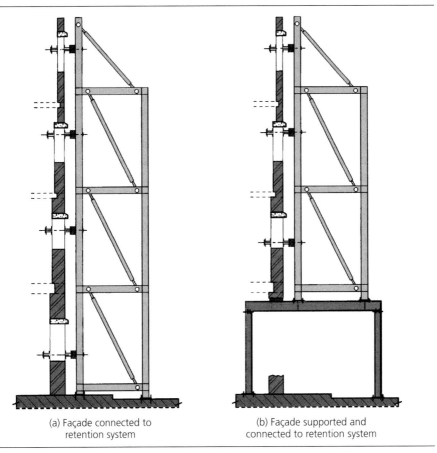

(a) Façade connected to
retention system

(b) Façade supported and
connected to retention system

floors prior to their demolition. As the demolition of floors progresses downwards, subsequent lower level internal supporting frames can then be installed.

With all support systems, timber or proprietary frames may be used to brace up major openings in the façade, to maintain the shear capacity and prevent lateral displacement.

26.4. Loads to be considered
26.4.1 General
The temporary works designer for a retained façade should consider all potential modes of failure. Temporary works offices and designers have traditionally used permissible stress methods with equipment manufacturers quoting 'safe working loads' in literature. The actual deflections need to be calculated in the service condition. When design uses 'limit state', the relevant partial safety factors will therefore need to be included. Particular care is necessary when using Eurocodes as future suppliers' literature may quote

Figure 26.3 Typical horizontal frame arrangements with diagonal bracing: façade supported by (a) external framing and (b) internal framing

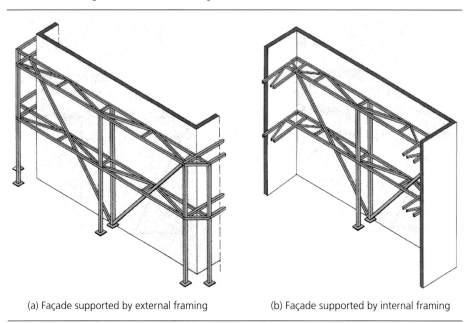

(a) Façade supported by external framing   (b) Façade supported by internal framing

'characteristic values' for equipment; note, however, that a characteristic value is *not* a safe working load. The following loads and practical considerations typically need to be addressed in the design process from concept to installation, monitoring and use.

26.4.2 Vertical loads

Vertical dead loads include the self weight of the façade, self weight of access or storage platforms, hoists, sheeting and site offices (space is often at a premium). If vertical supports are removed (columns or piers replaced due to deterioration or strengthening), then the self weight of the façade must be supported by means of needling schemes or vertical dead shores. Elastic shortening of the support system and settlement of any temporary foundations can be partially overcome by pre-loading (pre-deflecting the supports by jacking load into the system). Settlement and possibly undermining may also be caused by adjacent works such as trenching or excavating for a basement. Differential settlement (between existing structure and temporary works) is likely to be most problematic and can lead to the greatest degree of damage to the retained structure. When considering vertical dead load, 'favourable' and 'unfavourable' conditions exist. The self weight of façade alone is the only true dead load when considering resistance to overturning, as cabins, storage, working platforms, etc. may be moved as the work progresses. Further guidance can be found in C579 (CIRIA, 2003a; section 8.3).

26.4.3 Construction operation loads

Imposed vertical loads during construction will include working platforms, stored materials or snow. The retention scheme should be easily inspected. CIRIA C579

(CIRIA, 2033a) recommends that working platforms be normally designed for service class 2 loading (1.5k N/m²) minimum for minor repair work, or higher if significant rebuilding is necessary. Material storage areas, loading bays or site cabins need to be separately considered. Further guidance can be found in C579 (CIRIA, 2003a; section 8.4).

26.4.4 Impact loads

Accidental impact loads occur from falling debris, vehicles or a swinging load suspended from a crane. These should be assessed by an appropriate risk assessment. Minor damage can be repaired; however, disproportionate collapse should be considered and protective measures may be provided as necessary. Ideally the design risk assessment should be used to reduce or eliminate impact on temporary façade structures. Impact loads are listed in Table 26.1 and should be considered to act in any direction on critical members. Vehicle impact is considered in the bottom 1 m of the structure, but a lower impact loading of 10 kN is considered at higher levels to represent a swinging crane load. CIRIA C579 (CIRIA, 2003a; section 8.5) gives further guidance. BS 5975 (BSI, 2011; clause 17.4.3.3) recommends that designers should 'refer to contract specification' when considering the design of vehicle crash barriers.

26.4.5 Wind loading

Wind loading is generally the main loading to be considered, and is calculated to the withdrawn BS 6399-2 in C579 (CIRIA, 2003a). The wind code is BS EN 1991-1-4 (BSI, 2005) and a simplified method, based on the Eurocode for use in all temporary façade retention structures, recommends that when used in the UK both the seasonal

Table 26.1 Lateral load combination
Data taken from CIRIA C579 (2003a)

Load case	Weight of actual façade	Self weight of retention structure	Wind load Maximum	Wind load Working	Impact load	Out of plumb	Other vertical loads
Overturning greater of either	1.5% of total	1.5%	Full	n/a	No	No	1.5%
or	No	1.5%	Full	n/a	No	Yes	1.5%
Connections to façade as greater of	2.5% at level	No	Local at level	n/a	No	No	No
or	No	No	Local at level	No	No	Full at level	No
Impact loads	No	No	No	Yes	10 kN in any direction	No	No
Vehicle impact	No	No	No	Yes	25 kN horizontal up to 1 m	No	No

factor c_{season} (formerly referred to as S_s) and the probability factor c_{prob} (formerly S_p) are taken as 1.0. Unlike falsework, scaffolding and formwork, there is no reduction for the short-term loading (less than 2 years) for façade temporary works. The basic equation for the peak wind velocity pressure (q_p) is given in Section 22.33.5 of Chapter 22 on falsework. The façade is generally considered as a solid impermeable face (due to sheeting and boarding-up of openings). If the wind can be 'trapped' in a corner then the wind force may be increased. Positive wind pressures as well as wind suction are considered; see CIRIA (2003a; section 8.6) for further guidance.

26.4.6 Notional lateral forces

In a similar way to the minimum disturbing force allowed for in falsework (see Section 22.3.9 in Chapter 22 on falsework), the temporary façade retention system has to resist notional lateral forces. It is recommended in CIRIA C579 (CIRIA, 2003a) that the supports are designed for a minimum lateral load of the greater of the following loads.

- 1.5% of the vertical load at that point acting horizontally which includes the self weight of façade, retention structure, other dead loads and imposed loads affecting the retention structure (such as storage and site cabins), but the actual lateral load should be calculated (the lateral load could be as much as 10% of the vertical load).
- The actual lateral load from eccentricity of the façade (due to out of plumb, corbels, balconies, etc.) plus 1.5% of the total vertical load on the retention structure which will include its self weight plus other dead and imposed loads (self weight of the façade is not included).

This lateral load is considered as acting as a uniformly distributed load over the façade surface and is applied to the retention scheme at the connection points. It is added to the wind loading as shown in Figure 26.4. The wind loading will generally be significantly

Figure 26.4 Wind loading plus lateral load applied to support points
Courtesy of RFK Consult Ltd

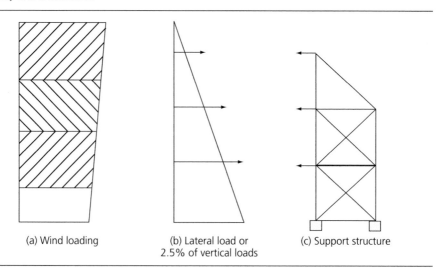

(a) Wind loading   (b) Lateral load or 2.5% of vertical loads   (c) Support structure higher than the self weight component of lateral load. A clear load path to the ground should be identified; see CIRIA (2003a; section 8.8) for further guidance.

26.4.7 Other loads

Existing basement walls will be subject to earth, water and surcharge pressures (traffic, plant, rubble or kentledge blocks); see CIRIA (2003a; section 8.7) for further guidance.

CIRIA C579 (2003a; section 8.9) provides advice on other loads to be considered. Dynamic loads (such as traffic) generating vibration are generally ignored and any loosening of fixings can be addressed by using lock nuts or regular inspection. Fatigue is generally not taken into account in temporary works. However, there have been cases whereby a retention scheme has had to support a façade for many years due to planning or financial issues, and fatigue and corrosion can become issues. Seismic activity is not taken into account in the UK. Thermal movement, due to expansion and contraction of the materials of the façade and support system, may occasionally need to be considered when specifying 'acceptable' levels of movement in the façade.

Older façades tend to be of substantial stone or masonry thickness and have greater thermal mass, hence respond slowly to daily temperature variations. Excessive thermal movement can lead to cracking of the façade. CIRIA Technical Note 107 *Design for Movement in Buildings* (CIRIA, 1981) and BRE Digest 251 (BRE, 1995) give further advice. If a retained façade is within a potential flood risk area or next to water then these effects should be considered; ice formation is not deemed to be a major issue.

26.5. Design considerations
26.5.1 General

The support scheme must be positioned to allow the demolition and rebuilding to be carried out. This normally involves the temporary works being positioned externally (assuming sufficient available space and local authority permission) as internal temporary works (see Figure 26.3b) makes demolition and re-building more challenging.

External schemes need to consider interfaces with the general public and appropriate safety measures should be taken. Security is a significant consideration with adequate protection necessary.

Provision may be required to allow for the scheme to be altered due to variations in wall locations discovered during demolition and/or any unexpected items discovered on site. Large openings in the façade may require bracing with timbers or steel frames to maintain overall shear capability. The effects of fire are occasionally considered and an appropriate risk assessment should be carried out. Lightning protection with adequate earthing should be provided to steel support frames.

26.5.2 Overall stability

Overall stability must be maintained in all directions as wind loading or other loads (impact) could act in any direction. The retention scheme must resist the overturning moment as well as moments generated by eccentric dead loads (out of plumb, corbels, balconies, not plumb, etc.) and imposed loads to provide overall stability. The structure may also tilt during demolition or reconstruction work as support conditions change due to re-supporting the vertical weight of the façade, settlement or heave. The new support positions should be provided as close as possible to the original condition in the existing structure. It must, however, be remembered that wind loading on the façade may change after the existing building has been demolished. The points of support to the façade should be at relatively close centres to prevent excessive deflection.

Section 8.14 of CIRIA C579 (CIRIA, 2003a) recommends a factor of safety of 1.5 against overturning; This is larger than that used for falsework in BS 5975 (BSI, 2011). Any kentledge required is then calculated as:

$$\frac{\text{maximum overturning moment} \times 1.5}{\text{lever arm to the kentledge}}$$

and potential settlement of the kentledge should be considered.

26.5.3 Deflection criteria

The support system must be stiff enough to prevent excessive movement, which may cause cracking to the fabric of the façade and should ideally replicate that of the existing structure. When retaining a party wall some degree of pre-loading (pre-deflecting) of the support system may be possible to reduce potential movement. The positioning of the jacking points should coincide with strong points in the retained building. The degree of permitted movement of any façade being retained should be discussed carefully with the structural engineer and client. The nature and state of repair of the façade will determine this, and should be monitored during the course of demolition and rebuilding. See, for example, the monitored movement shown in Figure 6.4 of CIRIA R589 (CIRIA, 2003b). CIRIA C579 (CIRIA, 2003a; clause 8.10.1) recommends that, in the absence of more onerous limits set by the Permanent Works Designer (PWD), the following limit be adopted:

$$\text{lateral deflection } \theta_H \leqslant \frac{H}{750}$$

where H is the height to the restraint level under consideration above the point at which the façade is considered fixed and θ_H is the lateral deflection. The limit was first quoted by Goodchild and Kaminski (1989).

CIRIA C579 (2003a) further states that: '... there appears to be no evidence that working with this limit has resulted in distress to façades. Equally there is no evidence to warrant recommending a more liberal limit.' In addition, a maximum floor to floor deflection of 5 mm over 3 m is often quoted. Designers of temporary works façades should be aware that the movement of the ground in response to partial demolition and subsequent reconstruction are inherent in the scheme and should be considered by the client's consultant. The lateral deflection limit of the system defined above will be used by the temporary façade designer, unless tighter limits are set. This limit could be unacceptable for a party wall, creating large gaps between it and the return walls/

floors within the adjacent building. BRE Digest 251 (BRE, 1995) discusses crack widths and repairs. Damage category 2 is generally considered appropriate with cracks of <5 mm requiring only decorative repair, but agreement should be reached with the party wall surveyors. Owners of supporting party walls of occupied buildings may be less tolerant of movement causing cracking, and deflection limits may need to be reviewed. Excessive vibration during demolition should be avoided.

26.5.4 Connections and restraint

Designing the connections to the façade is important. When making connections into old brickwork, expanding anchors should be avoided and bonded (resin or similar) type or thin wall sleeve expansion anchors should be used. Old bricks may have soft cores or may be loose (mortar may have weathered) and may not provide a positive fixing; alternatively, the anchors may work loose under cyclic loading. The number of drilled connections into a listed façade is usually limited by planning and architectural constraints. Fixings into brickwork should be tested to establish capacity for design purposes.

Local restraint is provided by the strength and stiffness of the support scheme prior to demolition of the existing supporting structure. When the existing structure is removed, the effective length of the façade dramatically increases and the supporting connections must provide sufficient restraint to the façade. CIRIA C579 (2003a; section 8.11) recommends that connection should be designed for the greater of the following loads (to be effective in resisting lateral buckling of the wall).

- 2.5% of the total gravity load on the façade at the level of the connection being considered, plus the wind force on the area of the façade restrained by the connection.
- The lateral load arising from offsets and out of plumb of the façade at the level of the connection, as a uniformly distributed load along the length of a linear element (waling).

26.5.5 Lateral restraint

The load combinations in Table 26.1 should be considered in the design process. The combination of the wind load and the connection lateral load is shown diagrammatically in Figure 26.4. Effectively, the façade itself has to span vertically between the connection points. Because the dead weight of the structure increases near the bottom of the façade, its ability to withstand lateral wind forces increases. It is, therefore, not uncommon to notice that, contrary to expectations, the vertical spacings between connections are closer together near the top.

Where kentledge blocks are used to cater for the lateral loads in sliding, then sufficient friction must be generated. If the blocks are partially or fully buried, then passive resistance can be considered. The kentledge blocks can also be designed to spread vertical load and limit settlement. If the kentledge is to be cast in situ, then polythene must not be used to protect the pavement as it will act as a slip membrane. CIRIA C579 (2003a; section 8.14) recommends a factor of safety of 2.0 against sliding. When considering sliding, only permanent loads should be used to provide beneficial restoring moment or sliding resistance. Uplift and sliding needs to be considered in combination as the uplift will reduce sliding resistance.

26.6. Demolition, monitoring and inspection

In order to install a retention scheme, some additional temporary works items may be necessary (e.g. bracing in window openings) and some localised partial demolition (generally using hand-held tools) may be required. Demolition should be a careful and systematic process following an agreed sequence of works in order to maintain stability and prevent damage. Demolition should be carried out by competent persons in accordance with BS 6187 (BSI, 2000). Further shoring of main structural members or 'protection/containment platforms' may be necessary to facilitate a safe demolition sequence. To prevent overloading, debris should not be allowed to accumulate on existing floors and chutes or conveyors should be used to remove rubble. Particular attention should be given to avoiding or protecting existing services. A common safety measure is to provide vertical scaffold boards or netting around cut edges to prevent loose masonry falling from the façade during the works.

A monitoring system is usually established prior to demolition. The purpose is to check for movement of the façade during the work. Readings are taken on a regular basis (at least weekly during demolition and following high winds). The readings should be assessed to identify potential problems, with the following trigger levels.

- green (low movement): no problems, continue taking readings
- amber (generally three-quarters of the maximum designed deflection): increased movement hence increase frequency of readings
- red (maximum designed deflection): significant movement leading to a thorough investigation of the causes and possible remedial measures having to be taken.

Inspection should be carried out on a regular basis, checking: that ties, wedges and fixings are tight (they can work loose in cyclic wind loads); that the structure and its state of repair is as expected by the design; and for any signs of damage due to impact during demolition or construction.

REFERENCES

BRE (Building Research Establishment) (1995) Assessment of damage in low rise buildings. Digest 251. BRE, London.

BSI (2000) BS 6187: Code of practice for demolition. BSI, London.

BSI (2005) BS EN 1991-1-4: Eurocode 1: Actions on structures. Part 1–4: General Actions: Wind Loads. BSI, London (including Amendment No. 1, January 2011).

BSI (2011) BS 5975: 2008 + A1: 2011 Code of practice for temporary works procedures and the permissible stress design of falsework. BSI, London.

CIRIA (Construction Industry Research & Information Association) (1981) Design for Movement in Buildings. Technical Note 107. CIRIA, London.

CIRIA (2003a) Masonry Façade Retention: Best Practice Guide. Report C579. CIRIA, London.

CIRIA (2003b) Masonry Façade Retention: Best Practice Site Handbook. A5 size Report C589. CIRIA London.

CIRIA (1986) Structural Renovation of Traditional Buildings. Report 111. CIRIA, London.
Goodchild SL and Kaminski MP (1989) Retention of major façades. *The Structural Engineer* **67**(8): 131–138.

FURTHER READING

BRE (1992) Good Building Guides. GBG1, GBG10, GBG15. HSE, London.
BSI (1981) BS 5977-1: Lintels. Part One Method for assessment of load. BSI, London.
BSI (1993) BS 5080 Part 1. Structural Fixings into Concrete and Masonry. BSI, London.
CIRIA (1994) A Guide to the Management of Building Refurbishment. Report 133. CIRIA, London.
Doran D, Douglas J and Pratley R (2009) *Refurbishment and Repair in Construction*. CIOB (Chartered Institute of Building), Ascot.
Highfield D (1991) *The Construction of New Buildings Behind Historic Façades*. Spon Press, London.
HSE (Health and Safety Executive) (1984) Health and Safety in Demolition Work (four parts). Guidance GS29. HSE, London.
HSE (1985) Safe Erection of Structures (four parts). Guidance GS28. HSE, London.
HSE (current version) Roof-work: prevention of falls. Guidance GS10. HSE, London.
HSE (current version) Façade Retention. Guidance GS51. HSE, London.
Knight LR (1984) The façade can be a nightmare. *Civil Engineering Magazine*, March: 29–31.
Lamsden BS (1988) Remedying defects in older buildings. Technical Information Service 89. CIOB (Chartered Institute of Building), Ascot.
NSWC (New South Wales Construction) (1992) Façade Retention. Code of Practice. New South Wales, Australia.
Thorburn S and Littlejohn GS (1992) *Underpinning and Retention*, 2nd edition. Taylor & Francis, London.

Useful web addresses

Construction Industry Research and Information Association (CIRIA): http://www.ciria.org.uk
National Federation of Demolition Contractors: http://www.demolition-nfdc.com
National Access and Scaffolding Confederation: http://www.nasc.org.uk

Temporary Works: Principles of Design and Construction
ISBN 978-0-7277-4177-6

Chapter 27
Bridge installation techniques

Keith Broughton HOCHTIEF UK Construction
John Gill HOCHTIEF UK Construction

Bridge installation techniques range from straightforward construction methods to highly complex and unusual methods developed for a specific project. Construction techniques covered in earlier chapters are adequate to describe normal bridge construction. In this chapter, more unusual and complex techniques are described which use the bridge structure as part of the temporary works, dependent on bridge design concept and specific project constraints. With the more unusual techniques, the installation technique will often drive the final bridge design and certainly the detailing. Techniques considered here include: partial deck erection schemes; deck erection as a single unit; erection by tunnelling and mining; and segmental deck erection. Factors to consider in the design of the temporary works for these bridge installation techniques include significant stability issues (global and local), robustness, foundations and supports, plant and equipment (mechanical and motive systems design), contingency planning, control and monitoring systems and independent review and validation.

27.1.   Introduction

Installing bridges is one of the more high-profile aspects of Civil Engineering, and generates significant media and public interest. It takes a brave project team to invite public scrutiny, however, as the risks in these projects can be high. The rewards for engineers working in this field are great.

Most people will have heard of the Millau Viaduct, watched a local bridge construction project or seen one of the 'Mega Structures' films. This chapter will help readers appreciate the effort needed to make the techniques look simple, and enthuse them to investigate further.

Bridge installation techniques discussed use the structure itself to provide all or most of its support during erection. The required design is covered in this chapter, but only in concept.

Some of the concepts are subject to patents and intellectual property rights. Many companies have particular specialist knowledge which goes much deeper than described within this text. Current best practice is generally project specific and many details do not necessarily translate to another project.

The rate of development is rapid and techniques quickly evolve such that some of the details here will become obsolete within a few years. As with permanent design, future developments in material technology and mechanical plant will change our view of the possible. However, engineers will always return to the basic principles and concepts such as those in the erection schemes described here.

27.2. Preparation and selection of installation technique

There has been a continuous drive by UK Clients and Contractors to achieve cost benefits and improve risk management. This has in turn led to a greater consideration of the erection technique at the design stage. Contractors intuitively look to remove expensive temporary works schemes, particularly the 'bridge to build a bridge' solutions. Within densely populated and industrial areas, there is a greater need to devise erection schemes that minimise erection periods, maintain traffic flows, reduce the need for service diversions or incorporate the efficient demolition and replacement of a worn-out structure.

Selecting a bridge installation technique is a major decision, which requires careful and thorough preparation in order to have all the required information to hand. The range of information includes

- health and safety hazards
- installation constraints
- bridge design principles
- experience and current practice
- cost and time
- detailed site information.

A useful debate at an early stage of a project is whether the client should prepare a fully developed scheme, or leave the design and installation techniques entirely to the tendering contractors. Experience suggests that the optimum is part way between these extremes. Early contractor involvement is successful when developing a scheme prior to a full tender. A negotiated contract can also be successful, where tenderers develop and submit their technical solutions and obtain client feedback during a tender process leading to a final pricing stage, but this is expensive for both parties. For such schemes, Clients should carefully consider and review the allocation of responsibility of the major risk events.

A large number of solutions are available for bridge installation, and most can be grouped into the headings used for the following sections: partial deck erection schemes, deck erection as a single unit, erection by tunnelling and mining and segmental bridge construction.

27.3. Partial deck erection schemes

27.3.1 Large crane erection to single and multi-span bridges

27.3.1.1 General description of erection technique

This technique is used for bridge designs incorporating composite steel and concrete decks and pre-cast concrete bridge beams. The composite design requires a reinforced concrete deck, bonded with welded shear studs to an upper steel flange. Bolted or air welded joints would be located between 1/3 and 1/4 points of span. Pre-cast beam solutions also require an in situ stitch arrangement. Large-piece erection uses either tracked or telescopic cranes.

27.3.1.2 Base requirements

These include a good access for crane and materials, stable crane platforms with the ability to carry large outrigger leg loads (see Chapter 5 on site roads and working platforms) and no overhead restrictions. For multiple-span structures, provision may be required for temporary supports to form bolted or welded joints. Large fabrication or storage lay-down areas are also required. Where the bridge is erected on a critical timescale, such as a rail or motorway possession, a trial erection is essential to ensure all components are complete on time and fit properly. For information relating to the crane selection and the lifting design, refer to Chapter 20 on heavy moves.

27.3.1.3 Risks and opportunities

For the sake of safety, working at height should be avoided if possible. This includes using permanent formwork systems for the soffit of in situ decks, installation of parapet formwork and working access onto the outer steel beams prior to lifting. The growth in hydraulic crane capacities now offers the opportunity for far larger deck sections. The capability for a single large deck panel lift over the railway is illustrated in Figure 27.1 in the construction of Bridge 12 at Stratford Olympic Park. There are, however, risks to be considered such as high winds when depending upon on a single lift during a disruptive Network Rail possession.

Stability and robustness. Considering the stability of the beams during the lift, it is preferable to erect the beams as braced pairs; otherwise, temporary bracing is required. The main beam design also needs to consider the construction load cases including placing of deck concrete. Bracing should be designed to ensure that any permanent formwork cannot slip off its bearing on the steel flanges, particularly in an area over road, rail or occupied sites. Pay particular attention to the lateral stability of edge beams as lifted and landed.

Foundations and support. Temporary trestles will require foundations designed to spread short-term loads into the ground while supporting beams until splices are completed (and sometimes until the deck is complete).

Plant and equipment. Erection cranes will typically be of the range 250–800 tonne mobiles, but the largest 1000 tonne mobile cranes or 1200 tonne gantry cranes may be required for high load and large radius lifts. Cranes utilising super-lift require a clear working area of up to 30 m diameter. A limitation on crane set-up near railways will be a significant constraint, and the congestion of city centre areas often prevents super-lift work.

Temporary stresses. A critical load case during concreting of an in situ composite deck, where additional temporary bracing will be required, occurs when concrete cast on the beams creates locked-in stresses as they deflect under wet concrete load.

Figure 27.1 Single large lift at Stratford Olympic Park
Courtesy of Hochtief UK

Independent review and validation. For any installation over railways, a full design and independent check of the temporary supports, stability and method statements will be required.

27.3.2 Precast concrete arch

This is a variation on segmental construction where a pre-cast concrete arch is formed in segments. There are generally two types of arch as follows.

1 A single-piece arch structure, spanning springing points. Erection moves progressively along the bridge alignment using a single crane or a tandem lift.

2 Three-pinned arch, comprising two pieces joined at the crown. The erection method requires the two initial pieces to be erected together, one held on the crane (or propped) until the other is positioned, offset by half a segment width. Once this is secure, both cranes release their support. The erection of the following segments progress alternately, using the previously placed arch segment for support.

The large pre-cast concrete sections are lifted onto a pre-constructed edge foundation that acts as a springing point for the arch. The most important aspect of the erection concerns the designer's assumptions of the shear capacity of the foundation and placement of the structural backfill. The temporary loads on the foundation generally govern design. The structural fill must be placed equally on both sides of the arch, taking care not to create an out-of-balance loading.

27.3.2.1 Base requirements
Consideration should be given to the following points.

- Early input from specialist suppliers is recommended to inform arch configuration and interaction with adjacent structures or earthworks.
- The delivery, handling and storage of pre-cast sections must be considered. Lifting points should be designed to be cast into the back of each section such that the section hangs on the hook in the configuration required for setting down. This avoids the need for pulling, kentledge or coarse adjustment.
- Control of material delivery, placement and compaction must be ensured in the method statement.

27.3.2.2 Risks and opportunities
The key benefit of such a structure is its speed of erection and the ability to prepare the foundation beams outside of the influence of the traffic. Consequently, they are often appropriate during possessions over railways and highways. A typical concrete arch structure is shown in Figure 27.2, constructed over the railway of the Greater Bargoed Community Regeneration Scheme in South Wales. An arch profile is sometimes adapted to the gauging of trains and vehicles. Quality control is obviously better with factory production. The placement of fill over the structure often provides the benefit of landscaping and planting. Edge walls can be created with reinforced earth structures or simple pre-cast concrete spandrel panels.

Figure 27.2 Lifting in a pre-cast arch at the Greater Bargoed Community Regeneration Scheme
Courtesy of Hochtief UK

27.3.2.3 Design considerations

Stability and robustness. A fundamental aspect of the design is the changing load distribution from first installation through backfilling and any nearby construction. The backfill sequence assumed in design must be followed and monitored on site as the arch is susceptible to small changes in load, particularly unequal loading. The case history on the failure at Gerrards Cross is useful for any temporary works designer to reflect on and learn from (NCE, 2005).

Stability of the initial arch is critical and may require temporary propping, kentledge or anchors to prevent toppling or spreading. The subsequent arch units are generally stable once the first units are fixed in position. Units are generally robust during lifting and handling provided attention is paid to positioning lifting points and the layout of the working areas. Two-piece arches are not robust when placed until all joint details are completed; for example, a stitch joint may be required at the crown and grouting may be required at the springing points. They are best used only where the load of a one-piece arch would be beyond the limit of the crane.

Foundations and support. Temporary foundations should not be required, although temporary props may be required to support units in storage or during final positioning. It is critical that the lifting arrangement is designed carefully to ensure that the final positioning is achieved with the piece in the correct orientation, which requires a calculation of the centre of gravity of the piece.

Contingency measures. A temporary trestle may be required to support the first section if two cranes cannot be used. Rapid-strengthening concrete could be used to complete joints or stitch details to prevent arch spread or to connect units (e.g. Ductal produced by Lafarge).

Control and monitoring. Control measures should cover final position, alignment and inspection of bearing areas to ensure no point loads are introduced. Monitoring of arch units during and after installation is important to ensure that deflections are within expected limits.

Independent review and validation. It is crucial that the interface between specialists' design of the arch system and the global design into which it fits is considered and that all temporary load cases are developed. A number of failures during construction have occurred and it is recommended that the designer review literature on these while developing the design.

27.4. Deck erection as a single unit
27.4.1 Launching
27.4.1.1 General description of erection technique

This is an installation technique in which the deck is fabricated in part or in whole behind one abutment, and pulled or pushed into position over rollers or skids located at the abutment and the intermediate supports. A lightweight launching nose is usually required and ballast may be required at the tail. Due to the deflection of the nose, there may be a vertical jacking requirement at the intermediate supports. It is complex and costly, and chosen only for multiple spans or after all other options have been discarded. The effect of the rolling load on the lower soffit or flange means that the temporary loads to deck and substructure are often the most onerous loading conditions and define the design of the structure. A clean straight launch path is preferred, although a circular path is possible. Fully varying soffits or 'corkscrew' decks have been launched, but are extremely complex and require multiple vertical jacking points to prevent over-loading of individual elements.

A variation less frequently used is to launch the bridge sideways from a temporary construction position alongside the final alignment. This requires temporary abutments and piers with a slide track to the permanent abutments and piers. A benefit is the shorter timescale for the final installation, which usually requires an existing road deck to be closed for a very short time.

Such methods were employed during the construction of the A38 Marsh Mills Viaducts project (see Figure 27.3) near Plymouth, where traffic disruption was minimised using a side launch technique (permitting the two viaducts to be replaced with only two weekend road closures). The picture shows the viaduct deck on temporary supports, carrying live traffic, before the demolition of the existing pre-cast concrete deck and the eventual slide onto the newly constructed piers.

Figure 27.3 Sideways slide at Marsh Mills Viaduct
Courtesy of Hochtief UK

27.4.1.2 Base requirements

The Client should consider a contract that allows for the combination of temporary and permanent design both to the deck structure and the loads applied to the substructure. The length of preparation during the pre-construction/design period should not be underestimated. A specialist jacking subcontractor is required. If this solution is being applied to a project with multiple stakeholders, then it can be very beneficial to bring them in closely to the project at the earliest stages.

27.4.1.3 Risks and opportunities

Launching systems are favoured where the underlying ground is inaccessible (e.g. because of a river or an operating road or railway). A large area behind one abutment is required to erect the deck launch. For side launching, a linear site is required for the full length of the bridge. The design process will go through several iterations due to the effects of the temporary loads on the permanent design. There are advantages in the speed of erection and the avoidance of over-sailing craneage.

The minimisation of friction at bearing positions will reduce jacking loads. However, consider restraints for sideward sliding and the requirement for a braking system.

If technically feasible, it is normally beneficial to install the bridge in as close to a complete state as possible (i.e. track and ballast in place, or surfacing and white lining complete). On the Paddington Bridge Project (Figure 27.4), it was possible to incorporate the foundations of the temporary loading towers into the permanent substructure. On completion of the deck launch, the new deck was also used to transport away the old truss structure.

27.4.1.4 Design considerations

Stability and robustness. Many serious failures have occurred during this form of construction, where temporary stability has played a significant part in the failure. A thorough appreciation of many factors affecting stability is required before designing a launched bridge system, covering global and local stability of the bridge and its components. Some factors to consider include the following

- loads on and resistances of substructures and foundations
- stability following out-of-tolerance movement
- flexibility of the whole system at all stages
- effects of environmental loads including wind, ice and temperature
- site controls and technical supervision
- monitoring and feedback control systems
- lower chord buckling at temporary supports.

Foundations and support. Normally the permanent substructures and foundations are used to provide support during the deck launch. This is often supplemented by temporary supports to reduce bending moments, shear forces and deflections. Careful attention is important to the interface between the sliding deck and the support to ensure adequate guidance is provided and to limit the resistance loads on the support.

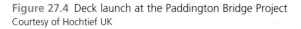

Figure 27.4 Deck launch at the Paddington Bridge Project
Courtesy of Hochtief UK

The pathway on the support can be provided by sliding or rolling bearings. The bearing design accommodates static friction (when the launch commences) and lesser dynamic friction (as launch proceeds) as well as lateral forces (imposed in restraining any lateral movement). The choice of rolling or sliding bearing will depend on requirements for tolerances, friction resistance, intensity of load at bearings and robustness. Final fixity of the deck is completed after the launch; permanent bearings will sometimes be carried in during the launch, but isolated out of use to prevent abnormal stresses.

Plant and equipment. The design of a deck launch should only be undertaken with the knowledge and support of specialist plant and equipment suppliers. Indeed, the design erection scheme will be partly defined by the size, capacity and applicability of the suppliers' hydraulic jacks, strand jacks and the associated power-pack. The motive power required to move the structure can be calculated from the frictional values estimated in the slide tracks, the roller bearings or at the structure/soil interface. Guidance to estimated frictional coefficients can be found in Chapter 20 (Section 20.2.4.3) on heavy moves and in the online Engineer's Handbook (http://www.engineershandbook.com).

Contingency measures. As with all high-risk schemes, contingency measures should be planned at critical stages of the erection. This may include the provision of additional jacking capacity, the means of reducing friction or simply a means to halt progress for a period for repair.

Control and monitoring. It is essential to monitor both movement and stress to the structure during erection. The structure should be modelled through all of the temporary design load conditions and allowance made for the effects of temperature. There may be a requirement for a braking restraint. The onsite teams should be highly integrated with well-understood lines of communication and clearly identified decision makers. This can involve specific specialists taking control of the site operations for the critical jacking operations, who then hand over to the overall site supervision team upon completion.

Independent review and validation. An independent design check must consider all aspects of the method of erection on the design. The checking engineer should be selected from consultants with the experience and ability to undertake similar complex schemes.

27.4.2 Self-propelled modular transporter (SPMT)
Note that relevant information relating to the capacity and arrangement of SPMT equipment is detailed in Chapter 20 (on heavy moves).

27.4.2.1 General description of erection technique
The application of SPMTs is a relatively recent development, in which multi-wheeled trailers incorporating hydraulic jacks lift and drive pre-constructed bridge forms into position. The jacks and wheels are capable of being moved by remote control with very fine tolerances, while lifting substantial loads.

27.4.2.2 Base requirements
The most important consideration is the preparation of the roadway formation on which the trailers must run. Clearly, the road formation must be strong enough to withstand the running and skewing of the multiple axles. In addition, the overall settlement of the loaded trailers must be within determinable limits. For this reason, steel plates, proprietary track and even laying an asphalt surface are used for the erection roadway. Distance travelled within the possessions should be limited by the close location of the construction yard or parking the structure within a short distance of the bridge site. Because of limited jacking heights, SPMTs do not have the ability to go over humpbacks with total vertical differentials of over 750 mm.

27.4.2.3 Risks and opportunities
The main advantage of the SPMT technique is the speed at which the deck or pre-cast form can be moved into position. They are therefore popular for bridge erections requiring railway possessions in which the tracks are lifted, an embankment is excavated, the bridge is driven into position and backfilled and the track is replaced, all within a long weekend. They are similarly popular for bridge replacements to over-bridge decks on the motorway system. If ground conditions are very good, then consideration might be given to carrying in the bridge foundations with the remainder of the portal. Such a scheme was successful at the Channel Tunnel Rail Link Contract (CTRL) 342, where the portal structure and foundations were installed in one possession (see Figure 27.5).

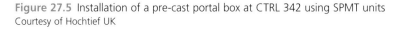

Figure 27.5 Installation of a pre-cast portal box at CTRL 342 using SPMT units
Courtesy of Hochtief UK

27.4.2.4 Design considerations

Stability and robustness. A critical calculation is to find the centre of gravity of the structure to be transported and to ensure the stiffness in the temporary transport configuration is accurately defined in the permanent structure modelling.

Foundations and support. While the transporter will spread the load well, the competence of the surface layers must be assured such that the transporter does not settle under load. The risk of transporter failure due to settlement of the wheels is significant in determining whether the work can be completed within a road or rail possession.

Plant and equipment. Appropriate transporters are readily available from a number of companies including Mammoet UK Ltd, Fagioli Ltd and ALE (Abnormal Load Engineering) Ltd.

Temporary stresses. The arrangement of the support system located on top of the transport bogeys will determine the stresses during the lifting process. If possible, it is preferable to incorporate the temporary load case in the permanent design. Beware of the danger of stresses created by distortions generated by the transport path.

Independent review and validation. An independent review is needed to ensure that all load cases have been considered within the final design and method, and incorporated either in the permanent design or within temporary works.

27.5. Bridge and deck erection by tunnelling and mining
27.5.1 General description of erection technique

Advances in the manufacture of hydraulic jacks and the development of slide tracks with very low values of friction have led to the jacking of ever-larger structures under existing road and rail embankments. The mining technique involves the pushing of a structure through an embankment, while material is excavated from within a mining shield at the front. This is done either by jacking a single box structure or by jacking the abutment and roof as separate elements. A key element in the design is the means by which the embankment above the roof is restrained in its original position, often known as the Anti-Drag System (ADS). Solutions include the use of thin steel sheets or steel ropes to minimise forward movement of the ground above the structure as it is jacked into position.

Whichever method is chosen, provision of a large anchorage restraining mechanism is required at the entrance portal. The design of the mining shield is also critical and must fully consider the ground conditions, proposed methods of excavation and shoring into consideration. The safety of the miners and operatives is imperative.

An alternative method is to construct foundations and slide tracks in advance through the embankment, for example, under a railway. Once the slide tracks are complete, the section of railway track and embankment above are removed and the pre-constructed bridge is jacked into position along the slide track onto the new foundations. The choice of method is determined by the construction programme and possession time available, the volume of material to be excavated and an assessment of risk by the contractor.

27.5.2 Base requirements

This method does not suit poor ground or high water tables. Mining within chalk and cohesive soils above the water table give the best results. The minimising of surface settlements is a major requirement. This can generally be mitigated by minimising the free area being mined at the face shield; the greater the potential for face loss, the greater the surface deflections. The limiting factor on the design will usually be the amount of jacking force required to move the structure. Large structures can be moved in sections by the introduction of intermediate jacking stations. A structure is initially jacked at the interface between the front sections and then progressively backwards, resulting in a caterpillar-like motion.

27.5.3 Risks and opportunities

In general, tunnelling and mining techniques should be considered high risk and only undertaken when all other options have been exhausted. The temporary works are expensive and require a high level of engineering expertise. The advantage of such a technique is in minimising the effect of construction on a key transport link. Contingency planning is essential in this type of scheme and fallback alternatives should be considered at every step, whether it involves the provision of more jacking power or the injection of bentonite to improve frictional values.

The calculation of the frictional resistance to jacking is critical and should only be undertaken by an experienced designer using reputable data sources. The final solution will be

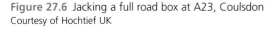

Figure 27.6 Jacking a full road box at A23, Coulsdon
Courtesy of Hochtief UK

obtained by numerous design reiterations in which the estimated costs and risks are repeatedly measured and balanced. On the A23 Coulsdon Town Improvement Scheme (Figure 27.6), a horizontal line of 600 mm diameter steel tubes were installed at high level beneath the rail ballast to act as the ADS. The tubes were filled with reinforced concrete, and locked into a concrete slab over the jacking pit to provide horizontal restraint to the rail track.

27.5.4 Design considerations
27.5.4.1 Stability and robustness
One of the most important design requirements is the ability of the structure to withstand the substantial local jacking loads imparted both at the back of the structure and at any intermediate stations. Typical horizontal jacking arrangements may consist of several 500 tonne capacity jacks, each with a stroke of up to 2.0 m. Upon achieving full extension, the jacks are retracted, spacer blocks inserted and the cycle repeated.

The safety of the miners, the loads from their machinery and the requirement to support the open face of the excavation determines the robustness of the design of the front mining shield. The shield is typically made either from heavy steel sections or from reinforced concrete with steel cutting edge. Guidance is available in the preparation of the specification for jacked box tunnelling including the requirements for the working environment, predicting and monitoring ground conditions and grouting (PCE, 2010).

27.5.4.2 Foundations and support

The provision of foundations at an early stage (e.g. within tunnels) has the advantage that the slide-path for the roof and walls provides the guidance of a straight jacking path. Box jacks that have no such restraints or guidance are more likely to incur errors in their final alignment. The largest frictional jacking forces are generated at the underside of box portal structures. There is a requirement for a casting bed or a pre-construction area at the box invert level within approach retaining walls, and consideration must be given to the means of resisting the substantial jacking forces. Often the casting slab and the retaining walls can be arranged to provide the jacking resistance. A head beam must be constructed at roof level of the entrance portal, to anchor the ADS mechanism that prevents the soil block over the roof from moving with the box (see Figure 27.6). The loads to be resisted here require a substantial beam and appropriate supports.

Various means are available to the designer to reduce the jacking loads. These might involve low friction materials such as PTFE on the slide paths, tunnelling muds such as bentonite injected into the over-excavated void around the structure and drag shields to the roof incorporating steel sheets or steel ropes.

27.5.4.3 Plant and equipment

Specialist suppliers provide the hydraulic equipment. Strand jacks could be employed to pull a bridge structure along a slide path. For further details regarding the design and capacity of such equipment, refer to Chapter 20 on heavy moves.

27.5.4.4 Independent review and validation

The assistance of an experienced checking engineer in the team will provide the assurance required by the contractor and client that all loading assumptions are reasonable and within an acceptable range.

27.6.   Segmental bridge construction

It is not the intention of this chapter to include the very largest span bridges which utilise design and erection techniques such as cable-stayed bridges, suspension bridge and balanced cantilever construction. Many of the details for these bridges would use temporary works described above and in earlier chapters, for example, using transporters to move large pre-cast sections for a balanced cantilever bridge (e.g. the second Severn Crossing), together with specialist techniques such as slip-forming. As an example, a particularly specialist process requiring great skill for a segmental concrete structure is the match-casting of adjacent segments to ensure a precise fit. This is usually undertaken on short-line casting beds. Similarly, the erection of the segments requires careful application of glue and pre-stressing.

An excellent example of a segmental erection scheme is shown in Figure 27.7 for the construction of the STAR Light Railway in Kuala Lumpur, where the deck is being

Figure 27.7 The erection gantry of a glued segmental bridge used for the STAR Light Railway in Kuala Lumpur
Courtesy of Vinci PLC and Mark Raiss, Benaim

constructed using a balanced cantilever construction in which segments are delivered along the previously built deck. Parag *et al.* (1999) provide a fuller description of such techniques.

REFERENCES

NCE (New Civil Engineer) (2005) Backfilling thought to be culprit in Gerrards Cross Tunnel collapse. New Civil Engineer (EMAP), August 2005.

ICE (Institution of Civil Engineers) (2010) Specification for Tunnelling, 3rd edition. British Tunnelling Society and Institution of Civil Engineers. Institution of Civil Engineers, London.

Parag CD, Frangopol DM, Nowak AS (1999) *Current and Future Trends in Bridge Design, Construction and Maintenance*. Thomas Telford Publishing, London.

FURTHER READING

Rosignoli M (2002) *Bridge Launching*. Thomas Telford Publishing, London.

Troyano LF (2003) *Bridge Engineering: A Global Perspective*. Thomas Telford Publishing, London.

Useful web addresses

Rapid strengthening concrete for jointing PC segments: http://www.ductal-lafarge.com

Commentary on design and construction of a balanced cantilever segmental bridge: http://www.cbrd.co.uk/histories/openingbooklets/pdf/m2medway.pdf

Numerous examples of heavy lifting: http://www.ale-heavylift.com; http://www.mammoet.com

Particularly useful for materials information: http://www.engineershandbook.com

Use of a jacked-box tunnelling under a live motorway and pre-cast segmental bridge construction: http://www.icevirtuallibrary.com/content/article/10.1680/geng.2004.157.4.229

Hochtief UK Construction Ltd: http://www.hochtief-construction.co.uk

Precast segmental bridge construction: http://www.tu-harburg.de/mb/PDF-Dokumente/segmental-bridges.pdf

Temporary Works: Principles of Design and Construction
ISBN 978-0-7277-4177-6

ICE Publishing: All rights reserved
http://dx.doi.org/10.1680/twpdc.41776.361

Index

access, 1, 6, 7, 11, 38, 44, 103, 122, 123, 142,
    148, 162, 181, 188, 193, 204, 219, 221,
    222, 223, 224, 231, 237, 239, 311, 314,
    317, 321, 325, 326, 330, 331, 334, 347, 352
  planning, design, and cost considerations,
    table, 28–29
  site compounds and set-up, 34–37
  see also platforms; scaffolding; site roads
access mats, 75
ALE Engineering Ltd, 355
aluminium, 75, 150, 263, 276, 277, 278, 279,
    281, 285, 287, 288, 291, 293, 294, 307,
    311, 312
American Society of Mechanical Engineers
    (ASME), 253, 255
anchorage, 137, 139, 140, 175–176, 187, 190,
    321, 322–323
  in-situ anchor head block, illustration,
    188
anti-drag system (ADS), 356, 357
Approval in Principle (AIP), 23

Bailey, DC, 221, 225, 232
Bailey Bridge, 222, 232
  modern day military logistical support
    bridge, illustration, 233
barges, 209, 210, 213, 214, 220–223, 225–227,
    256
  crane barges, 225
  hopper barges, 225
  jack-up barges, 223–224, 227–229
  typical barge with crane and ancillary plant,
    illustration, 221
barriers, 8, 11, 237, 337
basic soakage tests (BRE), 65
beams, bridge installation techniques, 346,
    347, 349
beams, soffit formwork, 311, 313, 314, 315

bearers, 277, 286, 287, 289, 290, 293, 300, 301,
    307, 308, 309, 310, 311, 312
bearing piles, 203–207
  analytical process, 207
  cross-bracing of piles for lateral loading
    and effective length, illustration,
    206
  ground parameters, design, 205
  installation methods, 204
  load factors, 205–206
  loadings, 206
  use of, 203–204
Beaufort Scale Force, 281
Beeby, AW, 315
Bell, FG, 93
Bennett *et al.*, 228
bentonite, 164–166, 197
  table, Bentonite support fluid compliance
    testing, 165
  typical diaphragm wall Bentonite farm
    set-up, illustration, 167
Berry *et al.*, 106
Bill of Quantities, 275
birdcage scaffolds, 260
Bishop, AW, 125
Black and Lister, 65
Bolton *et al.*, 175
Bond, A, 87
boreholes, 21, 29, 37, 39, 83, 84, 85, 106, 110,
    126, 127
Boulanger, R, 103
boundary of site, 11
box-out, 186
BR394, 315
BR470, 72
Bragg Report (1974, 1975), 3, 4
    1975, 6, 16, 17, 19, 275
bridges, 318